AQA

GCSE separate sciences

Authors

Graham Bone

Simon Broadley

Philippa Gardom Hulme

Sue Hocking

Mark Matthews

Jim Newall

Contents

How to use this book

Welcome to the continuation of your AQA GCSE courses in Biology, Chemistry, and Physics. This book has been specially written by experienced teachers and examiners to match the 2011 specifications.

On these two pages you can see the types of pages you will find in this book, and the features on them. Everything in the book is designed to provide you with the support you need to help you prepare for your examinations and achieve your best.

Unit openers

Specification matching grid: This shows you how the pages in the unit match to the exam specification so you can track your progress through the unit as you learn.

Why study this unit: Here you can read about the reasons why the science you're about to learn is relevant to your everyday life.

You should remember: This list is a summary of the things you've already learnt that will come up again in this unit. Check through them in advance and see if there is anything that you need to recap on before you get started.

Opener image: Every unit starts with a picture and information on a new or interesting piece of science that relates to what you're about to learn.

Main pages

Learning objectives: You can use these objectives to understand what you need to learn to prepare for your exams. Higher Tier only objectives appear in pink text.

Key words: These are the terms you need to understand for your exams. You can look for these words in the text in bold or check the glossary to see what they mean.

Questions: Use the questions on each spread to test yourself on what you've just read.

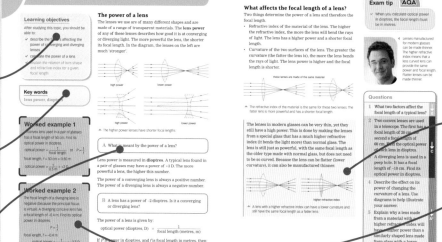

Higher Tier content: Anything marked in pink is for students taking the Higher Tier paper only. As you go through you can look at this material and attempt it to help you understand what is expected for the Higher Tier.

Worked examples: These help you understand how to use an equation or to work through a calculation. You can check back whenever you use the calculation in your work.

Summary and exam-style questions

Every summary question at the end of a spread includes an indication of how hard it is. These indicators show which grade you are working towards. You can track your own progress by seeing which of the questions you can answer easily, and which you have difficulty with.

When you reach the end of a unit you can use the exam-style questions to test how well you know what you've just learnt. Each question has a grade band next to it.

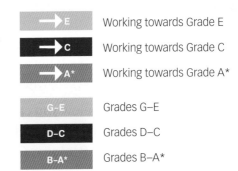

E — Working towards Grade E

C — Working towards Grade C

A* — Working towards Grade A*

G–E — Grades G–E

D–C — Grades D–C

B–A* — Grades B–A*

Course catch-ups

Revision checklist: This is a summary of the main ideas in the unit. You can use it as a starting point for revision, to check that you know about the big ideas covered.

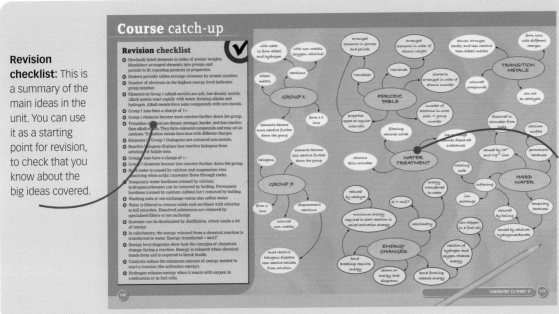

Visual summary: Another way to start revision is to use a visual summary, linking ideas together in groups so you can see how one topic relates to another. You can use this page as a start for your own summary.

Upgrade: Upgrade takes you through an exam question in a step-by-step way, showing you why different answers get different grades. Using the tips on the page you can make sure you achieve your best by understanding what each question needs.

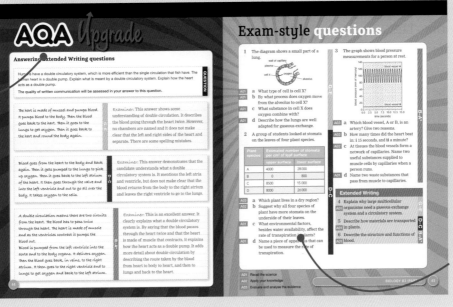

Exam-style questions: Using these questions you can practice your exam skills, and make sure you're ready for the real thing. Each question has a grade band next to it, so you can understand what level you are working at and focus on where you need to improve to get your target grade.

Matching your course

The units in this book have been written to match the specifications, so that you can take three separate GCSEs in science.

In the diagram below you can see that the units and part units can be used to study either for **GCSE Science**, leading to **GCSE Additional Science**, or as part of **GCSE Biology**, **GCSE Chemistry** and **GCSE Physics** courses.

	GCSE Biology	GCSE Chemistry	GCSE Physics
GCSE Science	B1 (Part 1)	C1 (Part 1)	P1 (Part 1)
	B1 (Part 2)	C1 (Part 2)	P1 (Part 2)
GCSE Additional Science	B2 (Part 1)	C2 (Part 1)	P2 (Part 1)
	B2 (Part 2)	C2 (Part 2)	P2 (Part 2)
	B3 (Part 1)	**C3 (Part 1)**	**P3 (Part 1)**
	B3 (Part 2)	**C3 (Part 2)**	**P3 (Part 2)**

GCSE Biology, GCSE Chemistry, and GCSE Physics assessment

The units in this book match the exam papers on offer. The diagram below shows you what is included in each exam paper to progress to three separate science GCSEs. It also shows you how much of your final mark you will be working towards in each paper.

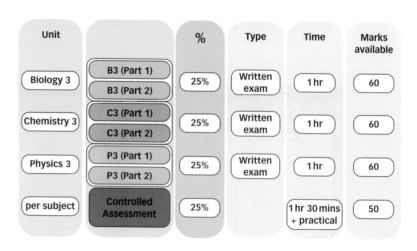

Unit		%	Type	Time	Marks available
Biology 3	B3 (Part 1)	25%	Written exam	1 hr	60
	B3 (Part 2)				
Chemistry 3	C3 (Part 1)	25%	Written exam	1 hr	60
	C3 (Part 2)				
Physics 3	P3 (Part 1)	25%	Written exam	1 hr	60
	P3 (Part 2)				
per subject	Controlled Assessment	25%		1 hr 30 mins + practical	50

Understanding exam questions

When you read the questions in your exam papers you should make sure you know what kind of answer you are being asked for. The list below explains some of the common words you will see used in exam questions. Make sure you know what each word means. Always read the question thoroughly, even if you recognise the word used.

Calculate

Work out your answer by using a calculation. You can use your calculator to help you. You may need to use an equation; check whether one has been provided for you in the paper. The question will say if your working must be shown.

Describe

Write a detailed answer that covers what happens, when it happens, and where it happens. The question will let you know how much of the topic to cover. Talk about facts and characteristics. (Hint: don't confuse with 'Explain')

Explain

You will be asked how or why something happens. Write a detailed answer that covers how and why a thing happens. Talk about mechanisms and reasons. (Hint: don't confuse with 'Describe')

Evaluate

You will be given some facts, data or other information. Write about the data or facts and provide your own conclusion or opinion on them.

Outline

Give only the key facts of the topic. You may need to set out the steps of a procedure or process – make sure you write down the steps in the correct order.

Show

Write down the details, steps or calculations needed to prove an answer that you have been given.

Suggest

Think about what you've learnt in your science lessons and apply it to a new situation or a context. You may not know the answer. Use what you have learnt to suggest sensible answers to the question.

Write down

Give a short answer, without a supporting argument.

Top tips

Always read exam questions carefully, even if you recognise the word used. Look at the information in the question and the number of answer lines to see how much detail the examiner is looking for.

You can use bullet points or a diagram if it helps your answer.

If a number needs units you should include them, unless the units are already given on the answer line.

Controlled Assessment in GCSE Science

As part of the assessment for your GCSE Biology, GCSE Chemistry, and GCSE Physics courses, you will undertake Controlled Assessment tasks.

What is Controlled Assessment?

Controlled Assessment has taken the place of coursework for the new 2011 GCSE Science specifications. The main difference between coursework and Controlled Assessment is that you will be supervised by your teacher when you carry out your Controlled Assessment task.

What will my Controlled Assessment task look like?

Your Controlled Assessment task will be made up of four sections. These four sections make up an investigation, with each section looking at a different part of the scientific process.

	What will I need to do?	How many marks are available?
Research	• Independently develop your own hypothesis. • Research two methods for carrying out an experiment to test your hypothesis. • Research the context of the investigation. • Carry out a risk assessment.	
Section 1	• Answer questions relating to your own research.	20 marks
Practical investigation	• Carry out your own experiment and record and analyse your results.	
Section 2	• Answer questions relating to the experiment you carried out. • Select appropriate data from data supplied by AQA and use it to analyse and compare with the hypothesis. • Suggest how ideas from your investigation could be used in a new context.	30 marks
	Total	50 marks

How do I prepare for my Controlled Assessment?

Throughout your course you will learn how to carry out investigations in a scientific way, and how to analyse and compare data properly.

On the next three pages there are Controlled Assessment-style questions matched to the biology, chemistry, and physics content in B3, C3, and P3. You can use them to test yourself, and to find out which areas you want to practise more before you take the Controlled Assessment task itself.

Overview: There is a link between exposure of plants to direct sunlight and the number of stomata found on the undersides of their leaves. **You must develop your own hypothesis to test.** You will be provided with a microscope, microscope slides, clear nail polish, sticky tape, fine forceps, cover slips, a dropper pipette and distilled water, leaves from plants (eg ivy) grown in shade conditions, and leaves from the same plants grown in full sunlight.

Download the Research Notes and Data Sheet for B3 from **www.oxfordsecondary.co.uk/aqacasestudies**.

Research

*Record your findings in the **Research Notes table**.*

1. Research two methods to explore the link between the amount of direct sunlight to which a plant is exposed and the number of stomata found on the underside of its leaves.
2. Find out how the results of the investigation might be useful for garden centres when advising customers about their houseplants.

Section 1   Total 20 marks

Use your research findings to answer these questions.

1. **(a)** Name the two most useful sources that you used for your research.
   (b) Explain why these sources were the most useful. [3]
2. Write a hypothesis about how exposure of plants to light or shade affects numbers of stomata on the lower surfaces of their leaves. Use your research findings to explain why you've made this hypothesis. [3]
3. Describe how to carry out an investigation to test your hypothesis. Include the equipment needed and how to use it, the measurements to make, how to make it a fair test, and a risk assessment. [9]
4. Use your research to outline another possible method, and explain why it was not chosen. [3]
5. Draw a table to record data from the investigation. You may use ICT if you wish. [2]

Section 2   Total 30 marks

1. Display the **Group A data** on a graph. *This data has been provided for you to use instead of data that you would gather yourself.* [4]
2. **(a)** What conclusion can you draw from the **Group A data** about a link between the amount of direct sunlight to which a plant is exposed and the number of stomata found on the underside of its leaves? Use any pattern you can see in the **Group A data** and quote figures from it. [3]
   (b) (i) Compare the **Group A** and **Group B data**. Do you think the **Group A data** is reproducible? Explain why. *The **Group B data** has been provided for you to use instead of data that would be gathered by others in your class.* [3]
   (b) (ii) Explain how you could use the repeated results from Group B to obtain a more accurate answer. [3]
   (c) Look at the **Group A data**. Are there any anomalous results? Quote from the data. [3]
3. **(a)** Sketch a graph of the results in **Case study 1**. [2]
   (b) Explain to what extent the data from **Case studies 1–3** support or contradict your hypothesis. Use the data to support your answer. [3]
   (c) What change could you make to the way the investigation was carried out in **Case study 3** to obtain data that may support the results of **Case study 2**? [3]
4. Look at **Case study 4**.
   (a) State three environmental conditions that the scientists kept constant when measuring the mass of the detached leaves over 48 hours. [3]
   (b) Explain how the ideas from **Case study 4** and from the **Group A** and **Group B data** could be used by a garden centre in customer advice on watering houseplants. [3]

C3 Controlled Assessment-style questions

Overview: The position of a metal in the reactivity series may be linked to the amount of heat energy released when it reacts with copper sulfate solution. **You must develop your own hypothesis to test.** You will be provided with zinc, iron, tin, and lead metals, copper sulfate solution, a thermometer, and common laboratory glassware.

Download the Research Notes and Data Sheet for C3 from **www.oxfordsecondary.co.uk/ aqacasestudies**.

Research

*Record your findings in the **Research Notes table**.*

1. Research two methods to explore the link between the position of a metal in the reactivity series and the energy released when the metal reacts with copper sulfate solution.
2. Find out how the results of the investigation might help in choosing the best metal to add to copper sulfate solution to heat a ready meal.

Section 1   Total 20 marks

Use your research findings to answer these questions.

1. **(a)** Name the two most useful sources that you used for your research.
   (b) Explain why these sources were the most useful. [3]
2. Write a hypothesis about how the position of a metal in the reactivity series affects the energy released when it reacts with copper sulfate solution. Use your research findings to explain why you've made this hypothesis. [3]
3. Describe how to carry out an investigation to test your hypothesis. Include the equipment needed and how to use it, the measurements to make, how to make it a fair test, and a risk assessment. [9]
4. Use your research to outline another possible method, and explain why it was not chosen. [3]
5. Draw a table to record data from the investigation. You may use ICT if you wish. [2]

Section 2   Total 30 marks

1. Display the **Group A data** on a graph or bar chart. *This data has been provided for you to use instead of data that you would gather yourself.* [4]
2. **(a)** What conclusion can you draw from the **Group A data** about a link between position in reactivity series and energy released? Use any pattern you can see in the **Group A data** and quote figures. [3]
   (b) (i) Compare the **Group A** and **Group B data**. Do you think the **Group A data** is reproducible? Explain why. *The **Group B data** has been provided for you to use instead of data that would be gathered by others in your class.* [3]
   (ii) Explain how you could use the repeated results from Group B to obtain a more accurate answer. [3]
   (c) Look at the **Group A data**. Are there any anomalous results? Quote from the data. [3]
3. **(a)** Sketch a bar chart of the results in **Case study 1**. [2]
   (b) Explain to what extent the data from **Case studies 1–3** support or contradict your hypothesis. [3]
   (c) Compare the **Group A data** to the **Case study 4 data**. Explain to what extent the **Case study 4 data** supports or contradicts your hypothesis. [3]
4. A company developing a new ready meal warmer wants to choose the most efficient pair of substances. A chemist develops a hypothesis that the higher a metal is in the reactivity series, the more energy is released when it reacts with copper sulfate solution.
   (a) Does the **Group A data** support or contradict this hypothesis? [3]
   (b) Explain how the company could use ideas from the **Group A data** and the case studies, and suggest why it might decide against using copper sulfate solution to heat the ready meal. [3]

P3 Controlled Assessment-style questions

Overview: The length of a pendulum affects the frequency of the swing. **You must develop your own hypothesis to test.** You will be provided with a length of string, a pendulum bob, a stopwatch, retort stand, clamp, boss, and a metre rule.

Download the Research Notes and Data Sheet for P3 from **www.oxfordsecondary.co.uk/aqacasestudies**.

Research

*Record your findings in the **Research Notes table**.*

1. Research two methods to investigate how the length of a pendulum affects the frequency of the swing.
2. Find out how the results of the investigation might be useful in designing a simple swing for a children's playground.

Section 1   Total 20 marks

Use your research findings to answer these questions.

1. (a) Name the two most useful sources that you used for your research.
   (b) Explain why these sources were the most useful. [3]
2. Write a hypothesis about how the length of a pendulum affects its frequency. Use your research findings to explain why you've made this hypothesis. [3]
3. Describe how to carry out an investigation to test your hypothesis. Include the equipment needed and how to use it, the measurements to make, how to make it a far test, and a risk assessment. [9]
4. Use your research to outline another possible method, and explain why you did not choose it. [3]
5. Draw a table to record data from the investigation. You may use ICT if you wish. [2]

Section 2   Total 30 marks

1. (a) Display the **Group A data** on a graph. *This data has been provided for you to use instead of data that you would gather yourself.* [4]
   (b) What conclusion can you draw from the **Group A data**? Use any pattern you can see in the **Group A data** and quote figures from it to support your answer. [3]
2. (a) (i) Compare the **Group A** and **Group B data**. Do you think your results are reproducible? Explain why. *The **Group B data** has been provided for you to use instead of data that would be gathered by others in your class.* [3]
   (ii) Explain in detail what might account for the slight differences between the readings from each group. [3]
   (c) Look at the **Group A data**. Are there any anomalous results? Quote from the data to explain your answer. [3]
3. (a) Sketch a graph of the results in **Case study 1**. [2]
   (b) Explain to what extent the data from **Case studies 1–3** support or contradict your hypothesis. Use the data to support your answer. [3]
   (c) Explain whether the **Case study 4 data** supports or contradicts your hypothesis. State any other conclusion that can be drawn from the data. Use examples of data from **Case study 4** and the **Group A data**. [3]
4. (a) (i) Explain how the length of a pendulum with a time period of exactly 1.00 s might be found from the data in the case studies. [2]
   (ii) In order to find a more precise value for this length, suggest three more lengths to be tested. [1]
   (b) Suggest how the results of your investigation and the case studies might be useful in designing a simple swing for a children's playground. [3]

B3 Part 1

Exchange and transport

Why study this unit?

The bodies of the human and the flowering plant are exquisitely balanced machines. It is vital that the cells of these bodies are supplied with a constant supply of life-supporting molecules like water, oxygen, carbon dioxide, and nutrients. In this unit you will discover how these molecules reach those cells.

You will study the ways in which molecules get into and out of cells. Keeping our bodies well hydrated and well fuelled is important. Larger plants and animals have needed to develop special exchange surfaces, like gills, lungs, and leaves, in order to pick up useful molecules from the outside. Once molecules have entered a plant or animal, they need to be moved around. The movement of water in the plant will be studied in this unit. In animals, the development of the circulatory system has allowed transport of molecules around the body. The circulatory system includes blood, blood vessels, and the living pump, the heart.

You should remember

1 The process of diffusion, allowing some molecules to enter cells.

2 The plant organs, and their structure and function.

3 How plant and animal organ systems compare.

4 The structure of cells.

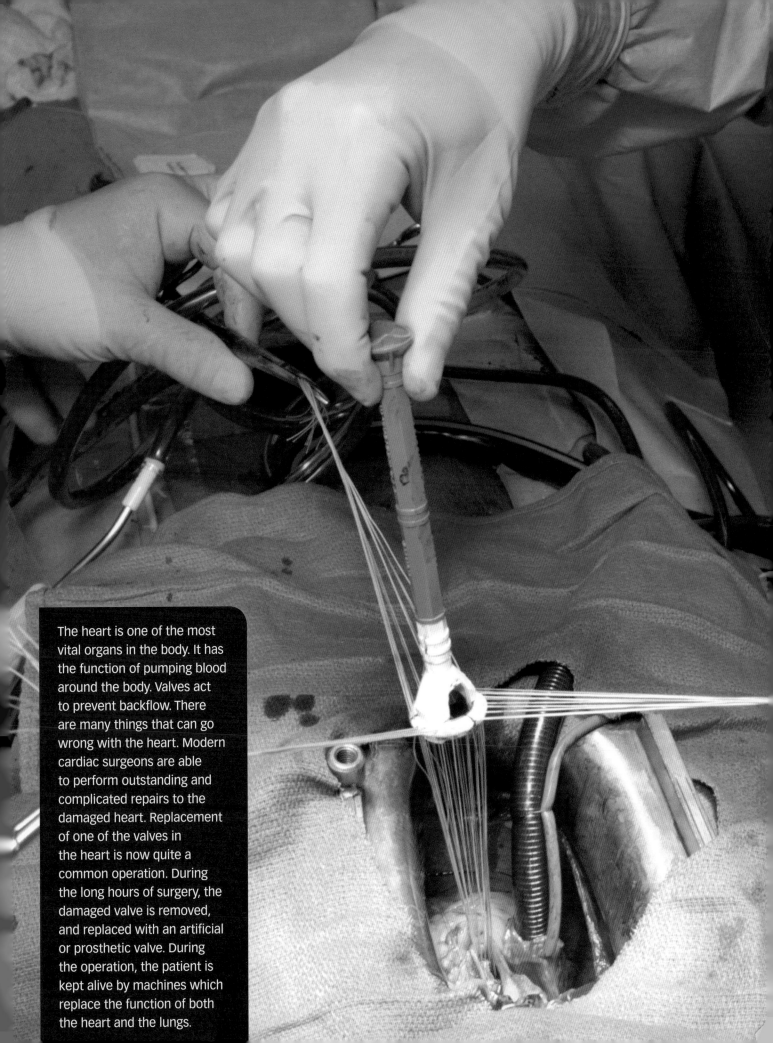

The heart is one of the most vital organs in the body. It has the function of pumping blood around the body. Valves act to prevent backflow. There are many things that can go wrong with the heart. Modern cardiac surgeons are able to perform outstanding and complicated repairs to the damaged heart. Replacement of one of the valves in the heart is now quite a common operation. During the long hours of surgery, the damaged valve is removed, and replaced with an artificial or prosthetic valve. During the operation, the patient is kept alive by machines which replace the function of both the heart and the lungs.

Learning objectives

After studying this topic, you should be able to:

✔ understand the process of osmosis

✔ know the effects of osmosis on plant and animal cells

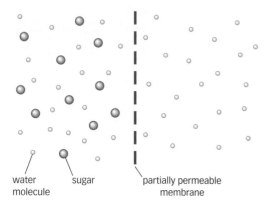

▲ A partially permeable membrane has pores that allow water molecules through, but not larger sugar molecules

> **A** In which direction do water molecules move in osmosis?
>
> **B** What is a partially permeable membrane?

▲ A wilted coleus plant. The cells have lost water by osmosis.

Moving molecules

There are three processes by which substances can move into or out of cells. Dissolved substances (molecules or ions) move by

- diffusion
- active transport.

Moving water

Osmosis is a special kind of diffusion. Water moves into and out of cells by osmosis.

The cell membrane has tiny holes called **pores**. Larger molecules such as sugars and proteins are too big to pass through the pores, but very small molecules, including water, can pass through. This type of membrane is called a **partially permeable membrane**, because only some molecules can pass through it.

The diagram on the left shows a dilute sugar solution separated from pure water by a partially permeable membrane. The sugar molecules are too big to pass through the pores. Water molecules pass from the pure water to the sugar solution by diffusion. This dilutes the sugar solution.

In osmosis, water will move from an area of high water concentration (pure water or a dilute solution) to an area of low water concentration (a more concentrated solution) across a partially permeable membrane.

Osmosis and cells

Water can move into or out of cells by osmosis. This movement of water is important for both plants and animals, because it keeps their cells in balance.

When plant cells take up water by osmosis, the cells become firm. The cell contents push against the inelastic cell wall. When plant cells are firm like this, they help support the plant. If they lose water, the cells become soft and the plant wilts.

Osmosis is also important in animals. There is no cell wall in animal cells, so they are very sensitive to water concentrations. If they take in or lose too much water, the cells are damaged and can die.

Osmosis and plant cells

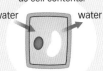
water   water

Surroundings are a less concentrated solution than cell contents (higher water concentration).

Surroundings have the same concentration as cell contents.

Surroundings are a more concentrated solution than cell contents (lower water concentration).

water

water   water

water

Cell placed into a dilute solution. It takes up water by osmosis. The pressure in the cell increases; this is called turgor pressure. The cell becomes firm or turgid.

Cell placed into a solution with the same concentration as its contents. There is no net movement of water. The cell remains the same.

Cell placed into more concentrated solution. It loses water by osmosis. The turgor pressure falls and the cell becomes flaccid (soft). Eventually the cell contents collapse away from the cell wall. This is called a plasmolysed cell.

▲ Water movement by osmosis in plant cells

Osmosis and animal cells

isotonic solution

water   water

Surroundings are a less concentrated solution than cell contents (higher water concentration).

Surroundings have the same concentration as cell contents.

Surroundings are a more concentrated solution than cell contents (lower water concentration).

water

water   water

water

Cell placed into a solution that is more dilute than its contents. It takes up water, swells, and may burst. This is called lysis.

Cell placed into a solution with the same concentration as its contents. There is no net movement of water. The cell remains the same.

Cell placed into a more concentrated solution. It loses water by osmosis. The cell becomes crenated (it crinkles).

▲ Water movement by osmosis in animal cells

◄ A normal red blood cell and a crenated red blood cell

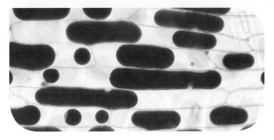

▲ Soft plant cells

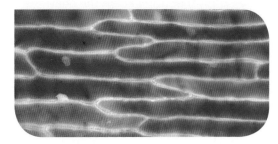

▲ Firm plant cells

Key words

osmosis, pore, partially permeable membrane

Questions

1 Name three ways in which substances can move into or out of cells.

2 A piece of potato is weighed and then placed into a concentrated sugar solution. After 24 hours it is removed, dried, and weighed again:

  (a) Describe what would happen to the mass of the potato piece after 24 hours.

  (b) Explain why this has happened.

3 A casualty from a road accident has lost blood. Why are they given a transfusion of blood, not water?

2: Sports drinks

▲ You sweat more during strenuous exercise

A What is the recommended water intake for an adult?

B Name two substances that are lost from the body during sweating.

C Explain why water is important in keeping muscles healthy.

A body of water

The human body contains about 60–70% water. The water gets into your cells by osmosis. If the level of water in your body falls, your cells become **dehydrated** and they do not function properly. It is important to replace lost water by drinking fluids:

- Inactive people need two to three litres of fluid per day to remain hydrated.
- You need more fluid during exercise.
- You can sweat up to two litres of water per hour on a hot day.
- When you sweat, you lose not only water but also ions from your body. The body's balance of water and ions is now disturbed.

The importance of hydration

Fluids protect organs such as the brain, by forming a liquid buffer layer.

Fluids keep the skin, mouth, and the lining of the nose and lungs moist.

Mineral ions are carried around the body dissolved in water.

Water and ions are needed for the temperature regulation of the body.

Fluid lubricates the joints.

Substances such as glucose for respiration are carried to and from muscle cells dissolved in water. When oxygen leaves the blood cells it travels to the muscle cells dissolved in water, and so does carbon dioxide as it moves from the muscle cells into the blood.

The effect of exercise

When you exercise, you use energy. The energy is released from sugars during respiration. Respiration also generates heat. To help cool your body down, sweating occurs. Most exercise sessions result in some sweating. You must replace the fluids lost to stop you dehydrating. Good tips are:

- Always start an exercise session fully hydrated.
- Drink 400–600 ml of water during the two hours before exercise.

Sports drinks

Sports drinks contain

- water to hydrate the body
- carbohydrates such as glucose for respiration, to provide energy
- mineral ions to keep the muscles healthy
- caffeine to make you feel awake.

There are three main types of sports drink:

▲ Sports drinks keep your body hydrated, and also replace glucose and mineral ions

Type of drink	What it contains	How it helps the body
Hypotonic drinks	In these drinks, the concentrations of dissolved substances are lower than in the body. There is usually less than 4 g of carbohydrate per 100 cm³ of the drink.	Being more dilute than the blood, a lot of water will move from the gut quickly into the blood by osmosis. This type of sports drink is mainly for hydration.
Isotonic drinks	These drinks have concentrations of dissolved substances at about the same level as in the body. They usually have a carbohydrate concentration of between 4 and 8 g per 100 cm³ of the drink.	Being the same concentration as the blood, some water will move from the gut into the blood by osmosis. Some sugar is also absorbed. This type of drink provides both hydration and fuel replacement.
Hypertonic drinks	In these drinks, the concentrations of dissolved substances are higher than in the body. They typically have sugar levels above 8 g per 100 cm³ of the drink.	These drinks provide high sugar levels for absorption. They are often called 'power' drinks. They are mainly for supplying fuel to the muscles. They can cause a sudden sugar rush, followed by a crash, which can cause problems.

Questions

1 List four ingredients in a typical sports drink.

2 Explain why long-distance runners would need isotonic sports drinks.

3 Why are hypertonic drinks often referred to as 'power' drinks?

4 Explain how the water in a hypotonic sports drink is able to get into the blood from the gut.

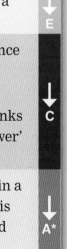

3: Active transport

Against the flow

Diffusion and osmosis are not the only ways that particles can get into or out of cells. Some dissolved molecules or ions need to move from a low concentration to a high concentration, against a **concentration gradient**. This can happen by a process called **active transport**.

> **A** Active transport is one process by which molecules can move into or out of a cell. Name two others.

An example of active transport is the movement of sodium ions out of nerve cells in the human body.

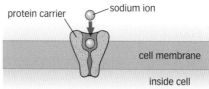

1. The ion attaches to the protein carrier.

protein carrier — sodium ion

cell membrane

inside cell

There is a high concentration of sodium ions on the outside of the nerve, and a low concentration on the inside.

There are **protein carriers** in the nerve cell membrane. Sodium ions fit into these carriers.

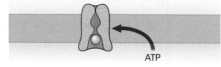

2. The protein uses energy to change shape.

ATP

The proteins can change shape. This uses energy from a molecule called ATP, which is made in respiration.

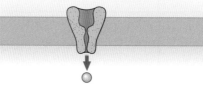

3. The ion moves to the inside of the cell.

As the protein changes shape, it moves the sodium ion from the inside of the membrane to the outside.

The sodium ion falls off the protein carrier.

The protein immediately returns to its normal shape.

▲ Protein carriers in the membrane bring about active transport. Unlike diffusion and osmosis, the process requires energy.

Here are some key features of active transport:

- It pumps substances against a concentration gradient (from low to high concentration).
- It requires energy from respiration, which it obtains from the molecule ATP.
- It needs a protein carrier in the membrane.

> **B** What are the three distinctive features of active transport, which make it different from the other methods?

Examples of active transport

Active transport is involved in:

- the absorption of mineral ions by cells, for example in roots
- the absorption of sugars by cells.

Plants need mineral ions to maintain healthy growth. Mineral ions are at low concentrations in the soil – lower than their concentrations in the plant's cells. The minerals therefore cannot move into the plant by diffusion. Root hair cells on the outsides of roots are highly adapted for the uptake of minerals by active transport. They have long, fine extensions that fit between soil particles, and many protein carriers in their cell membranes which take up mineral ions from the soil. Each protein carrier is specific to one ion.

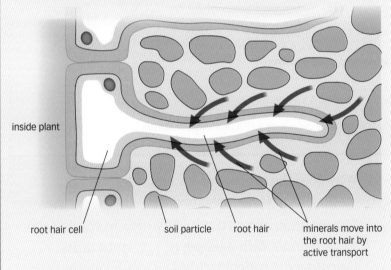

inside plant

root hair cell · soil particle · root hair · minerals move into the root hair by active transport

▲ Dissolved mineral ions are taken into plants through the root hairs. They move against a concentration gradient, by active transport.

Glucose can also be taken up by active transport. Glucose is absorbed by the cells lining the gut by active transport. There is often more glucose in the gut cells than in the fluid in the gut. For example, a hypotonic sports drink does not contain a lot of glucose. The cells lining the gut have membrane proteins that take up the glucose by active transport. These proteins absorb both glucose and sodium at the same time. Sports drinks often contain sodium ions, to help ensure glucose uptake.

Questions

1. What is energy used for in active transport? E

2. Explain why active transport is needed in roots to absorb minerals from the soil.

3. Suggest why a poison such as cyanide, which stops respiration, will stop active transport. C

4. Why is active transport affected by high temperatures?

5. Explain why root hairs need more than one type of carrier protein. A*

Key words

exchange system, villus

The problem with being big

As organisms get bigger, they reach a size at which the surface area of their body is no longer large enough to allow sufficient materials to be exchanged with their surroundings. Important molecules such as oxygen cannot get into the body quickly enough to keep the organism alive.

As cells or organisms get bigger, their surface area to volume ratio gets smaller. As the ratio falls, exchange over the body surface becomes inefficient. To overcome this problem, organisms have developed specialised exchange surfaces.

 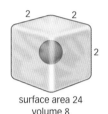 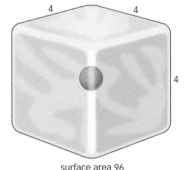

surface area 6
volume 1

surface area 24
volume 8

surface area 96
volume 64

surface area : volume ratios

6 : 1
24 : 8 = 3 : 1
96 : 64 = 3 : 2 or 1.5 : 1

▲ The surface area to volume ratio falls as a cell, or organism, gets bigger

A Why does the process of exchange become inefficient in larger organisms?

B The diagram shows the surface area to volume ratio for cube cells with a length of 1, 2, and 4 units. Calculate the ratio for cube cells with lengths of 3 and 5 units.

Exchange systems

Larger organisms have developed many organ systems that are involved in exchange. These **exchange systems** include

• the surface of the lungs in land animals, for gaseous exchange

• the surface of the gills in aquatic animals, for gaseous exchange

• the digestive system of mammals and other animals, for uptake of nutrients

• the leaf, for gaseous exchange in plants

• the roots, for uptake of water in plants.

▲ The axolotl is an aquatic amphibian. It has external gills for gaseous exchange in water.

Features of exchange systems

At first, the various exchange systems of different organisms and for different functions look very different. But they all have common features:

- Large surface area: this provides a larger area over which diffusion can occur. This will increase the rate of diffusion.
- Thin surface: this provides a very short distance over which diffusion has to occur. This will also increase the rate of diffusion.
- Blood supply: a good blood supply over the exchange surface allows any particles that are taken up to be moved away quickly. This will maintain a greater concentration gradient.
- Turnover: the molecules or ions being exchanged need to be constantly replaced. For example, the air inside the lungs is constantly changed by ventilation – breathing in and out – and food is regularly supplied to the gut. This turnover maintains a high concentration gradient.

The villus – efficient by design

The small intestine is the major site of absorption of digested foods by both diffusion and active transport. It has many adaptations for absorption.

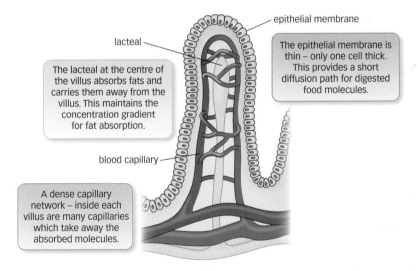

lacteal

epithelial membrane

The lacteal at the centre of the villus absorbs fats and carries them away from the villus. This maintains the concentration gradient for fat absorption.

The epithelial membrane is thin – only one cell thick. This provides a short diffusion path for digested food molecules.

blood capillary

A dense capillary network – inside each villus are many capillaries which take away the absorbed molecules.

▲ Exchange across the villus. Each villus increases the surface area for both active transport and diffusion.

It has a large surface area for exchange – the small intestine is long (about 6.1 m), and its internal surface area is increased further by the presence of millions of finger-like projections called **villi**.

Exam tip

- Whenever you see a question about exchange surfaces, remember to look for the features listed on the left.

C Identify the two features of exchange surfaces in the axolotl that are clearly evident.

D Explain how breathing helps to maintain the concentration gradient in the lungs.

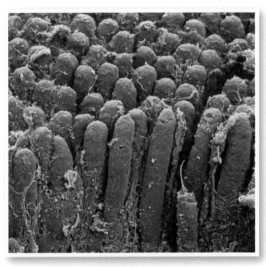

▲ The villus is well adapted for the absorption of digested food – it shows all the features of an exchange system

Questions

1 List three adaptations of a villus for exchange.

2 For each adaptation named above, describe how it helps maintain exchange.

3 Explain why a specialised surface is needed in humans for absorbing food.

Learning objectives

After studying this topic, you should be able to:

- ✔ know that the lungs are the organs of gas exchange in the human
- ✔ explain the process of gas exchange in the lungs
- ✔ explain the sequence of steps in the ventilation of the lungs

Key words

lung, alveolus, ventilation

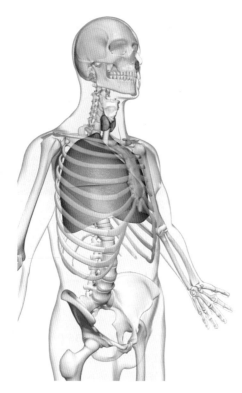

▲ The lungs are located in the thorax, surrounded by the ribs

A Where precisely does gaseous exchange occur in the lungs?

A breath of fresh air

The **lungs** are the specialised organs of many land animals for gaseous exchange. They are located in the chest or thorax, surrounded by the ribcage. The ribs protect the lungs and are also used during the process of breathing.

The thorax is separated from the abdomen by the muscular sheet called the diaphragm. This encloses the lungs in the thorax, and also plays a role in breathing.

Exchanging gases in the alveoli

You breathe air in through your nose and mouth. Here it is warmed, and many microbes are filtered out. This warmed air passes down your windpipe or trachea, which branches right and left into each of two lungs.

The airways continue to branch many times, getting smaller and smaller each time. Eventually, the tubes end in millions of tiny air sacs called **alveoli**. The alveoli have an excellent blood supply. It is in the alveoli that gaseous exchange occurs.

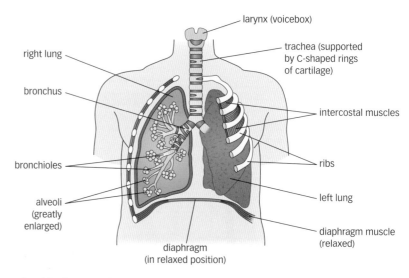

▲ This diagram shows a surface view of the left lung, and a section through the right lung showing the airways and air sacs inside

Breathing in brings air that is high in oxygen into the alveolus. Oxygen diffuses from this area of high oxygen concentration into the blood, where the oxygen concentration is low. At the same time, the carbon dioxide concentration is high in the blood arriving at the alveolus, and low in the air inside the alveolus. So carbon dioxide diffuses out of the blood into the alveolus. The stale air inside the alveolus becomes lower in oxygen and higher in carbon dioxide, and is breathed out.

The alveolus greatly increases the surface area for gas exchange. This maximises the rate of diffusion.

The wall of the alveolus is very thin – just one cell thick, and that cell is flattened, making it even thinner. This makes the diffusion pathway very short.

capillary

from pulmonary artery

red blood cell

ventilation

oxygen enters red blood cells

diffusion of oxygen

to pulmonary vein

diffusion of carbon dioxide

carbon dioxide passes into alveolus

epithelium of alveolus

film of moisture

There is a dense blood supply to take away the absorbed gases. This maintains the concentration gradient.

The lining of the alveolus is moist. This allows dissolved gases to diffuse.

▲ How the alveoli and capillaries in the lungs aid gaseous exchange

B Which gases are exchanged in the lungs?

The composition of inhaled and exhaled air

Gas	Inhaled air	Exhaled air
nitrogen (%)	78	78
oxygen (%)	21	17
carbon dioxide (%)	0.04	4
other gases (%)	1	1
water vapour	little	saturated

Ventilation

Ventilation is the process of breathing in (inhaling) and breathing out (exhaling) as shown in the diagrams.

Breathing in – inhaling

1. The intercostal muscles between the ribs contract, lifting the ribcage up and out. This expands the thorax.

2. The diaphragm muscle contracts, flattening the diaphragm. This also expands the thorax.

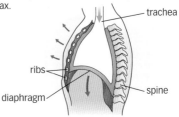

trachea

ribs

spine

diaphragm

3. The volume inside the lungs has increased, and the pressure inside has decreased.

4. Air rushes into the lungs due to the lower pressure.

Breathing out – exhaling

1. The intercostal muscles relax, and the ribs fall, reducing the volume of the thorax.

2. The diaphragm muscle relaxes, and arches up. This also reduces the volume.

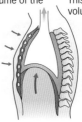

3. The volume inside the lungs has decreased, increasing the pressure in the lungs.

4. The higher pressure forces the air out.

Questions

1 Explain what causes the ribcage to move up and down during ventilation.

2 As you breathe in, describe the role of the diaphragm.

3 Describe the adaptations of the alveolus that make it an effective exchange surface.

4 Sketch a graph to show the pressure changes inside your lungs for two breaths in and out. Label the parts when you are inhaling and exhaling.

↓ E

↓ C

↓ A*

Exam tip

✓ Ventilation is a sequence of events. Learn the four steps in order.

Learning objectives

After studying this topic, you should be able to:

✔ know that plants exchange substances across their roots and leaves

✔ understand the process of transpiration

✔ describe gaseous exchange in the leaf and the role of the stoma

Key words

transpiration, transpiration stream, stomata

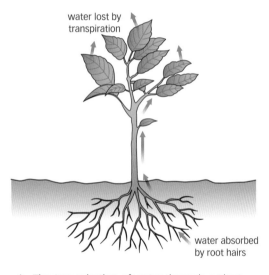

▲ The transpiration of water through a plant

water lost by transpiration

water absorbed by root hairs

In and out of plants

Plants also need exchange surfaces. There are two major exchange surfaces in plants:

*   roots
*   leaves.

Plants need water

Water is important for plants for a number of reasons:

1. Water is needed for the process of photosynthesis.
2. When water evaporates from the leaf it has a cooling effect.
3. Water enters the cells of the plant by osmosis, and makes the cells firm. This helps to support the plant.
4. As water moves through the plant, it transports dissolved minerals.

Transpiration

Plants take up water and minerals from the soil through their root hairs, which extend into the soil. The root hairs greatly increase the surface area of the root for the absorption of water and dissolved mineral ions.

The water flows up the stem and into the leaves. Water exits the plant by evaporation through the leaves in a process called **transpiration**. The flow of water from the roots to the leaves is called the **transpiration stream**. Leaves are also well adapted for exchange – their flattened shape gives a large surface area, and they have many internal air spaces.

A   By what process does water move into the plant?

B   Where does water:
(a) enter a plant   (b) leave a plant?

C   State two uses of water by the plant.

Controlling water loss: stomata

Leaves are highly adapted to be efficient at photosynthesis. A consequence of these adaptations is that the leaves can lose a lot of water by transpiration. To help reduce this, the leaf can control water loss through pores in the leaf, called **stomata**.

- Most stomata are on the lower leaf surface. There are very few on the upper leaf surface. More water would evaporate through the stomata on the upper surface because this area is warmed by the Sun.
- Each stoma can be opened or closed. When the plant is photosynthesising the stomata are open. The stomata are closed at night. When the stomata are closed, this reduces water loss.
- If there is little water, a plant is in danger of losing water faster than it can be replaced. The stomata do not open when the plant is short of water, and this reduces water loss. This prevents the plant dehydrating and wilting.

There are two special cells, called guard cells, on either side of the stoma. When there is plenty of light and water, the guard cells take up water by osmosis, swell, and become firm. This causes them to bend and open the stoma. Water then leaves via the stoma. If there is little water, then the guard cells cannot become firm. Then they do not open the stoma.

Gaseous exchange in the leaf

The leaf is the site of gaseous exchange in the plant. When the stomata are open, gases can both enter and leave.

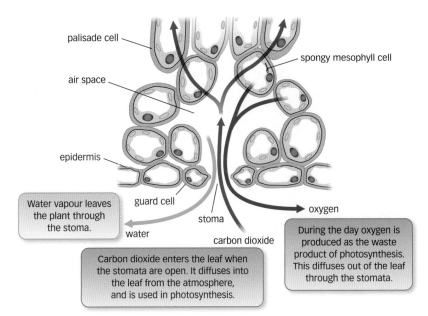

Water vapour leaves the plant through the stoma.

Carbon dioxide enters the leaf when the stomata are open. It diffuses into the leaf from the atmosphere, and is used in photosynthesis.

During the day oxygen is produced as the waste product of photosynthesis. This diffuses out of the leaf through the stomata.

palisade cell
spongy mesophyll cell
air space
epidermis
guard cell
oxygen
stoma
water
carbon dioxide

▲ Gaseous exchange in the leaf

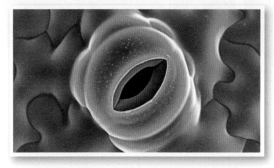

▲ When conditions are good for photosynthesis, the guard cells are turgid, opening the stoma. Carbon dioxide can enter the leaf and water can leave.

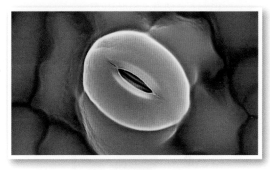

▲ When conditions are not good for photosynthesis, the guard cells close the stoma. This reduces water loss from the plant.

D List two ways that a plant can reduce water loss.

E Describe three occasions when osmosis plays a part in the movement of water through the plant.

Questions

1 Which gases are exchanged through the stomata during the day? ↓E

2 Describe the process by which stomata can open. ↓C

3 Wilting is a response of the plant to dehydration. Suggest how wilting helps prevent further dehydration. ↓A*

Learning objectives

After studying this topic, you should be able to:

✔ know that the rate of transpiration can change

✔ describe and explain how environmental factors can change the rate of transpiration

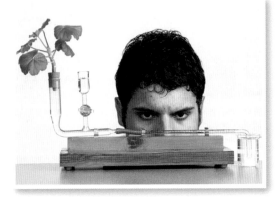

▲ A bubble potometer

A A rate is a speed, which is distance divided by time. What two measurements would you need to take in an experiment using a potometer, in order to calculate the rate of transpiration?

B Increasing the light intensity will increase the rate of transpiration. How would you notice this using the bubble potometer?

C When comparing the rate of transpiration in two plants, why is it important to conduct the experiments at the same time of day?

Factors affecting the rate of transpiration

There are four main factors in the environment that can affect the rate of evaporation of water. Anything that affects evaporation will affect how quickly water moves through the plant – the **rate of transpiration**. The following factors make the rate of transpiration faster:

- an increase in light intensity
- an increase in temperature
- an increase in air movement
- a decrease in humidity.

Biologists use a piece of apparatus called a bubble **potometer** to measure the rate of transpiration. You can change a factor such as the light level, or temperature, and note the change in the rate of transpiration using a bubble potometer, by measuring how fast a bubble moves along a glass tube. The bubble shows how quickly water is moving through the plant.

Increasing the rate of transpiration
Higher light intensity

Stomata close in the dark and open in the light. When the light intensity is greater, more stomata will open. This allows more water to evaporate, so the rate of transpiration will be faster.

◄ A higher light intensity increases the rate of transpiration. The stomata open to allow oxygen into the leaves for photosynthesis.

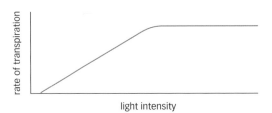

▲ Graph of transpiration rate against light intensity. The rate increases until all the stomata are open, and transpiration is at a maximum.

Increase in temperature

The higher the temperature, the faster the particles in the air will move. This means that water molecules move faster and evaporate from the leaf quicker. So the rate of transpiration will increase.

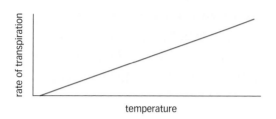

▲ A warmer temperature increases the rate of transpiration

Increased air movement

When air moves over the leaf, it moves evaporated water molecules away from it. The faster the air movement, the quicker the water will be moved away. This increases the diffusion of water out of the leaf, because water molecules do not build up in the air outside the leaf. The concentration of water outside the leaf is kept lower, keeping a high concentration gradient between the inside of the leaf and the air outside. So the rate of transpiration increases.

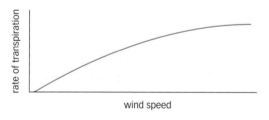

▲ The rate of transpiration is higher on a windy day

Decreased humidity

The less humid the air, the less water there is in it (it is drier). This again makes for a greater concentration gradient between the inside and the outside of the leaf. Water molecules will diffuse out more quickly, increasing the rate of transpiration.

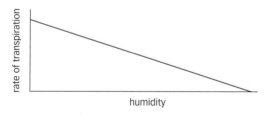

▲ The rate of transpiration is higher when the air is less humid

Key words

rate of transpiration, potometer

Exam tip

✔ Try to remember the factors affecting the rate of transpiration by thinking of the best conditions for drying clothes.

Questions

1 Why do gardeners need to water their plants more in the summer?

2 Explain why plants on a sand dune will lose water faster than plants in a woodland.

3 Why do florists spray ferns with water to help keep them healthy?

↓ E

↓ C

↓ A*

Learning objectives

After studying this topic, you should be able to:

- ✔ understand that substances are transported around the body by the circulatory system
- ✔ know that circulatory systems can be medically assisted

Key words

blood, plasma, trauma

A Explain why single-celled organisms do not need a transport system.

Why do you need a transport system?

Diffusion in single-celled organisms

Small organisms such as amoebae do not need a circulatory system. They have a large surface area compared to their volume. They are surrounded by the water they live in. Dissolved oxygen diffuses from this water into the cell through the cell membrane. Waste material diffuses out of the cell. There is no need for a special transport system.

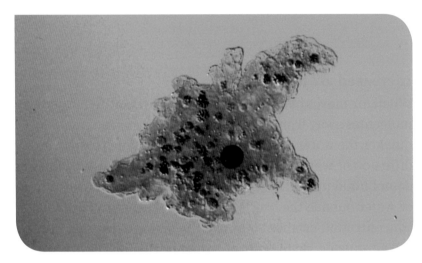

▲ *Amoeba proteus,* a single-celled organism. It lives at the bottoms of ponds and puddles. It is between 0.2 and 0.5 mm long.

Larger animals need a circulatory system, because diffusion alone cannot efficiently transport substances to and from their cells. They need blood to do this.

The human transport system

The **blood** is your main transport system. It takes oxygen and nutrients, such as glucose and amino acids, to cells. It collects and removes waste, such as urea and carbon dioxide, from cells.

Blood is a tissue. Red blood cells, white blood cells, and platelets are suspended in the fluid **plasma**.

B Name three substances that blood carries to your body cells.

C Name two substances that your blood carries away from your body cells.

Artificial blood

If people have lost a lot of blood, or have a problem with their blood, doctors may infuse their blood with extra 'artificial blood'. Various artificial blood products are available, but none contain red or white cells or platelets, so they are really substitutes for blood rather than artificial blood. Some are for increasing the blood volume, and some are for carrying oxygen.

Increasing the blood volume

These volume expanders are used by paramedics in emergency situations. If a patient has lost a lot of blood, but there is no real blood of the correct type to infuse, saline (salt) solution can be used instead. Some volume expanders also contain sugars and proteins. The volume expanders can maintain normal blood pressure, and the remaining haemoglobin in the patient's blood will carry enough oxygen to the body tissues to sustain a motionless patient.

Oxygen carriers

If the blood loss was such that more than two-thirds of your red cells were lost, you would need artificial blood that can carry oxygen. Some types contain chemicals that can carry and release oxygen. Other types contain encapsulated haemoglobin. Haemoglobin cannot be used free in the blood without being in capsules, because it would be filtered out in the kidneys and would damage them. These types of oxygen carriers are undergoing trials on emergency patients.

Uses of artificial blood products

Unlike real blood, artificial blood products do not have to be matched to patients. They could be useful

- for treating war casualties
- in countries where blood transfusions may not be safe, as blood may not be screened for disease
- to rapidly treat **trauma** patients who have serious injuries, often as a result of violence or an accident
- because they can be stored for one to three years at room temperature
- because they immediately restore full oxygen-carrying capacity to recipients, whereas this takes 24 hours with real blood.

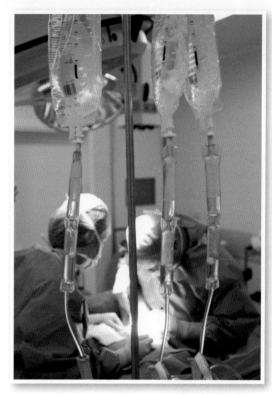

▲ Saline drips replace fluid lost by a patient during an operation

Questions

1 What are blood expanders, and when might they be used?

2 What are oxygen carriers?

3 Why might the remaining haemoglobin in a trauma patient's blood be enough to sustain a motionless patient, but not someone who is mobile?

4 Evaluate the usefulness of artificial blood products.

Exam tip   AQA

✓ If you are asked to evaluate something, try to think of some benefits and some risks.

Learning objectives

After studying this topic, you should be able to:

- ✔ know the names and locations of the four main chambers of the heart
- ✔ understand that there are two separate circulation systems, one to the lungs and one to the rest of the body
- ✔ understand the functions of ventricles and heart valves

Key words

ventricles, atria, valves

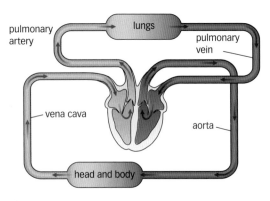

▲ The human double circulatory system

A The double circulatory system allows mammals to be very active. Why do you think this is?

B Draw a simplified diagram showing the double circulatory system. Label the atria, ventricles, aorta, vena cava, pulmonary artery, and pulmonary vein.

Two separate circulatory systems

Humans and other mammals have a double circulatory system. There are two circuits from the heart.

Blood passes
- from the heart to the body organs and tissues
- back to the heart
- to the lungs to remove carbon dioxide and collect oxygen
- back to the heart before going to the body again.

Because the blood makes two circuits from the heart, the heart needs four chambers. It is a double pump. Blood in a double circulatory system is under high pressure and so it transports material more quickly around the body.

The heart

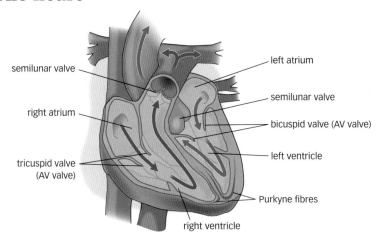

▲ Section through the human heart. Red arrows show the path of oxygenated blood. Blue arrows show the path of deoxygenated blood.

Your heart is an organ. Its function is to pump blood around the body. The wall of the heart is made of muscle. It is a specialised type of muscle called cardiac muscle.

The walls of the **ventricles** (lower chambers) are thicker than the walls of the **atria** (upper chambers). The left ventricle wall is thicker than the right ventricle wall. Blood leaving the left ventricle goes all around the body. Blood leaving the right ventricle goes to the lungs:
- Blood enters the atria of the heart, from veins.
- The atria contract and force blood into the ventricles.
- The ventricles contract and force blood out of the heart, into arteries.
- Blood flows from the heart to the organs, in arteries.
- Blood returns from the body organs to the heart, in veins.

Artificial parts for hearts

Heart valves

The **valves** in the heart prevent the blood from flowing backwards. Surgeons can replace diseased or damaged heart valves. The valves used may be synthetic, or taken from other animals such as cows or pigs. There is no risk of rejection of these valves, as heart valves have no capillary blood supply. This means that white blood cells do not patrol the heart valves.

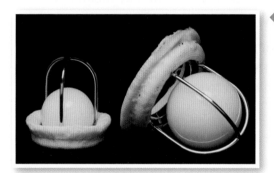

◀ Artificial heart valves. The one on the left is closed and the one on the right is open. They are made of inert plastic and metal that will not react with any chemicals in blood.

Artificial hearts

The Jarvik-7 artificial heart is made from polyurethane and titanium. It was developed by Dr Robert Jarvik and a biomedical engineer, Dr Lyman. The inside is smooth and seamless so it does not cause blood clots that would cause strokes. Many people have had this type of artificial heart implanted while waiting for a heart transplant. However, the wires protrude through the skin.

In France in 2008, Professor Alain Carpentier, a cardiac surgeon, and engineers from the group that makes the Airbus aircraft, developed a new artificial heart that has been tested on calves and will soon be tested on humans.

Questions

1 Explain why artificial hearts and valves are made of inert materials.

2 Why do you think it is important for biomedical engineers to continue to develop better artificial hearts?

3 Explain why the risk of rejection would be a serious problem if heart valves had a capillary blood supply.

↓ E
↓ C
↓ A*

> **Did you know...?**
>
> In the future, it may be possible to use artificial hearts instead of heart transplants. This would be useful, because there is a shortage of donors for heart transplants. Many recipients of heart transplants are young and otherwise healthy, so using artificial hearts may one day save many lives.

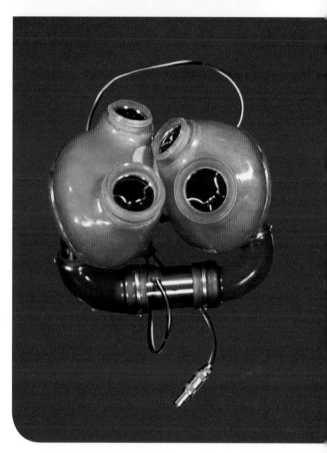

▲ The Jarvik-7 artificial heart

> **Exam tip**　**AQA**
>
> ✓ You need to learn the names and functions of the aorta, pulmonary artery, vena cava, and pulmonary vein.

Learning objectives

After studying this topic, you should be able to:

✔ describe the structural features of arteries and veins

✔ understand how the structures of arteries and veins enable them to carry out their functions

✔ describe how stents may be used

Key words

elastic, muscle, lumen, stent

Did you know...?

A five-year-old child could crawl through the aorta of a blue whale.

A Explain why the lining of arteries is folded.

B Explain why measuring your pulse tells you how fast your heart is beating.

Arteries

Every time your heart beats, the ventricles contract and force blood out of the heart, into arteries. The two arteries leaving the heart are the aorta and pulmonary artery.

The aorta:
- leaves the left ventricle
- carries oxygenated blood to your body tissues
- smaller arteries branch off from it to take blood to the head and brain, and to your other body organs.

The pulmonary artery:
- leaves the right ventricle
- takes deoxygenated blood to the lungs.

Because blood is forced out of the ventricles of the heart at each beat, it enters the arteries in high-pressure spurts. Artery walls contain
- a lot of **elastic** fibres to allow them to stretch, when each spurt of blood enters, and then to recoil. This pulsation helps smooth the flow of blood
- a lot of **muscle** fibres to withstand and maintain the high pressure
- a folded inner lining that can expand as the walls stretch with each high-pressure spurt
- a narrow **lumen** (the space inside the artery).

Arteries have a pulse. You can feel your pulse where an artery crosses over a bone and/or is near to your skin. Measuring your pulse tells you your heart rate, as each pulse corresponds to each beat of your heart.

▲ Light micrograph of transverse section of an artery (left) and a vein (right) (× 30). Notice the thick wall and small lumen of the artery, and the thin wall and wide lumen of the vein.

Veins

- Veins carry blood back from body tissues to the heart.
- Blood in your veins is under very low pressure.
- Their lumen is wide to allow low resistance to blood flow.
- The walls are thin as they do not have to withstand high pressure.
- Their walls contain less muscle and fewer elastic fibres.
- The inner lining is smooth.
- Veins are surrounded by skeletal muscles. When your leg muscles contract, this helps push blood through the veins, up towards your heart.
- They have valves to prevent backflow of blood.

The vena cava brings deoxygenated blood back to the right atrium. The pulmonary veins bring oxygenated blood from the lungs to the left atrium.

What happens if your arteries become narrow?

As you age, and especially if you eat a lot of saturated fat, your arteries can become narrower. Fatty deposits form under their linings, and this obstructs the lumen. This could reduce blood flow and even cause a clot. If this happened in a coronary artery, supplying the heart muscle, you would have a heart attack.

A **stent** can be inserted into a narrowed or blocked artery. It makes the lumen wider again and eases the flow of blood. A stent is a narrow mesh tube that is inserted into the blocked artery. As it expands, it widens the artery lumen.

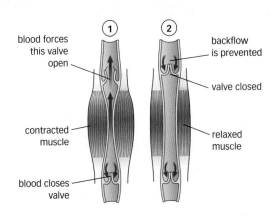

▲ How the valves in veins prevent the backflow of blood

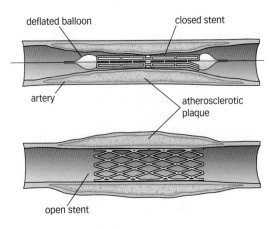

▲ A coronary stent

Questions

1. Make a table to compare arteries and veins.
2. Name the artery that carries deoxygenated blood.
3. Name the vein that carries oxygenated blood.
4. Explain how blood gets back to the heart in veins, even though there is no pulse and the blood in veins is under very low pressure.
5. Some hospitals treat patients who have had a heart attack within 24 hours, and insert a stent into the blocked coronary artery. This minimises damage to the heart muscle. Explain how a stent widens a blocked artery.

Exam tip   AQA

- ✔ Remember, arteries take blood from ventricles, and veins take blood to atria.
  Always V and A.

▲ Light micrograph of a capillary network branching off from an arteriole (× 200)

Capillaries: where exchange takes place

As arteries reach the body tissues, they branch into narrower vessels called arterioles. Arterioles divide into smaller vessels called **capillaries**. Capillaries allow substances to be exchanged between blood and tissues. Capillaries then join to form venules, and these venules join to make veins. Veins take blood back to the heart.

The structure of capillaries

Capillaries are the smallest of your blood vessels:

- They have a wall that is made of just one layer of flattened cells. There are tiny gaps between the cells that make up the capillary walls. These gaps allow blood plasma to leave the capillaries.
- Blood in capillaries is at low pressure and so will not damage their thin walls.
- Their lumen diameter is just wide enough to let through red blood cells, usually one at a time in single file.
- Your blood flows slowly in capillaries.
- Capillaries form vast networks at the tissues of each of your organs.
- This gives a large total surface area for the exchange of materials.

▲ False-coloured scanning electron micrograph of a capillary (pink) carrying blood to muscle fibres (grey) (× 7000). Notice how just one red blood cell at a time can pass through.

A What are the functions of capillaries?

B Explain how the structure of capillaries enables them to carry out their functions.

Did you know...?

In the seventeenth century, William Harvey, a doctor at St Bartholomew's hospital in London, published a book showing how blood circulated in the body, from the heart and back, and to and from the lungs. He realised that the pulse in arteries was linked to the contraction of the left ventricle of the heart. He discovered that veins have valves to prevent backflow. He postulated that there were capillaries, but did not see them as he did not have a microscope.

What is exchanged?

Capillaries deliver blood to your tissues, carrying substances such as:

- oxygen for aerobic respiration
- glucose for respiration
- amino acids for making proteins for growth and repair
- other nutrients, such as fatty acids to be stored
- water to keep cells hydrated
- hormones to cause their target cells to respond.

At your tissues, some of the liquid blood plasma is forced out through the tiny gaps in the capillary walls. This liquid, now called tissue fluid, bathes your cells. Substances dissolved in tissue fluid can diffuse into your cells. Substances made in your cells can diffuse into your tissue fluid. This tissue fluid goes back into your capillaries and then into your veins and back to your heart.

Because there is a great network of capillaries at each organ, none of your cells is very far from a capillary. This is how capillaries deliver oxygen, nutrients, and other useful substances such as hormones, to your cells.

Your cells carry out all sorts of chemical reactions (your metabolism) and these reactions produce waste products.

Capillaries carry waste products away from cells and tissues, including:

- carbon dioxide from aerobic respiration
- lactic acid from anaerobic respiration
- urea from the breakdown of excess amino acids and haemoglobin from old red blood cells (in liver cells)
- spent hormones
- water, a by-product of respiration
- heat made by respiring muscles and liver cells
- hormones from the cells of glands where they are made.

Questions

1 List four substances that your capillaries deliver to your tissues.

2 If you gain a pound of fat tissue, one mile of new capillaries will be made to serve those fat cells. How can a mile of capillaries fit into such a small amount of tissue?

3 Where in your body do you think the heat that your blood carries away from your muscle cells is dissipated?

4 Which organs do you think deal with the urea that your blood carries away from your liver?

Learning objectives

After studying this topic, you should be able to:

✔ understand the structure and functions of blood

Key words

tissue

A What makes blood a unique tissue?

B Where in your body is blood made?

C State the three functions of blood.

Did you know...?

Normal blood has a pH of 7.2. If it changes to above 7.4 or below 6.8, you are in serious danger.

Blood is a tissue

Blood is a **tissue**. It consists of red blood cells, white blood cells, and platelets suspended in a non-living, straw-coloured fluid (liquid) called plasma. Because blood is liquid, it can flow around your body. Blood is the only fluid tissue in your body.

Blood is made in the red bone marrow of your long bones. You have about five litres of blood in your body. This volume has to be maintained, otherwise your blood cannot circulate properly. Blood is slightly alkaline and its temperature is a little higher than your body temperature, at 38 °C.

Blood is for

- transport
- protection
- regulation.

Transport

Red blood cells carry oxygen from your lungs to your heart, and then to your tissues.

Plasma carries
- soluble products of digestion from your small intestine to other organs
- urea from the liver to the kidneys
- carbon dioxide from the organs to your lungs
- hormones from glands to target cells.

Protection

If you cut yourself, your blood clots and forms a scab over the wound. This stops blood loss and prevents pathogens entering.

If pathogens do get into your body, certain white blood cells deal with them.

Regulation

Your blood helps to maintain your
- body temperature – by distributing heat from respiring muscles and liver cells to other organs and to your skin
- pH in body tissues – some of the plasma proteins act as buffers, which means they resist changes in pH.

Plasma

Plasma contains about 90% water. There are many dissolved substances in it. Some are being carried to and from cells. These dissolved substances include:

- glucose
- amino acids
- fatty acids
- vitamins
- hormones
- cholesterol
- carbon dioxide and hydrogencarbonate ions
- mineral ions, such as sodium, calcium, potassium, and chloride
- fibrous proteins that are important for blood clotting when you cut yourself
- antibodies.

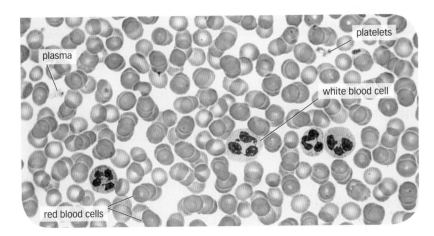

▲ Human blood smear as seen with a light microscope

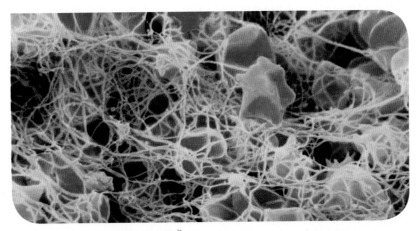

▲ False colour scanning electron micrograph of a blood clot forming (×2000). Soluble blood proteins have come out of solution to form threads that make a mesh and trap red blood cells.

Exam tip

✔ Remember that blood is a tissue – a collection of different types of cells that work together to perform certain functions.

Questions

1 Name four substances carried by the blood. For each one, state where it is being carried to and from. **E**

2 List ten substances dissolved in your blood plasma.

3 How does your blood protect you?

4 How does your blood help regulate your body temperature? **C**

5 Explain the importance of maintaining a constant blood pH. How does the blood resist changes in pH? **A***

Did you know...?

You have about 5 billion red blood cells in each cm³ of your blood. This means you have five thousand billion in each litre of blood, so you have 25 million million red blood cells in your body. This is about 30–40% of the total number of cells in your body. You have about 600 times more red blood cells than white blood cells. People who live in a high-altitude area have even more red blood cells.

A What is the function of red blood cells?

B Explain how the size and shape of red blood cells enables them to carry out their function.

Red blood cells

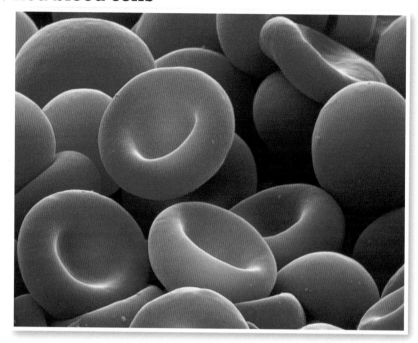

▲ Coloured scanning electron micrograph of human red blood cells (×7000)

Red blood cells are made in your bone marrow. Just before they get into your bloodstream, their nucleus breaks down. This gives them their characteristic shape. Each is a biconcave disc – each side caves inwards.

Each red cell is packed with **haemoglobin**. Haemoglobin is a protein that also contains iron.

In your lungs, oxygen diffuses from the alveoli into your blood, and then into red blood cells. Because red blood cells are very small and biconcave, they have a large surface area compared with their volume. Oxygen can easily diffuse through their cell membrane and reach all the haemoglobin molecules inside the cell. Oxygen combines with haemoglobin in red blood cells, to form **oxyhaemoglobin**.

The oxygenated blood returns from your lungs to your heart and then travels all over your body. At respiring tissues, oxyhaemoglobin splits into oxygen and haemoglobin. The oxygen diffuses into your cells to be used for aerobic respiration.

Red blood cells live for about four months. They cannot divide. Old ones are broken down in your liver. They are replaced by new ones being made in your bone marrow.

White blood cells

White blood cells have a nucleus. There are different types of white blood cell. They form part of your body's defence system against microorganisms. Some types ingest pathogens and other foreign particles. Some produce antibodies.

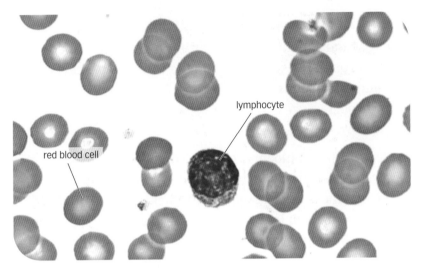

▲ A purple-stained lymphocyte amongst red blood cells, seen under a light microscope. Most lymphocytes are the same size as red blood cells, about 7–8 μm in diameter. Before they produce antibodies they become bigger and may reach 16 μm in diameter. This one is 12 μm in diameter.

Platelets

Platelets are small cell fragments. Platelets do not have a nucleus. They are very important in helping blood to clot at a wound. Each platelet lasts for about a week, but new ones are being made all the time in your bone marrow. You should have about 300×10^9 platelets in each litre of your blood. Old platelets are destroyed by phagocytes (another type of white blood cell) in your liver.

Questions

1 State two functions of white blood cells.

2 Why do you think red blood cells cannot divide?

3 If red blood cells are 7.5 μm in diameter, calculate the diameter of the platelets in the electron micrograph on the right.

4 Red blood cells lack mitochondria. What type of respiration can they use?

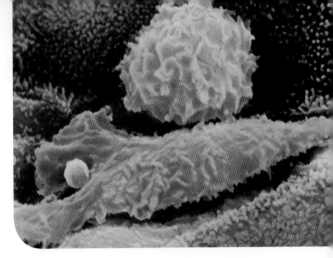

▲ False-coloured scanning electron micrograph of two macrophages in the lungs. One is elongated to engulf (ingest) a round particle. Macrophages in your lungs remove dust particles, pollen, and pathogens.

C Knowing that the lymphocyte in the picture on the left is 12 μm in diameter, calculate the magnification of this light micrograph.

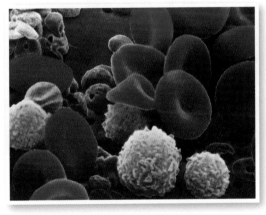

▲ Coloured scanning electron micrograph of blood cells. The small, pink cell fragments are platelets.

Exam tip AQA

✓ If you are asked to 'suggest', or are asked 'why do you think?', you need to use your knowledge from other biology topics that you have studied and apply it to a new situation.

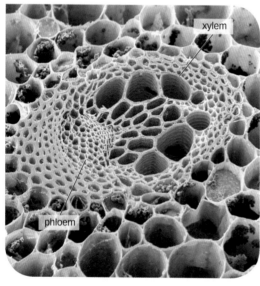

▲ A section through a buttercup stem to show the vascular bundles (× 150)

A Explain why it is important that xylem vessels are hollow.

B Describe the distribution of the vascular bundles in the stem.

Inside a plant

Inside a plant organ are tissues made up of similar cells working together. Two major tissues are **xylem** and **phloem**, which are found in the vascular bundles.

A closer look at vascular bundles

The vascular bundles form a continuous system from the roots, through the stem, and into the leaves. They carry out two major functions:

*   transport
*   support.

Both xylem and phloem are involved in the transport of water and dissolved substances through the plant.

*   Xylem: these cells are dead and stacked on top of one another to form long, hollow, tube-like vessels. Xylem is involved in the transport of water and dissolved minerals from the roots to the shoots and leaves.
*   Phloem: these cells are living and are also stacked on top of one another in tubes. They transport the food substances made in the leaf to all other parts of the plant.

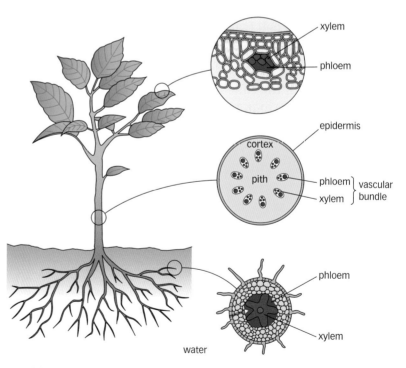

▲ This drawing shows sections cut through the root, stem, and leaf. It shows the different tissues involved in transport around the plant.

Moving substances through the plant

Plants can be very big. They need to move substances from one part of the plant to another. They need to move the water absorbed in the root, and the sugars made in photosynthesis in the leaves, throughout the plant to the parts that need them. Plants move substances in the vascular tissue – the xylem and phloem.

The transpiration stream

Xylem continually transports water and minerals up from the root to the leaf in the transpiration stream.

C What is the name of the process by which water is transported?

D What is the difference between transpiration and translocation?

E Which plant tissue is responsible for the transport of dissolved sugars?

upper skin of leaf

leaf vein

leaf

xylem vessels in the stem

stoma   guard cell

water and minerals

Water moves into the leaves. It evaporates from leaf cells and escapes through stomata as water vapour.

The root hair takes in water and dissolved minerals from the soil

Water and minerals move from cell to cell through the root until they reach xylem vessels

Water and minerals move up through the xylem vessels to the stem and the leaves

▲ The process of transpiration

Translocation

Phloem transports the sugars made by photosynthesis in the leaf (known as the source) to areas of the plant that are for storage or are still growing (known as the sink). This process is called **translocation**.

Glucose is made in the cells of the leaf by photosynthesis. The glucose is converted to sucrose, which dissolves easily. It is moved into the phloem by active transport. It is then transported to areas of the plant where it is needed, such as the growing tips, or storage areas like fruits.

Questions

1 What is: (a) a source, and (b) a sink?

2 Why is glucose converted to sucrose for transport in the phloem?

3 Describe how the distribution of vascular bundles in the plant changes at ground level.

4 The water in the xylem is under tension. Explain how the walls of the xylem are adapted to cope with this.

E

C

A*

Course catch-up

Revision checklist

- Dissolved substances can move into or out of cells by diffusion or active transport. Water moves in and out of cells by osmosis.
- Water keeps cells and bodies hydrated. Exercise uses glucose and causes loss of water and ions in sweat. Sports drinks can replace these.
- Active transport moves substances across cell membranes against the concentration gradient, using protein carriers.
- As organisms get bigger, their surface area to volume ratio becomes smaller. They need special exchange surfaces such as lungs, gills, villi, leaves, and roots.
- Exchange surfaces are thin, have a large surface area, may be supplied with blood, and have a concentration gradient.
- Breathing brings air, with oxygen, into the lungs. Gaseous exchange occurs at the alveoli.
- Plants lose water by transpiration (evaporation from stomata).
- Factors such as air movement, light intensity, temperature, and humidity affect the rate of transpiration. Rate of transpiration can be measured with a potometer.
- Large, complex organisms need a circulatory system that transports substances around the body. The circulatory system can be medically assisted.
- Humans have a double circulatory system. Artificial hearts and valves may treat some heart problems.
- Arteries carry blood away from the heart and veins return blood to the heart.
- At body tissues, substances are exchanged between blood in capillaries and cells.
- Blood is a tissue, consisting of different cells suspended in liquid plasma. It is for transport, protection, and temperature regulation.
- Red blood cells contain no organelles and are full of haemoglobin. They carry oxygen. New ones are made in the bone marrow.
- White blood cells are for defence. Some ingest pathogens, some make antibodies.
- Platelets are for blood clotting.
- Plants have a transport system. Xylem carries water and dissolved minerals from roots to leaves; phloem carries food substances made in the leaves to other parts of the plant.

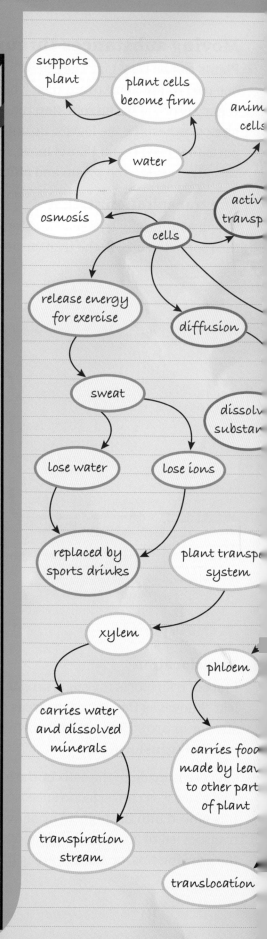

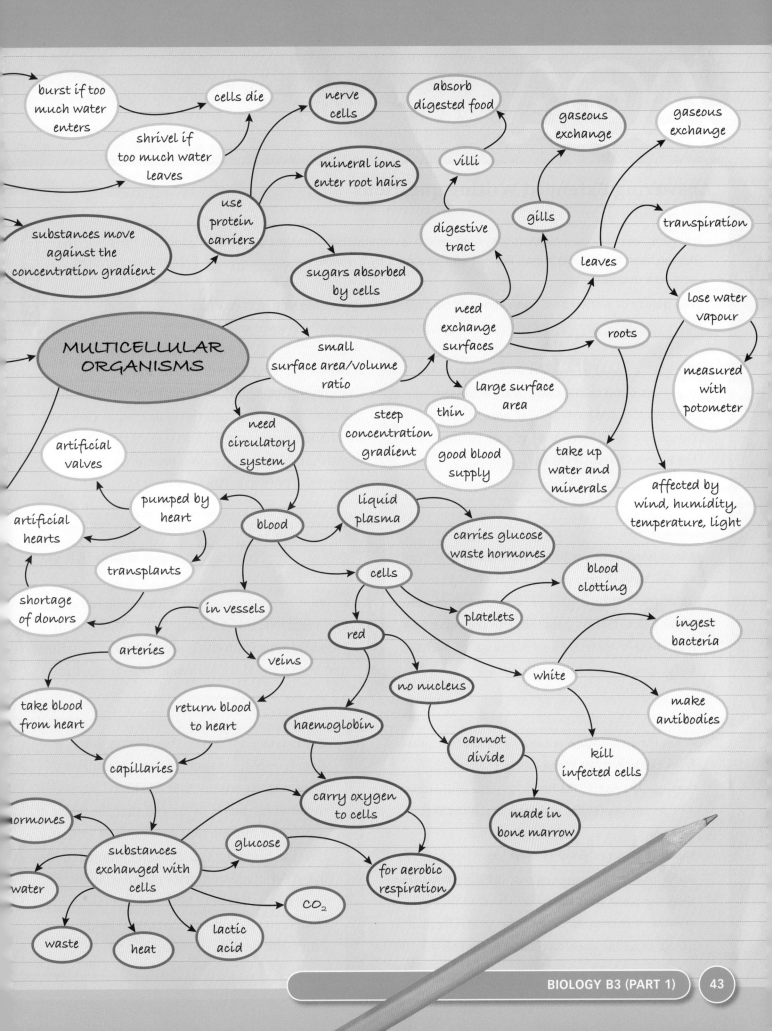

burst if too much water enters

cells die

nerve cells

absorb digested food

gaseous exchange

gaseous exchange

shrivel if too much water leaves

villi

gills

transpiration

use protein carriers

mineral ions enter root hairs

digestive tract

leaves

lose water vapour

substances move against the concentration gradient

sugars absorbed by cells

need exchange surfaces

roots

MULTICELLULAR ORGANISMS

small surface area/volume ratio

large surface area

take up water and minerals

measured with potometer

steep concentration gradient

thin

good blood supply

affected by wind, humidity, temperature, light

artificial valves

need circulatory system

pumped by heart

blood

liquid plasma

carries glucose waste hormones

blood clotting

artificial hearts

transplants

cells

platelets

ingest bacteria

shortage of donors

in vessels

red

white

make antibodies

take blood from heart

arteries

veins

no nucleus

kill infected cells

capillaries

return blood to heart

haemoglobin

cannot divide

made in bone marrow

hormones

substances exchanged with cells

glucose

carry oxygen to cells

water

CO_2

for aerobic respiration

waste

heat

lactic acid

AQA Upgrade

Answering Extended Writing questions

Humans have a double circulatory system, which is more efficient than the single circulation that fish have. The human heart is a double pump. Explain what is meant by a double circulatory system. Explain how the heart acts as a double pump.

The quality of written communication will be assessed in your answer to this question.

The hart is made of mussel and pumps blood. It pumps blood to the body. Then the blood goes back to the hart. Then it goes to the lungs to get oxygen. Then it goes back to the hart and round the body again.

G–E

Examiner: This answer shows some understanding of double circulation. It describes the blood going through the heart twice. However, no chambers are named and it does not make clear that the left and right sides of the heart and separate. There are some spelling mistakes.

Blood goes from the heart to the body and back again. Then it gets pumped to the lungs to pick up oxygen. Then it goes back to the left atrium of the heart. It then goes through the valve and into the left ventricle and out to go all over the body. It takes oxygen to the cells.

D–C

Examiner: This answer demonstrates that the candidate understands what a double circulatory system is. It mentions the left atria and ventricle, but does not make clear that the blood returns from the body to the right atrium and leaves the right ventricle to go to the lungs.

A double circulation means there are two circuits from the heart. The blood has to pass twice through the heart. The heart is made of muscle and as the ventricles contract it pumps the blood out.

Blood is pumped from the left ventricle into the aorta and to the body organs. It delivers oxygen. Then the blood goes back, in veins, to the right atrium. It then goes to the right ventricle and to lungs to get oxygen and back to the left atrium.

B–A*

Examiner: This is an excellent answer. It clearly explains what a double circulatory system is. By saying that the blood passes through the heart twice and that the heart is made of muscle that contracts, it explains how the heart acts as a double pump. It adds more detail about double circulation by describing the route taken by the blood from heart to body to heart, and then to lungs and back to the heart.

Exam-style questions

1 The diagram shows a small part of a lung.

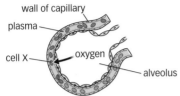

- **A01** **a** What type of cell is cell X?
- **A01** **b** By what process does oxygen move from the alveolus to cell X?
- **A01** **c** What substance in cell X does oxygen combine with?
- **A01** **d** Describe how the lungs are well adapted for gaseous exchange.

2 A group of students looked at stomata on the leaves of four plant species.

Plant species	Estimated number of stomata per cm² of leaf surface	
	upper surface	lower surface
A	4000	28 000
B	0	800
C	8500	15 000
D	8000	26 000

- **A03** **a** Which plant lives in a dry region?
- **A02** **b** Suggest why all four species of plant have more stomata on the underside of their leaves.
- **A01** **c** What environmental factors, besides water availability, affect the rate of transpiration in plants?
- **A01** **d** Name a piece of apparatus that can be used to measure the rate of transpiration.

3 The graph shows blood pressure measurements for a person at rest.

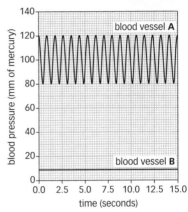

- **A03** **a** Which blood vessel, A or B, is an artery? Give two reasons.
- **A03** **b** How many times did the heart beat in: **i** 15 seconds, and **ii** a minute?
- **A02** **c** At tissues the blood vessels form a network of capillaries. Name two useful substances supplied to muscle cells by capillaries when a person runs.
- **A01** **d** Name two waste substances that pass from muscle to capillaries.

Extended Writing

4 **A01** Explain why large multicellular organisms need a gaseous exchange system and a circulatory system.

5 **A01** Describe how materials are transported in plants.

6 **A01** Describe the structure and functions of blood.

G–E

D–C

B–A*

G–E D–C B–A*

A01	Recall the science
A02	Apply your knowledge
A03	Evaluate and analyse the evidence

BIOLOGY B3 (PART 1)   45

B3 Part 2

Regulating the human and natural environments

Why study this unit?

In this unit you will find out about regulation of the internal conditions within the human body, as well as the impact humans have on their external environment. We all need to understand how our activities can disrupt the balance of the external environment, as these disruptions will affect other living organisms, and ultimately affect us.

In this unit you will learn how your body temperature and the amount of salt and water in your body are regulated, and what might happen if they are not properly regulated. You will also learn how we can grow enough food to feed our growing population, and how we can meet our increased demand for fuel as fossil fuels run out. These activities will inevitably affect the environment, and you will learn how we may minimise and repair any environmental damage.

You should remember

1 You are made of cells organised into tissues, organs, and systems – such as the reproductive system.

2 Plants make food by photosynthesis, and form the basis of nearly all food chains.

3 Consumers may be herbivores or carnivores. Humans are omnivores, as they eat plants and meat.

4 Farming alters the environment and may disrupt food chains.

5 Human activities may have significant effects on the environment.

Research on marine wood borers – has taken a new turn. Researchers hoping to find ways to reduce the damage done by these wood-eating organisms have instead discovered a means of producing biofuels more efficiently. They found that these creatures can produce an enzyme that digests cellulose in plant waste, such as agricultural waste products from crops like maize (pictured) more efficiently than the cellulase enzymes that are currently used. The gene for the wood borers' enzyme has been sequenced, and it is hoped that it can be mass-produced and used in the production of biofuels such as bioethanol from maize. This research is an example of serendipity – research into one topic has produced valuable information about a totally different aspect with an important application.

Learning objectives

After studying this topic, you should be able to:

✔ understand the need to remove toxic waste products from the body

✔ understand why body temperature and blood glucose must be kept within narrow limits

Key words

excretion, urea

Exam tip AQA

✔ Do not confuse the terms secretion and excretion. Glands secrete useful substances. Excretory organs excrete toxic waste made in your body.

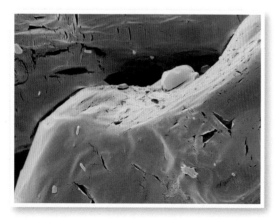

▲ Electron micrograph of urea, a waste product excreted by the kidneys in dissolved form

Staying in balance

In each of your cells there are always many chemical reactions going on. Many of these reactions produce toxic by-products. If these toxins were not removed from your body, you would die. Removal of toxic substances made in your body is called **excretion**.

Internal conditions that are controlled include:
- pH
- water content
- ion (salt) content
- temperature
- blood sugar levels.

Carbon dioxide

Respiring cells produce carbon dioxide. If carbon dioxide accumulated it would lower the pH of your cells, tissue fluid, and blood. The drop in pH would interfere with enzyme action and could also change the shapes of other protein molecules such as receptors on cell membranes. This would be very harmful.

The carbon dioxide produced in respiring cells diffuses into your blood to be carried to the lungs. It diffuses from your blood into your alveoli, from where you breathe it out.

A If your muscle cells respire anaerobically, what waste product do they make?

B How might this be harmful if it were not carried by the blood to the liver to be broken down?

Urea

Your liver cells break down excess amino acids and make ammonia. This is very alkaline and would raise the blood pH to a dangerous level. In liver cells, ammonia reacts with carbon dioxide to make **urea**. This is still alkaline, but is less toxic than ammonia and is carried in your blood to your kidneys in order to be removed.

Water and ions

You take water and ions into your body when you eat and drink. Your blood plasma is about 90% water. It also contains ions. If there were too much water in your blood, your blood cells would take in water by osmosis and would swell and burst. If there were too little water in your blood, your blood cells would shrivel and not function. Water would also leave your body cells to go into your blood. Your body cells would dehydrate and not be able to carry out their functions.

▲ Food and drinks contain water and ions

Temperature

Your body temperature may fluctuate slightly depending on your age, the time of day, and how active you are, but it is kept within narrow limits. Normally, human body temperatures are between 36°C and 37.5°C.

Most of your enzymes would still work at temperatures a bit higher than these, but other proteins in your body and your cell membranes would be damaged if your temperature rose above 40°C. Humans, like other mammals, can regulate their body temperature so it stays fairly constant regardless of the outside temperature.

Blood sugar

Your blood should always have about 900 mg of sugar (glucose) in each litre of blood. Your cells need a continuous supply of glucose for respiration. This is delivered to them by your blood. If your blood sugar level dropped, you would feel faint and tired. If there was too much sugar in your blood, water would leave your body cells by osmosis. This would make your cells dehydrate.

Did you know...?

Some types of cells in your body can respire other substances as well as glucose, such as fatty acids. However, your brain cells can only respire glucose. Having the right amount of sugar in your blood is crucial for your brain to function properly.

Questions

1. Explain why your body temperature has to be regulated.

2. Explain why your blood sugar level has to be regulated.

3. How do you think raising the blood pH would be harmful to your body?

4. By what process would water leave your body cells?

Key words

filtration, reabsorption

Urea

Proteins are digested into amino acids, which are absorbed into the blood from the small intestine. If you eat more protein than you need for growth and repair, the excess amino acids are carried in the blood to your liver. Here, your liver cells convert them to ammonia. The ammonia then reacts with carbon dioxide to make urea. The urea passes into your blood and is carried to your kidneys to be removed from the body in the urine.

Urea is toxic because it is alkaline. If it accumulates in your blood, it will make the blood far too alkaline.

How your kidneys filter your blood

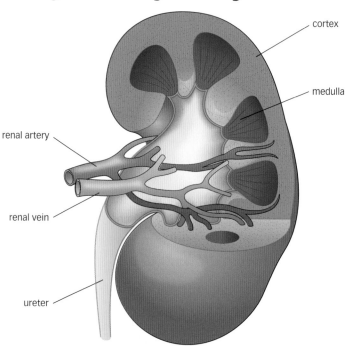

cortex

medulla

renal artery

renal vein

ureter

▲ The structure of the kidney. Blood flows in through the renal artery, is filtered and leaves the kidney in the renal vein. The waste urine, containing water, salts, and urea, passes down the ureter to the bladder.

Did you know…?

Your kidneys help regulate the pH of your blood. Besides removing alkaline urea, they also remove excess hydrogen ions that would otherwise make the blood more acidic. So the pH of urine can vary. Your kidneys also produce some hormones, one of which stimulates the production of red blood cells in your bone marrow.

A Describe how urea is made in the body.

B Explain why urea has to be removed from the body.

C How is urea transported from where it is made to the kidneys?

Each of your kidneys has about one million **filtration** units. Blood enters your kidney in the renal artery. It is filtered under high pressure and lots of substances are filtered out of your blood:

- glucose
- salts (ions)
- water
- urea.

Then the useful substances:

- all the glucose
- the ions that are needed by your body
- as much water as your body needs

are **reabsorbed** into the blood. The remaining liquid, called urine, contains urea, excess ions, and water. It passes down the ureter to the bladder. It is stored in the bladder and passed out when convenient.

As well as removing urea, your kidney also regulates the amount of salt and water in your body.

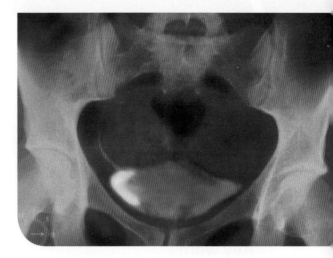

▲ A coloured X-ray urogram of urine collecting in the bladder

Questions

1 Why is all the glucose that was filtered out of the blood by the kidney reabsorbed?

2 Why do you think it is harmful for your blood to become more alkaline?

3 Explain why it is important for the amount of salts (ions) and water in your body to be regulated.

4 How do you think the amount of urea in your urine would change if you started eating a high-protein diet? Explain your answer.

5 How do you think the water content of your urine would change if you drank a lot of tea and lemon squash? Explain your answer.

6 How do you think the water content of your urine would change on a hot day if you ran around and did not drink any extra water? Explain your answer.

7 How do you think your urine would change after you ate a very salty meal?

↓ E

↓ C

↓ A*

Exam tip

✓ You do not need to learn the structure of the kidney. The diagram on the opposite page is to help you understand how the kidney filters blood to remove urea, and reabsorbs the useful substances.

A What is renal failure?

B Explain the difference between acute and chronic renal failure.

Renal failure

Renal failure is a condition where your kidneys fail to function adequately. 'Renal' means relating to the kidney. There are many causes of renal failure.

Acute renal failure

Sometimes the condition is acute (sudden and short lived). Acute renal failure is usually caused by an infection or drugs, and the patient will recover with treatment. The patient may need dialysis whilst recovering.

Chronic renal failure

Renal failure may be chronic (long lasting), and the patient will not recover. Chronic renal failure may develop slowly. It may be caused by overuse of some medicines, by diabetes, or it may be genetic.

In cases of chronic renal failure the kidneys do not filter efficiently, and urea accumulates in the blood. The ion balance of the body is disrupted. There are many symptoms, including:

• feeling sick and losing weight
• muscle paralysis
• back pain
• anaemia
• swollen ankles, feet, face, or hands.

People with chronic renal failure need regular renal **dialysis**, which filters their blood artificially. They may have dialysis while waiting for a kidney transplant to replace the damaged kidney, which cannot be repaired or cured.

Renal dialysis

The patient's blood is taken from their forearm and passed via tubes into a dialysis machine. An anticoagulant such as heparin is added to the blood to prevent clots forming whilst the blood flows through the machine.

Inside the machine, the blood flows on one side of a partially permeable membrane. On the other side of the membrane is the dialysis fluid, which contains

• water and ions of the same concentration as should be in your blood
• glucose in the same concentration as should be in your blood.

The dialysis fluid and the membranes have to be sterile (very clean), so there is no risk of infection. The fluid is at body temperature, to prevent the blood losing or gaining heat as it passes through the machine.

The patient's blood passes through the machine several times over a period of about six hours, three to four times a week. During this time the patient cannot move around, so often the dialysis is done at night, whilst the patient sleeps.

If the patient's blood contains excess salts and water, these will diffuse across the partially permeable membrane into the dialysis fluid. Glucose will not pass across the membrane, as it is at the same concentration in the dialysis fluid as it is in the patient's blood.

Patients with renal failure have to regulate their diet carefully. They must limit their fluid, salt, and protein intake. However, whilst they are actually undergoing dialysis they can treat themselves to extra drinks and salty snacks.

◀ This girl is undergoing renal dialysis. Tubes take blood from her forearm, into the machine. Here the blood is filtered and then passes back into her arm.

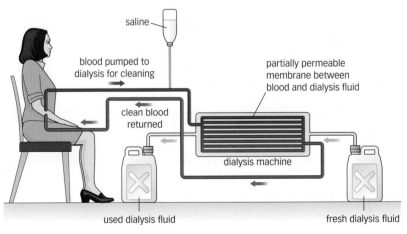

saline

blood pumped to dialysis for cleaning

clean blood returned

partially permeable membrane between blood and dialysis fluid

dialysis machine

used dialysis fluid

fresh dialysis fluid

▲ How a renal dialysis machine works

Questions

1 Why does the renal dialysis fluid and the rest of the machine have to be sterile?

2 Why is the dialysis fluid at body temperature?

3 Why is heparin added to the patient's blood before the blood enters the dialysis machine?

4 Explain why the dialysis fluid contains glucose in the same concentration as in healthy human blood.

5 Why do you think the renal dialysis fluid has to be changed after a dialysis session?

6 Why do you think people with renal failure get swollen ankles, feet, legs, and face?

7 Why do you think people with renal failure become anaemic?

Learning objectives

After studying this topic, you should be able to:

- ✔ understand the advantages of a kidney transplant
- ✔ understand the problems of rejection and how they may be overcome

Key words

donor, antigen, tissue-typing, rejection, immunosuppressant

Advantages of kidney transplants

You can survive with just one kidney. So if someone has renal failure and needs a transplant, only one kidney needs to be transplanted. The donated kidney could be taken from a close living relative, or the **donor** may have recently died.

If the kidney is from an unrelated person, tests are done to see if the tissue types of donor and recipient are similar. The donor and recipient should also be of the same blood group, and the organs may need to be matched for size.

The recipient's kidneys may be left in place and the donated kidney implanted in the abdomen, with its blood vessels joined to the recipient's iliac artery and vein. If the recipient had kidney cancer, the diseased kidney would be removed.

Having a functioning kidney inside your body means that you can live a normal life, as you do not need to be connected to a dialysis machine several times a week. You can go on holiday, for example. It is also cheaper for the NHS to carry out an operation than to provide a dialysis machine for you in the long term. However, the problem of rejection has to be overcome, and enough suitable donors have to be found.

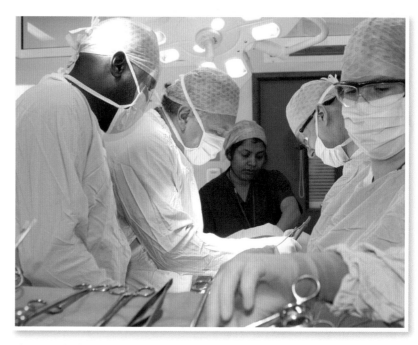

▲ A surgical team performing a kidney transplant operation. This is the safest and most commonly performed type of organ transplant. It has a high success rate, although patients have to take immunosuppressant drugs for the rest of their life to prevent rejection.

A What are the advantages of having a kidney transplant, compared with renal dialysis?

B What precautions does the medical team take to reduce the risk of rejection, when transplanting a kidney?

Rejection

You have proteins called **antigens** on the surface of all of your cells. Every one of us, except for identical twins, has particular antigens, unique to us. Your antigens may be similar to those of some of your close relatives. They may also, by chance, be similar to those of some unrelated people. **Tissue-typing** is about matching the antigens of donors and recipients.

Even with a close match, your immune system can recognise that the antigens on the transplanted kidney are not your own. Your white blood cells and antibodies may attack and destroy the cells of the transplanted kidney. The transplanted organ would cease to function and would die. This is called **rejection**.

Doctors give transplant patients **immunosuppressant** drugs. As their name suggests, these suppress the recipient's immune system to prevent rejection. If your immune system is suppressed, you are more at risk of infection. However, you can try and avoid contact with people who have colds and flu, and the benefits of having a successful kidney transplant outweigh the risks of infection.

Many people have had transplants and live healthy lives afterwards. Every year in the UK, a game of cricket is played between the England Transplant team and the Australian Transplant team. Every player has had at least one transplant (heart, kidney, liver, or heart–lung) and they are all fit and healthy.

Did you know...?

The most widely used immunosuppressant drug for transplant patients, cyclosporin, was discovered by 'accident'. In science this is called serendipity. It means making a useful discovery whilst looking for something else. In 1972 two Swiss doctors were testing cyclosporin as a treatment for cancer. They gave it to mice and found that it suppressed their immune systems. Cyclosporin is a short protein made by a fungus that lives in soil. It was approved for use as an immunosuppressant in 1983.

Questions

1 Why are transplant patients more at risk of infection?

2 Explain why a recipient may reject a transplanted kidney.

3 Some people carry a card and join the Organ Donor Register to say that they are willing to donate organs if they die. It is suggested that we should all be viewed as potential donors, and instead have to carry a card if we do *not* want to donate our organs. What are your views on this idea?

Exam tip

✔ For questions like Question 3, think of some pros and some cons. Then, if possible, reach a conclusion.

Learning objectives

After studying this topic, you should be able to:

- ✔ understand the role of the thermoregulatory centre in the brain and the temperature receptors in the skin
- ✔ describe the changes that bring the body temperature back to normal when it is too high

Key words

thermoregulation, **nerve impulses**, **evaporation**, **vasodilation**, **radiation**

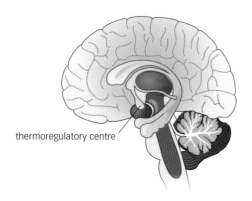

thermoregulatory centre

▲ The thermoregulatory centre (hypothalamus) in the brain

Did you know...?

If you overheat too much, your thermoregulatory centre shuts down. You get hotter and hotter and you would eventually die of heat stroke. You need to be immediately immersed in cool water and to drink lots of fluids, with some salt added.

Your body temperature

The temperature of the human body is normally kept at about 37 °C. This is the core temperature. At your fingers and toes it will be cooler. It is dangerous if your body temperature rises above 40 °C. **Thermoregulation** means keeping the body temperature within safe limits.

The thermoregulatory centre

A particular area of your brain, the thermoregulatory centre, monitors your blood temperature. It can do this because your blood flows through the brain every two or three minutes as it circulates your whole body. This area of the brain also receives information via nerves from your skin. You have special nerve endings in your skin that can detect changes in the external temperature. If your body temperature rises or falls, the thermoregulatory centre stimulates your body to make adjustments. This part of your brain acts as a thermostat. It consists of a heat-loss area and a heat-promoting area.

When you overheat

You may overheat when you

- exercise
- are dehydrated
- are exposed to very high external temperatures for too long.

Your blood carries heat away from respiring muscle tissue. As it flows through the brain your thermoregulatory centre detects the raised temperature. It then activates the heat-loss area, which causes more blood to flow to your skin. Your skin looks red because more blood flows through the capillaries, and more heat is lost.

How else does the thermoregulatory centre bring about heat loss?

Increased sweating

Nerve impulses stimulate the sweat glands in your skin to release large amount of sweat. This pours out onto your skin surface. The water in the sweat evaporates, which uses heat energy from your skin and blood. This **evaporation** cools you. It works best if the air is dry. In humid weather we feel hot and sticky because our sweat does not evaporate.

We can also seek shade or use a fan to move the air around us and promote evaporation and cooling. Removing some clothing may also help.

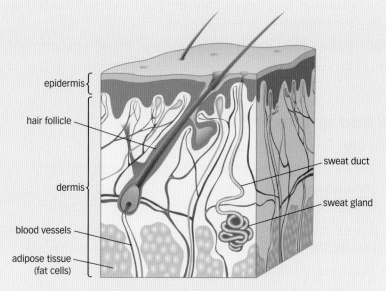

epidermis
hair follicle
dermis
blood vessels
adipose tissue (fat cells)
sweat duct
sweat gland

▲ Section through human skin showing sweat glands and sweat ducts. The sweat glands extract water and salts from the blood vessels. More sweat pours on to the surface of the skin when your body is overheating. Evaporation of the water in sweat takes heat from your body and cools you.

Vasodilation

Nerves stimulate the blood vessels (arterioles) that supply the capillaries in the skin to dilate (widen). This **vasodilation** allows more blood to flow though the skin capillaries. The excess heat from the blood is lost by **radiation**. Your skin looks flushed and feels hot because more blood is flowing just beneath it.

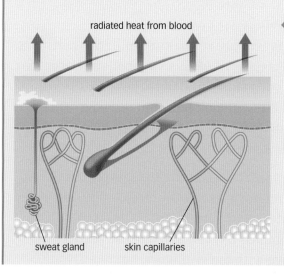

radiated heat from blood

◀ Blood vessels in the skin dilate and heat is lost by radiation. Your skin looks flushed and feels hot.

sweat gland   skin capillaries

A Explain why exercise can cause you to overheat.

B Why do you think being dehydrated could cause you to overheat?

Questions

1 Explain how increased sweating can cool you.

2 Explain why your skin looks red and feels hot when you are overheating.

3 Why do you think you should drink more water during hot weather?

 E

4 How does the thermoregulatory centre in your brain stimulate the blood vessels in your skin to widen?

C

5 Why do you feel cold when getting out of a swimming pool, even on a hot day?

6 Dogs do not sweat. Instead they pant. How do you think panting cools them?

 A*

7 Elephants and rabbits have large ears. When they are hot, more blood flows through their ears. How do you think this cools them?

Learning objectives

After studying this topic, you should be able to:

✔ describe the changes that bring the body temperature back to normal when it is too low

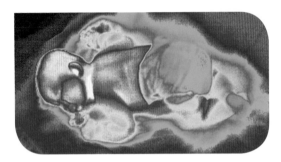

▲ Thermogram of a baby. The hottest areas are white. The temperature scale then goes red, yellow, green, blue, and purple (coldest).

A Why do you think it is dangerous if your core body temperature drops below 35°C?

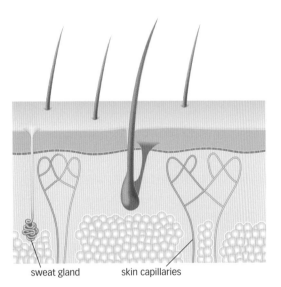

sweat gland   skin capillaries

▲ Blood vessels supplying skin capillaries constrict so less blood flows near your skin surface. This reduces heat loss. Core body heat is conserved.

Core and extremities

When we talk about body temperature we are referring to the temperature of your core – your internal organs. Your internal organs, including your brain, need to have their temperature maintained at around 37°C all the time. The temperature at your extremities (fingers and toes) is always lower. It is dangerous if your core temperature drops below 35°C.

When you overcool

You may lose heat when you

- are outside in cold weather for too long without good insulating clothing
- are immersed in cold water, even for a short period
- are elderly, especially if your home is not adequately heated
- are a baby, as you have a large surface area to volume ratio and much heat is lost through your surface.

If you lose too much body heat, your thermoregulatory centre initiates mechanisms to adjust your body temperature back to normal. It will stimulate heat-promoting mechanisms.

Reduced sweating

If you are cold, your sweat glands produce very little sweat. This reduces heat loss by evaporation.

B Explain why reduced sweating prevents you from overcooling.

Vasoconstriction

The arterioles that supply your skin capillaries constrict (get narrower). As a result of this **vasoconstriction**, less blood flows into your skin capillaries. Less heat is lost by radiation. Your skin will look pale and feel cold. This conserves heat at your core and protects your internal organs from heat loss and damage.

However, in extreme cases of prolonged exposure to cold, you could lose fingers or toes through frostbite. The cells at your extremities would die, as the reduced blood supply means that less oxygen and glucose reaches them. You could still live with fewer fingers, but not if your heart, liver, or brain died.

▲ The fingers of a young man with severe frostbite after a blizzard

Shivering

Your thermoregulatory centre stimulates **shivering** in your skeletal muscles. They contract and relax quickly to give a shuddering motion that is involuntary – it is beyond your control. Muscles need energy to contract, so they respire more when shivering. Respiration always releases some of its energy as heat, so increased respiration releases more heat.

You can of course also alter your behaviour to avoid overcooling, by putting on more clothes, moving about more, eating hot food or drinks, and hunching up and placing your hands under your arms to keep them warm.

Did you know...?

Babies do not shiver. Instead they have special fat called brown fat. The fat cells contain lots of mitochondria that contain iron, so this fat looks reddish/brown. When cold, babies respire this fat in a way that generates more heat than usual. Now scientists have found that adults also have some brown fat in the neck region. Thinner people have more brown fat than heavier people. Heavier people have more white fat that is not respired so readily.

Questions

1 State two reasons why you may overheat.

2 If your core body temperature drops below 35°C, you have hypothermia. Your heat-generating mechanisms do not get activated and you continue to lose heat. This would be fatal if not treated by being wrapped in an insulating blanket and gently warmed up. Why do you think untreated hypothermia would be fatal?

3 Why do you think people with more brown fat are thinner than people with less brown fat?

Exam tip

✔ Remember, 'hypo' means below, as in a hypodermic (below the skin) needle. So hypothermia is a reduced body temperature.

Learning objectives

After studying this topic, you should be able to:

✔ understand the roles of the pancreas, insulin, and glucagon in controlling blood glucose levels

Key words

glucose, insulin, glucagon

▲ Testing blood glucose level

Why does your blood glucose need to be regulated?

All your body cells need to respire the sugar **glucose**, to release energy for metabolic reactions, such as:

- making proteins including enzymes, antibodies, and haemoglobin
- muscle contraction
- cell division
- replication of DNA
- active transport of substances into and out of cells
- nerve action.

Glucose is your cells' energy source. Your blood carries glucose, so it is vital that it always has enough to deliver to all cells. However, it should not contain too much glucose, as this would make the blood too concentrated, and water would leave your body cells by osmosis. Your body cells would dehydrate and their enzymes would not function. The cells would not be able to carry out their chemical reactions.

Your blood glucose level has to be kept within narrow limits.

Your blood glucose level rises after you have eaten a meal. The glucose from digested carbohydrates is absorbed from the small intestine into your blood.

A Explain why your blood glucose level rises after you have eaten a meal.

B Explain why your blood glucose level drops when you have not eaten for several hours.

C Explain why your blood glucose level drops after you have been swimming.

The pancreas

Your pancreas sits within the U bend, or loop, of your duodenum. It is a double gland – as well as making digestive enzymes, it also makes hormones. As your blood flows through it, the pancreas monitors the blood glucose level.

If your blood glucose level rises above normal

Special cells in your pancreas secrete (make) the hormone **insulin**. The insulin passes straight into your bloodstream and is carried to all cells, including its target cells. Most cells in your body respond to insulin. Insulin causes the cells to take up more glucose from your blood. In some cells the glucose is used for respiration. In other cells (in the liver and muscles) the glucose is stored as glycogen (a large carbohydrate molecule). This taking up of more glucose into the cells lowers the blood glucose level back to normal.

If your blood glucose level drops below normal

However, as your blood continues to deliver glucose to respiring cells, if you have not eaten for a while, your blood glucose level may drop below normal. As your blood flows through the pancreas, this lower level of glucose is detected. Some other special cells in your pancreas make another hormone called **glucagon**. This hormone passes straight into the blood and is carried to all your cells, including its target cells. It causes your liver cells to break down some of their stored glycogen and release glucose into your blood, to top it up to normal levels.

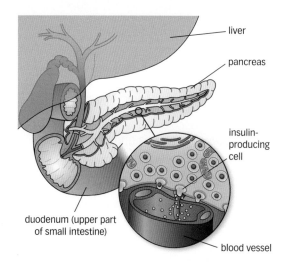

▲ The position of the human pancreas. Special cells secrete insulin straight into the bloodstream.

Did you know...?

Muscle cells also store glycogen, but it is only for their use. Their glycogen does not get released as glucose into the blood.

Questions

1 Which organ monitors your blood glucose level?

2 Which hormone is released into your blood when your blood glucose level rises above normal levels? ↓E

3 Which hormone is released into your blood when your blood glucose levels are lower than normal?

4 Explain how the hormone in Question 2 causes your blood glucose levels to drop back to normal. ↓C

5 Explain how the hormone in Question 3 causes your blood glucose level to rise back to normal.

6 Which of the following are carbohydrates and which are proteins?

    glucagon   glucose   glycogen   insulin ↓A*

7 Draw a flow diagram to show how your blood glucose level is regulated.

Exam tip   AQA

✓ Remember that glucagon is made when your glucose is low – when your glucose has gone.

✓ If you talk about *glycogen* being broken down to glucose, do not confuse it with *glucagon*. You must get the spellings correct.

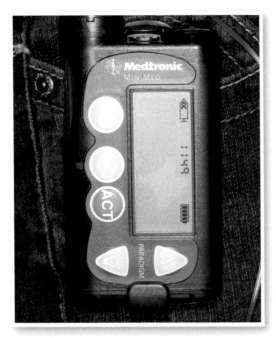

▲ A digital insulin pump. This can be attached to a belt and carried around by a person with diabetes. It delivers constant very small doses of insulin, and a larger dose before meals or if the blood glucose level is high.

What happens if you do not make enough insulin?

Some people do not make enough insulin in their pancreas. Their blood glucose level is not controlled. They suffer from a type of **diabetes** called type 1 diabetes.

If you do not make enough insulin, your blood glucose level will stay high after a meal, because there is no insulin to make your body cells take up the extra glucose.

When your blood is filtered by your kidneys, too much glucose is filtered out and the kidneys do not reabsorb it all.

Glucose passes out in your urine. A lot of water also goes with it, so you urinate more frequently and feel thirsty because your blood lacks water.

> A Explain why not producing insulin will lead to a permanently high blood glucose level.
>
> B What are the symptoms of type 1 diabetes?

How is type 1 diabetes treated?

People with type 1 diabetes have to pay careful attention to their diet. They should

• eat regular meals containing plenty of fibre and other complex carbohydrates, but not too much sugar. These complex carbohydrates are digested to sugar, but only slowly, and so after a meal the sugar is absorbed more steadily into the blood. More protein and unsaturated fats should replace sugary foods.
• take regular exercise
• regularly monitor their blood glucose level and inject insulin into their blood at mealtimes
• avoid alcohol.

Long-term consequences of diabetes

Careful treatment and management of type 1 diabetes is very important, as it can shorten the person's life expectancy. High blood glucose levels damage red blood cells and blood vessels.

Without proper control, diabetes can lead to
- blindness due to damage to the retina
- poor wound healing
- ulcers, which may lead to gangrene and loss of toes or feet
- increased risk of stroke
- increased risk of heart attack.

People with diabetes test their blood to see how much glucose is in it.

What causes type 1 diabetes?

In people with type 1 diabetes, the cells of their own immune system have destroyed the special cells in their pancreas that produce insulin.

Scientists are not certain why, in some people, the immune cells do this. There may be a number of factors.

There are environmental factors:
- They may have suffered from a particular viral infection, such as rubella. The white blood cells that deal with this virus as part of the immune system also destroy insulin-making cells.
- Some scientists think that giving babies cow's milk too early may increase the risk of type 1 diabetes in later life. It may cause them to make antibodies against proteins in the cow's milk, and these antibodies may also attack insulin-making cells.
- Certain antibiotics and anti-cancer drugs may destroy the insulin-making cells.
- Trauma injury and pancreatic tumours also destroy these cells.

There is also a genetic component, because these white blood cells and antibodies only attack insulin-making cells that have particular-shaped protein antigens on their surface.

Genes govern the way you make proteins. People with type 1 diabetes do not make enough of a certain protein that kills the white cells that destroy insulin-making cells.

There are cases of identical twins, one with type 1 diabetes and one without, so for type 1 diabetes to develop it seems you need particular genes plus an environmental trigger.

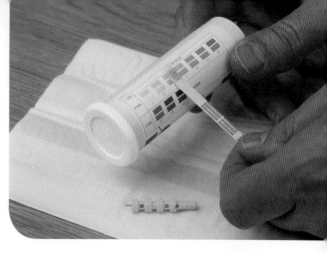

▲ A test strip placed against a scale, to test the blood glucose level. A yellow lancet was used to prick the finger and place a drop of blood on the test strip. The blood reacts with two coloured squares at the tip of the test strip. Depending on the blood glucose level, the squares change colour. The scale shows that this blood glucose level is normal.

Did you know...?

People with type 1 diabetes do not make enough of a certain protein, called TNF-α, that kills the white cells that destroy insulin-making cells. One scientist has successfully treated diabetic mice with this protein. Other scientists are researching the use of stem cells to replace destroyed insulin-making cells.

Questions

1 How do people with type 1 diabetes manage their condition? ↓ E

2 What are the long-term consequences of type 1 diabetes? ↓ C

3 Why do you think people with type 1 diabetes are advised to take regular exercise? ↓ A*

Learning objectives

After studying this topic, you should be able to:

✔ know that the human population is increasing

✔ understand that this increase is unsustainable and leads to pollution

Key words

population, pollution, sustainable

A Families had large numbers of children before 1900. Suggest why.

B The death rate decreased steadily after 1800. Suggest why this might have happened.

C What must happen to the birth rate and death rate to keep the population fairly constant?

The human population

The number of humans on the planet has been increasing. But the increase is not steady. Biologists have studied the growth of the human **population** and have found some interesting points.

1000 years ago, the population of the UK was stable:
* There was very little increase.
* The reason for this was that there were not many people to reproduce, and the food supply was limited.

Between 1600 and 1900, there was a steady increase.
* This was due to better farming methods and improving hygiene.

After 1900, there was a dramatic rise in the population:
* Diet improved.
* Hygiene improved.
* Healthcare improved.
* Infant mortality (death rate) fell.

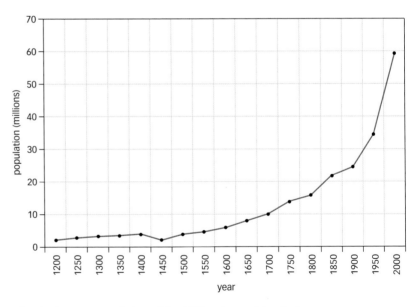

▲ The human population of the UK has been rising fast

The population explosion

The massive increase in human population seen in the UK since 1900 is repeated in most countries in the world. At the same time, the standard of living has improved in many countries. So there is much greater demand for material products and for the resources needed to make them.

These changes have a number of effects:

- There is a shortage of food in some countries.
- More land is being used for building and farming.
- More **pollution** is being produced.
- The world's resources are being used up more quickly than they can be replaced.

This growth is not **sustainable**. The impact of so many humans on the environment is harmful.

> **D** State why the human population explosion is not sustainable.
>
> **E** Biologists say that the use of resources must be sustainable. Describe what this might mean.

Sustainable development

Sustainable development is a term that is used increasingly often. It means using resources for human needs without harming the environment.

Humans use a lot of resources to live modern lifestyles. If these resources are taken from the environment without being replaced, so that they are being used up, this use is unsustainable. This was often the case in the past, and unsustainable use of resources has harmed both the environment and the organisms in it.

Humans need to manage their use of resources. There are two major approaches to this:

1. Replace resources where possible. For example, we use wood for many things, but new trees can be planted after felling.
2. Avoid overuse where resources cannot be replaced as quickly as they are used. For example, quotas are now used to stop overfishing in the oceans – limits are set on how many fish can be caught.

These methods require planning. As the population increases, our demand for resources grows. Resources, habitats, and species must all be considered. Planning for sustainable development needs to become increasingly global.

▲ Our modern way of life uses many more resources than lifestyles in the past

▲ Commercial replanting of conifers in a managed woodland

Questions

1. Recycling helps increase sustainability. Explain why this is the case. E

2. Explain why an increase in the human population might lead to an increase in pollution. C

3. Explain the shape of the human population curve shown on the previous page. A*

Did you know...?

Finland is a Green Champion. It was the first country to introduce a carbon tax. The government imposes a tax on companies that release carbon dioxide into the air.

Human influences on the environment

Humans have an impact on the environment by reducing the amount of land available for other animals and plants, and by producing pollution. These influences can be grouped into two major areas:

Agriculture

- use of fertiliser
- use of pesticides
- loss of habitat
- deforestation
- monoculture
- animal waste.

Towns and industries

- loss of habitat
- quarrying and extraction of raw materials
- dumping of wastes
- production of toxic chemicals
- sewage.

The development of towns, industries, and farms has a number of effects on the natural environment. Building projects remove large areas of Britain's natural woodlands. Agriculture and industry also produce a number of **pollutants** which affect the water, air, and land. Many land pollutants have their effect when they are washed from the land into waterways.

Air pollution

Pollutant	Source	Effect on environment

Sulfur dioxide and nitrogen oxides	Burning (combustion) of fossil fuels	Dissolves in rain to form acid rain:
		    damages plant leaves
		    acidifies lakes
		    changes minerals available in water supplies
		    causes bronchitis.

Carbon dioxide	Burning (combustion) of fossil fuels	Dissolves in rain to form acid rain (see above). A greenhouse gas which keeps more heat in the atmosphere, leading to global warming.
Methane	Cows and rice fields	Another greenhouse gas which contributes to global warming.

Smoke	Burning (combustion) of fuels	Releases particles into the air which cause:
		    bronchitis
		    reduction in photosynthesis.

CFCs	Aerosols and refrigerator coolants	Destroy the ozone layer in the upper atmosphere, allowing more ultraviolet radiation through and contributing to skin cancers.

▲ Smoke and steam from a petrochemical plant

▲ A biologist collecting water samples for testing

> **A** List three ways in which farming can adversely affect the environment.
>
> **B** How does sulfur dioxide produce acid rain?

Water pollution

Pollutant	Source	Effect on environment
Untreated sewage	Sewage works	Bacteria can cause disease, eg typhoid and cholera. Nitrates in the water lead to the death of fish by a process called eutrophication.
Fertilisers	Farms	Nitrates in the water lead to the death of fish by a process called eutrophication.
Pesticides and herbicides	Farms	These chemicals are washed into waterways and may build up in food chains to toxic levels.
Toxic chemicals	Factories and mining	Poison organisms directly, or may build up in food chains to toxic levels.
Detergents	Domestic use	Kill valuable microbes.
Oil	Tankers and pipelines	Kills birds and fish. Pollutes the sea bed.

Questions

1 Give: (a) the source, (b) the effects of smoke in the atmosphere. **↓ E**

2 Use information on these pages to explain why the increase in the human population is leading to more pollution of the air. **↓ C**

3 Explain why people in most towns are now only allowed to burn smokeless fuel.

4 Everybody wants the latest mobile phone. However, there is a cost to the environment in buying such products. Identify effects on the environment that producing mobile phones may have. **↓ A***

25: Deforestation

Learning objectives

After studying this topic, you should be able to:

- ✔ understand what deforestation is
- ✔ know the consequences of deforestation

Key words

deforestation, peat

Can't see the woods or the trees

Wood is a highly commercial product, and the land that trees grow on is sometimes prized even more. The large-scale felling of trees, called **deforestation**, can be a lucrative business. Deforestation is carried out for two major reasons:

- to provide timber for furniture, building, and fuel
- to use the forest land for farming, towns, and industries.

In many developing regions of the world, felling trees and selling the timber provides a quick income. What is more, generating farmland allows cash crops to be grown, which again generates a rapid income. However, while this has a short-term benefit to the local economy, the trees are often not replaced. This is happening on a massive scale, leading to a net reduction in the area of forest in the world. Deforestation has a lasting harmful impact worldwide.

> A State two major reasons for deforestation.
>
> B Why do many people in developing countries carry out deforestation?

▲ This truck is carrying logs from felled rainforest in Gabon, west central Africa

The cost of deforestation

1. Slash and burn	When forests are cleared for farms, the tree litter and stumps are often burnt to remove them. This releases carbon dioxide into the air.

2. Effect on global gases	Deforestation leads to a rise in carbon dioxide levels in the atmosphere by
	• the release of carbon dioxide during burning • the release of carbon dioxide during the decomposition of felled trees by microorganisms • a reduction in photosynthesis, so less carbon dioxide is taken up by trees and locked up in wood for many years.

3. Land for cattle and rice 	Forest land is often cleared for cattle farms or rice fields. Both of these release large quantities of methane gas into the atmosphere. Methane is a major greenhouse gas.
4. Land for biofuel crops 	Land can be cleared to grow crops to make biofuels based on ethanol. These are a low-polluting fuel. However, the loss of forest land still reduces the amount of carbon dioxide taken up.
5. Loss of biodiversity 	A diverse forest community is removed and replaced with a single crop. This provides few habitats and removes large amounts of the same mineral from the soil.
6. Loss of future resources 	With this loss of biodiversity, many species may become extinct, some of them as yet unknown to humans. These species, particularly tree species, may hold valuable potential uses for us, as cures for diseases, for example.
7. Soil erosion 	The removal of trees may lead to soil erosion, as there are no tree roots to hold the soil together. This allows heavy rain to wash the soil away.

Destruction of peat bogs

Peat is produced over thousands of years from sphagnum moss in very wet acidic boggy areas. The acid preserves the dead moss for thousands of years. The peat is very nutrient rich, and has been dug extensively, mainly to produce compost for the garden market. This gradually led to the removal of vast areas of peat bog. More than 90% of the bogs in England have been damaged or destroyed. Not only are we losing a diverse habitat, but as soon as the peat is aerated in gardens, the decay process begins, releasing carbon dioxide back into the atmosphere. Many gardeners now use peat-free composts.

Exam tip **AQA**

✔ Link the two major gases mentioned here, carbon dioxide and methane, to the process of global warming described in the next spread.

C Why is the drugs industry concerned about deforestation?

D Explain how trees prevent soil erosion.

Did you know...?

Peat bogs once covered 15% of Ireland. Much of this has been removed for burning as well as for gardens.

Questions

1 Explain how deforestation can lead to a rise in methane levels in the atmosphere. ↓ E

2 Explain three ways in which deforestation results in a rise in carbon dioxide in the atmosphere. ↓ C

3 Explain why peat-free composts are important for the environment.

4 Suggest how the human population can use wood in a sustainable way. ↓ A*

Too hot to handle

Global warming is an overall rise in average global temperatures. Most scientists think this is due to more heat being trapped in the Earth's atmosphere. The atmosphere naturally contains gases called **greenhouse gases**, which trap heat and make Earth warmer than it would otherwise be. However, we are producing more and more greenhouse gases, which increase the atmosphere's natural 'greenhouse effect'.

Biologists have become increasingly worried that global warming is happening at an alarming rate, caused by humans altering the balance of gases in the atmosphere.

Gases that trap heat in

The two major greenhouse gases that are increasing in the atmosphere and contributing to global warming are

- carbon dioxide – from increased combustion of fossil fuels to supply us with energy, and as a result of deforestation
- methane – from cattle, rice fields, and decaying waste.

The greenhouse effect

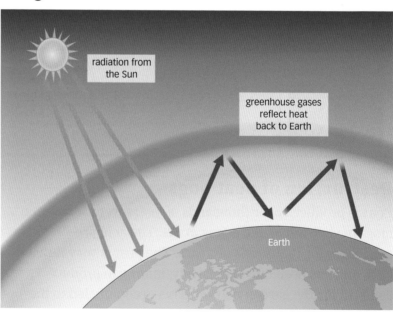

radiation from the Sun

greenhouse gases reflect heat back to Earth

Earth

▲ Greenhouse gases reflect heat back to Earth, keeping the temperature higher

Any activity that increases the amount of greenhouse gases in the atmosphere, such as combustion and deforestation, will lead to an increased greenhouse effect and global warming.

A Which two gases are the major greenhouse gases?

B What are the major sources of these gases?

Exam tip **AQA**

✔ When answering questions about global warming, you need to focus on the two major greenhouse gases, carbon dioxide and methane. You need to know how they cause global warming, and the effects of global warming.

The effects of global warming

A small rise in global temperatures may not feel significant to us. However, the global effects of a rise of just one or two degrees could be catastrophic:

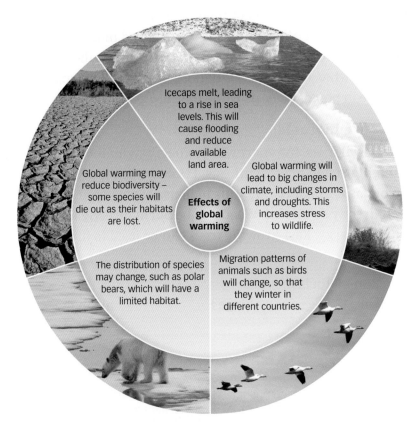

Icecaps melt, leading to a rise in sea levels. This will cause flooding and reduce available land area.

Global warming will lead to big changes in climate, including storms and droughts. This increases stress to wildlife.

Global warming may reduce biodiversity – some species will die out as their habitats are lost.

Effects of global warming

Migration patterns of animals such as birds will change, so that they winter in different countries.

The distribution of species may change, such as polar bears, which will have a limited habitat.

▲ Global warming may have many harmful effects on the environment

Oceans to the rescue

Large bodies of water absorb large amounts of carbon dioxide. So the oceans, lakes, and ponds of the world store carbon dioxide and remove it from the atmosphere in two ways:

- Phytoplankton absorb carbon dioxide during photosynthesis.
- Carbon dioxide dissolves directly in the water.

Both these processes increase as the carbon dioxide levels in the atmosphere rise. So the oceans are acting as a counterbalance to our increased release of carbon dioxide. However, they cannot counteract an excessive rise in atmospheric carbon dioxide levels.

Questions

1 Explain why there is an increase in the level of the two major greenhouse gases in the atmosphere at present. ↓ E

2 Explain why global warming is affecting the distribution of the polar bear. ↓ C

3 How might droughts affect biodiversity?

4 Draw a flow chart which starts with burning fossil fuels, and ends in the melting of icecaps. ↓ A*

5 Explain how carbon dioxide is taken out of the atmosphere.

Learning objectives

After studying this topic, you should be able to:

✔ know that biological materials can be used as a fuel source

✔ give examples of biofuels

✔ understand the production, uses, and composition of biogas

✔ know that fuel can be made from alcohol

Key words

biofuel

A What is the source of energy for making biofuels?

B Name three types of biofuel.

C State one advantage and one disadvantage of using biofuels.

▲ This researcher is culturing algae as part of research into biofuels

▲ Producing wood chips to be burnt in a wood-fired power station

Greener fuels

The burning of fossil fuels harms the environment, as it produces waste gases including carbon dioxide, which leads to global warming. A variety of fuels from biological materials can be used as an alternative. These are called **biofuels**. They are better for the environment because the carbon dioxide produced when they burn is balanced by the carbon dioxide they use in photosynthesis while they are growing.

What are biofuels?

As in fossil fuels, the energy in biofuels originates from sunlight used in photosynthesis. Photosynthesis produces the biomass in plants, and this biomass can be used directly or indirectly as biofuel. Wood can be burnt directly to release energy. Fast-growing trees can be used to fire power stations.

Common biofuels include:

- wood
- biogas
- alcohol.

Advantages of using biofuels	Disadvantages of using biofuels
Reduce fossil fuel consumption by providing an alternative fuel.	Cause habitat loss because large areas of land are needed to grow the plants.
No overall increase in levels of greenhouse gases, as the plants take in carbon dioxide to grow, and release it when burnt.	Habitat loss can lead to extinction of species.
Burning biogas and alcohol, produces no particulates (smoke).	

Balancing the books

To burn fuels while maintaining no overall increase in greenhouse gases is a difficult balancing act. When we burn biofuels we have grown, the carbon dioxide taken in during photosynthesis is then released during combustion.

However, land is needed to grow these crops. In some areas forests are cleared for the cash crop. This leads to a loss of plants to absorb carbon dioxide, and an increase in carbon dioxide released by decaying wood. It also causes a loss of habitat.

Biogas

Biogas is made by the fermentation of carbohydrates in plant material and sewage by bacteria. This fermentation occurs naturally, for example in marshes, septic tanks, and even inside animals' guts. Biogas is also produced at some landfill sites, where the gas can be burnt. Sometimes the biogas can explode, making the landfill site unusable for many years.

Biogas is a mixture of gases:

- methane (50–75%)
- carbon dioxide (25–50%)
- hydrogen, nitrogen, and hydrogen sulfide (less than 10%).

This mixture will burn in oxygen, so forms a useful fuel.

There are a few technical issues with the production of biogas. First, since many different waste materials are used, a large range of bacteria are needed to digest the waste.

Biogas is a cleaner fuel than petrol or diesel, as fewer particulates are released. However, burning biogas releases 4.5–8.5 kWh/m^3 of energy compared with natural gas, which releases 9.8 kWh/m^3. This is because biogas contains less methane than natural gas.

Biogas production on a larger scale

The gas is generated commercially in large anaerobic tanks. Wet plant waste or animal manure is constantly added, and the gas produced is removed. Gas production is fastest at a temperature of 32–35°C, because the fermenting bacteria grow best at this temperature. The remaining solids need to be removed from the tanks and can be used as a fertiliser in some cases.

Biogas has a number of uses:

- as vehicle fuel
- to generate electricity
- for heating systems.

Bioethanol

Alcohol is produced from plant material by yeasts in brewing. On a larger scale this alcohol can be used as a fuel. Mixed with petrol it produces gasohol, which can fuel cars. This is a particularly economic fuel in countries that produce large amounts of plant waste, such as Brazil. Brazil has no oil reserves and plenty of sugar cane waste to make the alcohol.

▲ A bioethanol fuel pump

Questions

1 Explain why biogas from landfill sites is particularly dangerous.

2 Give two reasons why gasohol is used in Brazil.

3 Why must a biogas digester be kept airtight?

4 Explain why using biofuels should not contribute to any net increase in greenhouse gases, in contrast to using fossil fuels.

Learning objectives

After studying this topic, you should be able to:

✔ know that fungi are used to produce foods

✔ understand how mycoprotein is produced

Key words

mycoprotein, fermenter

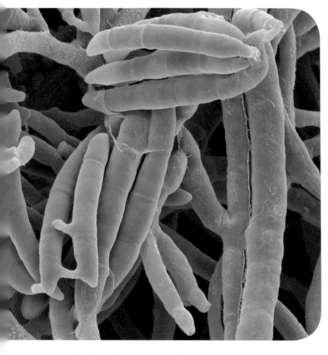

▲ *Fusarium venenatum*

> **A** Name some fungi that are eaten directly.
>
> **B** Name two foods produced by yeasts.
>
> **C** Which fungus is used to produce mycoprotein?

Fungal foods

A number of foods are produced with the help of fungi.

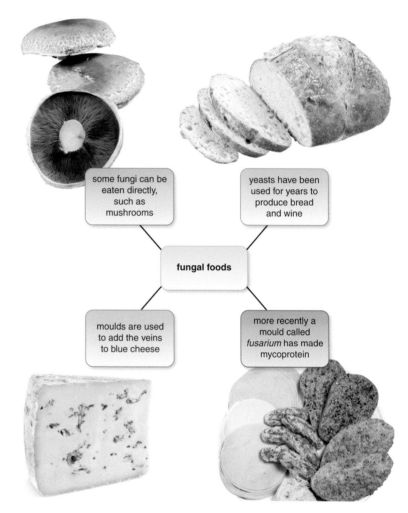

some fungi can be eaten directly, such as mushrooms

yeasts have been used for years to produce bread and wine

fungal foods

moulds are used to add the veins to blue cheese

more recently a mould called *fusarium* has made mycoprotein

▲ Some fungi are eaten directly in their natural state; others are used to produce foods

Mycoprotein

Why make mycoprotein?

In the 1960s, scientists became concerned about possibilities of food shortages as the world population increased. They were particularly concerned about producing enough protein to feed the world. Biologists looked for an organism that could convert waste plant materials into a protein-based food. In 1967 a fungus was discovered that could do this – *Fusarium venenatum*. After about ten years of research and development, **mycoprotein** was produced. This is a high-protein food product suitable for vegetarians.

Mycoprotein production

Mycoprotein is produced in large tanks called **fermenters**. The two largest fermenters in the world are used to produce mycoprotein. It is a continuous process. The fungi are placed in the tank filled with water and glucose syrup.

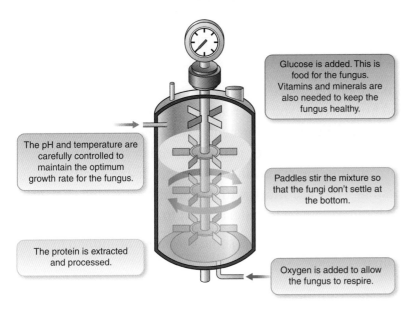

Glucose is added. This is food for the fungus. Vitamins and minerals are also needed to keep the fungus healthy.

The pH and temperature are carefully controlled to maintain the optimum growth rate for the fungus.

Paddles stir the mixture so that the fungi don't settle at the bottom.

The protein is extracted and processed.

Oxygen is added to allow the fungus to respire.

▲ A fermenter for producing mycoprotein

Nutrient	Amount (g) per 100 g of mycoprotein
protein	11.0
carbohydrate	3.0
all fat	2.9
saturated fat	0.7
fibre	6.0

▲ The nutrients in mycoprotein

Processing to give the finished product

The mycoprotein is removed from the fermenter. Next, a number of processing steps are carried out:

- The crude product is heated to 65 °C to remove excess nucleic acids. High levels of nucleic acid in the protein might cause gout.
- It is centrifuged – spun at high speed – to remove water.
- Egg is added to bind the product together.
- The mycoprotein is frozen to create fibres, making it resemble meat.

The nutritional value of mycoprotein

Mycoprotein is an excellent source of protein in the diet. As well as providing protein, it is a low-fat, high-fibre food, which many people think is healthier than meat.

Questions

1 What conditions must be kept constant in the mycoprotein fermenter?

E

2 Why is the product centrifuged?

3 What type of respiration occurs in a mycoprotein fermenter?

C

4 When mycoprotein was developed, some people didn't like the thought of eating a food produced by a microbe. Make a nutritional argument for eating mycoprotein.

A*

Energy transfer in food chains

You may remember that at each link in a food chain, the amount of energy and biomass becomes less. Some energy is transferred to the environment at each stage. So, as you move along a food chain, there is less and less of the original energy and biomass available. The longer the food chain, the less food is available to organisms at the end.

This affects our place in food chains. If you think about the food humans eat, you will realise that most of our food is either a producer or a herbivore. We seldom eat carnivores. Farming produces either plant material or herbivores for our consumption. This makes our food chains as efficient as possible. They are short, with fewer links at which energy and biomass can be transferred out to the environment.

The food web below shows some examples of human food chains:

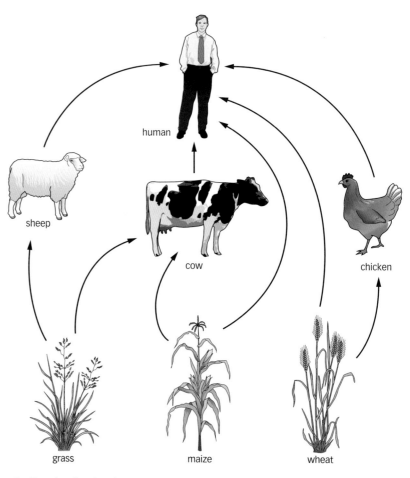

▲ Farming food web

A What two things become less available as you move along a food chain?

B List ten foods that a human might eat, and identify which level these foods occupy in a food chain.

C Why is it more efficient for humans to eat only herbivores and producers, rather than carnivores?

Maximising energy transfer

As biologists began to understand the ideas of energy transfer in food chains, they were able to look at farming methods and maximise the energy efficiency of their processes. For example, look at these two methods of rearing chickens – free range farming and intensive **battery farming**, in which large numbers of chickens are reared closely together indoors.

These principles are not just used for chickens – many other animals, such as pigs and calves, are reared intensively.

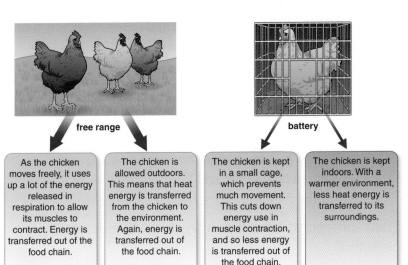

As the chicken moves freely, it uses up a lot of the energy released in respiration to allow its muscles to contract. Energy is transferred out of the food chain.	The chicken is allowed outdoors. This means that heat energy is transferred from the chicken to the environment. Again, energy is transferred out of the food chain.	The chicken is kept in a small cage, which prevents much movement. This cuts down energy use in muscle contraction, and so less energy is transferred out of the food chain.	The chicken is kept indoors. With a warmer environment, less heat energy is transferred to its surroundings.

▲ Intensive farming maximises efficiency and retains more energy in the food chain

▲ An intensive dairy farm

Advantages and disadvantages of energy-efficient farming

Advantages	Disadvantages
Less energy is transferred out of the food chain, so more energy is available for human consumption.	There is a greater risk of disease spreading through the animals as they are in close contact.
It is less labour intensive, as the animals are all contained in a limited area.	Some people feel that the technique is inhumane or cruel to the animals.
There is less risk of attack from predators such as foxes.	Some people believe that the quality of the product is poorer.
Production costs are cheaper.	

Questions

1 Give two ways in which energy is transferred out of the food chain when rearing animals. ↓ E

2 How do battery farming methods maximise energy transfer? ↓ C

3 Discuss why some people do not like to buy intensively reared meats. ↓ A*

▲ Dragnet fishing in the North Sea

▲ Cod has always been a popular fish with consumers, leading to a dramatic fall in cod populations

A Explain why more fish can now be caught than 100 years ago.

Gone fishing

When human populations were small, little farming occurred and most food was either hunted or gathered. As the population increased, more food was needed. This led to the development of farms. Some hunting still takes place, but the only hunting carried out on a more commercial basis today is open-ocean fishing.

Trawlers and nets

Commercial fishing features large ocean-going vessels, which lower large nets into the sea and catch shoals of fish. Modern developments in fishing fleets have resulted in greater numbers of fish being caught.

Modern fishing fleets benefit from technological advances such as:

- sonar to locate fish
- sophisticated net designs to prevent fish escaping
- well-designed boats to travel long distances and process and store the fish after they have been caught.

Many different species of fish are caught commercially, including:

- cod
- herring
- mackerel
- haddock.

Too efficient

Developments in fishing technology have provided bigger and bigger catches, but this has led to problems. Fishing fleets have overfished many seas, and the populations of some of our more popular fish have been seriously reduced. By the end of the 1960s, fish like cod were no longer common. The situation became so critical that international governments had to intervene.

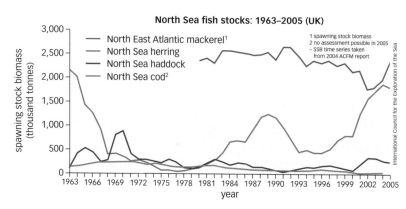

▲ Graph showing fish stocks of some species in the North Atlantic

The main fishing waters for British trawlers are the seas to the north of the UK. Figures have been recorded by the Department for Environment, Food and Rural Affairs (Defra), which have tracked **fish stocks** in the North Sea for several years. They show several key points:

- A general increase in fishing in response to increased demand by a growing human population.
- Stocks of many fish have fallen as a result.
- During the 1970s the levels of fish in the sea were very low.
- This level of fishing was unsustainable.
- The European Community (EC) intervened to protect the fish.
- This has allowed the recovery of some fish, such as herring.
- There is now a sustainable level of fishing.
- Some species, such as cod, are still dangerously low in numbers, and have been low for a long time.

Protecting fish stocks

National governments realised that they had to act to protect fish stocks in their own waters. Both the British Government and the EC looked for ways to allow the fish stocks to recover. The two major conservation methods they employed were:

- Net size – the size of the holes in the nets was increased. This would allow the smaller, younger fish to escape, as they would pass through the holes. These younger fish would then survive, breed, and help the population recover.
- Fishing **quotas** – each government set a limit on the number of fish of each species that could be caught. This meant that fewer fish from the species most in danger were removed, so the populations could recover.

These measures have enabled fishing to be sustainable in the North Sea. Fishing has been reduced to a level at which the fish populations can slowly recover. However, the disadvantage has been that many fishing communities have suffered unemployment as a result of reduced fishing.

C Which fish seems most likely to disappear from the North Sea?

D Why were the fishing methods of the 1960s unsustainable?

Questions

1 What actions have international governments taken to conserve fish populations? ↓ E

2 Look at the graph on the previous page. Which fish species has shown the greatest recovery in recent times? ↓ C

3 How effective have these government measures been, and how do we know this? ↓ A*

Course catch-up

- ○ Living organisms produce toxic wastes, such as carbon dioxide, urea, and heat, which must be removed.
- ○ Body temperature and blood glucose must be kept within narrow limits.
- ○ The water and ion content of the body has to be regulated.
- ○ Kidneys filter urea, excess salts, and water from the blood.
- ○ Renal (kidney) failure can be treated by dialysis or a kidney transplant.
- ○ Recipient and donor have to be matched for blood group and tissue type. The recipient must take immunosuppressant drugs to prevent rejection of the transplanted organ.
- ○ Sweating and vasodilation prevent overheating.
- ○ Reduced sweating, vasoconstriction and shivering prevent overcooling.
- ○ Insulin lowers the blood glucose level after meals.
- ○ Glucagon increases the blood glucose level after fasting.
- ○ Some people do not make enough insulin and they suffer from type 1 diabetes. Type 1 diabetes is treated with insulin injections.
- ○ The human population is increasing. More land will be needed to grow more food and to house the extra people.
- ○ This leads to depletion of resources and more pollution. Humans are developing sustainable development methods.
- ○ Agriculture and industry produce many pollutants that contaminate air and water.
- ○ Deforestation (removal of forests) increases the carbon dioxide and methane content of the air; reduces resources and biodiversity, and leads to soil erosion.
- ○ Increased methane and carbon dioxide in the air cause the greenhouse effect that leads to global warming.
- ○ Oceans can absorb some of the excess carbon dioxide.
- ○ Biofuels could replace use of fossil fuels and reduce the greenhouse effect. However, producing them takes up a lot of land that could be used to grow food.
- ○ Knowledge of how energy passes along food chains enables energy-efficient farming.
- ○ Modern fishing has been so efficient that fish stocks are dwindling. Some governments are acting to protect fish stocks.

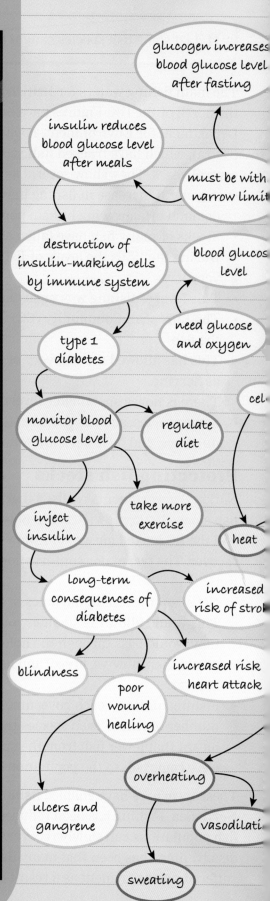

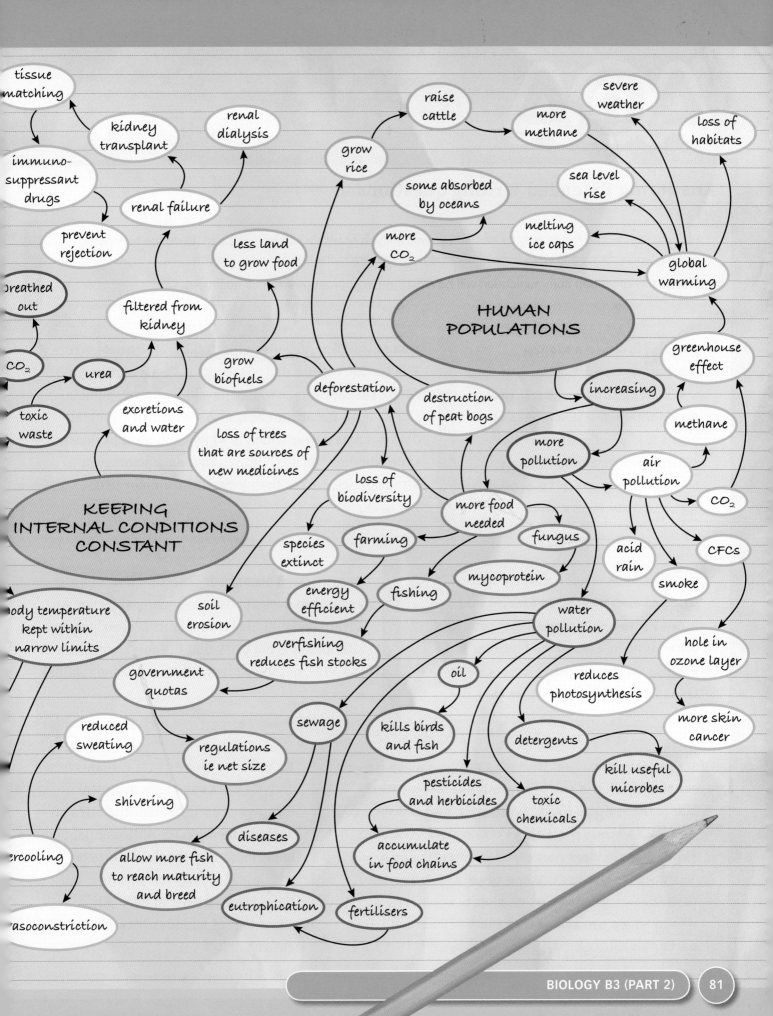

tissue matching

kidney transplant

renal dialysis

immuno-suppressant drugs

renal failure

prevent rejection

breathed out

CO₂

filtered from kidney

less land to grow food

grow biofuels

urea

toxic waste

excretions and water

loss of trees that are sources of new medicines

KEEPING INTERNAL CONDITIONS CONSTANT

body temperature kept within narrow limits

soil erosion

species extinct

loss of biodiversity

farming

energy efficient

fishing

overfishing reduces fish stocks

government quotas

reduced sweating

regulations ie net size

shivering

overcooling

allow more fish to reach maturity and breed

vasoconstriction

diseases

eutrophication

fertilisers

sewage

oil

kills birds and fish

pesticides and herbicides

accumulate in food chains

toxic chemicals

detergents

kill useful microbes

reduces photosynthesis

water pollution

mycoprotein

fungus

more food needed

raise cattle

grow rice

more methane

some absorbed by oceans

sea level rise

melting ice caps

more CO₂

HUMAN POPULATIONS

destruction of peat bogs

deforestation

increasing

more pollution

air pollution

severe weather

loss of habitats

global warming

greenhouse effect

methane

CO₂

CFCs

smoke

acid rain

hole in ozone layer

more skin cancer

AQA *Upgrade*

Answering Extended Writing questions

Patients with kidney failure may be treated by renal dialysis or with a kidney transplant. Describe how renal dialysis works. State one advantage of receiving a kidney transplant over having dialysis.

The quality of written communication will be assessed in your answer to this question.

Dialysis is using a kidney machine. it cleans the blood. it takes out salts and waste. if you have a transplant you have to have drugs to supress your ammune system for ever. With a kidney transplant you can eat a normal diet and have more drinks.

G–E

Examiner: Significant spelling and grammatical errors. The section on how dialysis works is vague and gives no detail. One advantage of having a kidney transplant is stated, but a disadvantage is also stated. The candidate does not make clear which is which. You need to clearly state whether you are talking about an advantage or a disadvantage, rather than leave the examiner to do the work.

The person has to use a kidney machine a few times a week. There blood goes into the machine. Poisonus waste, acess salts and water go acros a membrane into the fluid. Having this treatment is ecspensive. Kidney transplants are cheaper in the long run.

D–C

Examiner: This answer describes how dialysis works, but does not use any technical terms. An advantage of kidney transplants is clearly stated, although it is not clear that the cost savings are to the NHS, not the patient. There are some spelling errors.

The patient's blood goes through a dialysis machine. The blood is on one side of a membrane. On the other side is the dialysis fluid. Waste urea, and unwanted salts and water diffuse across the membrane into the fluid. Then the blood goes back into the patient's arm. This takes several hours 3 or 4 times a week and the patient can't go anywhere and has to watch their diet. If they have a transplant they can live a normal life and go on holiday.

B–A*

Examiner: This answer explains how dialysis works and uses technical terms such as 'diffusion' and 'urea'. It does not mention the anticoagulant heparin, or that the fluid has to be sterile and at body temperature, but there is enough detail here. An advantage of a kidney transplant is clearly stated.

Exam-style questions

1 The European Commission makes annual proposals for cod fishing quotas in EU waters, based on scientific data. Fishermen say that scientists are exaggerating the danger to cod stocks. Scientists say that fishermen are ignoring warnings about low cod populations, and that because they only fish in areas where there are lots of cod, fishermen get the wrong impression of the total population size.

A03 **a** Explain why scientists and fishermen have different ideas about the size of the cod population.

A03 **b** Suggest two reasons why the size of the catch allowed may not depend entirely on scientific data.

2 The table gives the composition of two drinks.

Drink	sugar (g per litre)	sodium (mmol per litre)	chloride (mmol per litre)
isotonic	73	24	12
cola	105	3	1

A03 Explain why the isotonic drink would be best for a runner on a hot day.

3 **a** Give three reasons why deforestation increases the carbon dioxide level in the atmosphere.
A01

A01 **b** Deforestation also leads to loss of biodiversity. What is biodiversity?

A02 **c** Why is it important to prevent the extinction of species of trees?

D–C (side tab)

G–E (side tab)

4 Describe the harmful effects of the following water pollutants:
A01 **a** sewage **b** fertilisers **c** oil.

5 Governments are encouraging businesses to reduce CO_2 emissions.
A01 **a** Explain the link between CO_2 and the greenhouse effect.

A01 **b** Describe two possible outcomes of the greenhouse effect.

6 The kidneys excrete water and urea. The graph shows the amount of sweat and urine produced at different temperatures.

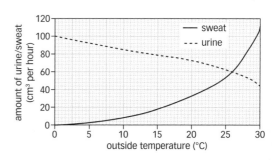

A03 **a** Describe how the amount of urine changes as temperature increases.

A02 **b** Explain what will happen to the amount of water in the urine as temperature increases.

Extended Writing

7 Describe how air pollution may harm the environment.
A01

8 Explain how the body prevents overheating and overcooling.
A01

9 Explain how insulin and glucagon regulate the blood glucose level, and why this is necessary.
A01

D–C (side tab)

B–A* (side tab)

G–E (side tab)

D–C (side tab)

B–A* (side tab)

A01	Recall the science
A02	Apply your knowledge
A03	Evaluate and analyse the evidence

BIOLOGY B3 (PART 2) 83

C3 Part 1

Water, energy, and the periodic table

Why study this unit?

Finding patterns and making predictions are key to science. Dmitri Mendeleev did just that when, in 1869, he created the first periodic table of the elements.

Clean drinking water is vital for life. Chemists are at the centre of the processes that make our water safe to drink.

Many people love their cars. But what will happen when fossil fuels run out? Chemists are working to bring hydrogen to our fuel tanks, creating a more sustainable transport future.

In this unit you will learn about the patterns in the periodic table, and how they help us to predict properties. You will discover how water safety and quality are ensured. You will also learn about energy changes in chemical reactions, and evaluate a new vehicle fuel – hydrogen.

You should remember

1 Everything is made up of atoms of about a hundred elements, listed in the periodic table.

2 Metals (on the left of the periodic table) are usually shiny, and good conductors of heat and electricity.

3 Non-metals (on the right of the periodic table) are not shiny, and most are poor conductors of heat and electricity.

4 Filtration is used to separate a mixture of a solid and a liquid. Distillation can be used to separate mixtures of liquids, or a liquid from a solution.

5 Exothermic reactions (such as combustion reactions) transfer energy to the surroundings, or give out energy.

6 Endothermic reactions take in energy from the surroundings.

7 Burning fossil fuels produces pollutants.

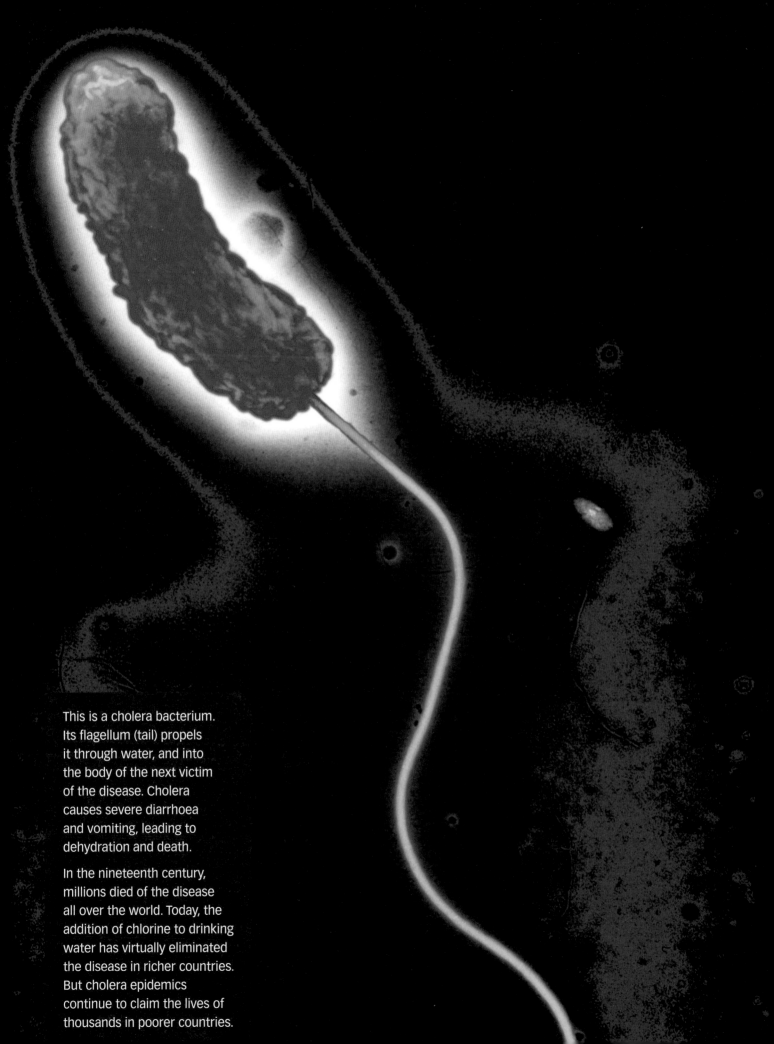

This is a cholera bacterium.
Its flagellum (tail) propels
it through water, and into
the body of the next victim
of the disease. Cholera
causes severe diarrhoea
and vomiting, leading to
dehydration and death.

In the nineteenth century,
millions died of the disease
all over the world. Today, the
addition of chlorine to drinking
water has virtually eliminated
the disease in richer countries.
But cholera epidemics
continue to claim the lives of
thousands in poorer countries.

▲ Fashionable women of the 1860s

▲ John Newlands was chief chemist in a London sugar factory

Decade of discovery

In Britain, fashionable women dressed like those shown on the left. In America, slavery was abolished. In France, the first true bicycles were invented. The decade? The 1860s.

The 1860s were important in chemistry, too. By then, chemists knew of more than 50 elements. The Italian Stanislao Cannizzaro had worked out their atomic weights. Chemists puzzled over properties, looking for patterns. Was there a link between an element's properties and its atomic weight? How could elements best be classified into groups?

Newlands' octaves

In the mid 1860s, John Newlands made progress in grouping the elements. He listed the 56 elements then known in order of increasing atomic weight. There was a pattern – every eighth element had similar properties. Newlands used this pattern to group the elements. He called his discovery the **law of octaves**, after the musical scale.

Newlands' grouping was not perfect. At a meeting of the London Chemical Society, chemists criticised his law of octaves. They asked why copper was grouped with lithium, sodium, and potassium, when its properties were so different. And did it make sense to include the metal nickel in the same group as fluorine, chlorine, and bromine?

A What information, supplied by Cannizzaro, helped Newlands to come up with his law of octaves?

B What problem did other chemists notice with Newlands' law of octaves?

Mendeleev's masterpiece

In 1869, a Russian chemistry professor made a vital breakthrough. On 1 March, Dmitri Mendeleev had planned to visit a cheese factory. But the weather was terrible, so he decided to work from home.

There, he made lots of small cards. On each, he wrote the name of an element, its properties, and its atomic weight. He tried placing the cards in different patterns.

By lunchtime, Mendeleev had come up with an arrangement that worked. The elements were in order of increasing atomic mass. At the same time, elements with similar properties were grouped together. Mendeleev wrote this arrangement on the back of an envelope. It was the first **periodic table**.

Filling in the gaps

Mendeleev knew he had discovered something important. But he realised that his periodic table was not perfect. For example, when placed in atomic weight order, iodine and tellurium seemed to be in the wrong groups. So Mendeleev swapped their positions. Iodine was now in a group with fluorine, chlorine, and bromine. All four of these elements have similar properties.

Mendeleev studied the patterns in his periodic table. He realised that it did not include all the elements. Had some elements not yet been discovered? Mendeleev left gaps for the missing elements, and predicted their properties. Over the next few years, other chemists searched for elements to fill the gaps:

- In 1875, Frenchman Paul-Émile Lecoq de Boisbaudran discovered the element under aluminium. He called it gallium. Its properties were those predicted by Mendeleev.
- In 1879, the Swede Lars Nilson found another missing element. He called it scandium. Again, its properties matched those predicted by Mendeleev.

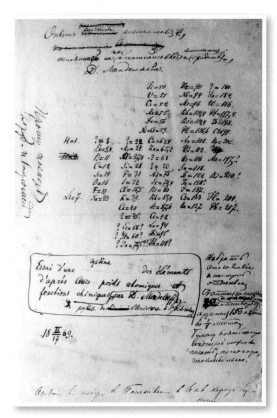

▲ The first periodic table

Did you know...?

The periodic table is so named because similar properties occur at regular intervals – just like the repeating pattern of menstrual periods.

Questions

1 Name the chemist who discovered the law of octaves.

2 Copy and complete: Mendeleev's periodic table listed the elements in order of increasing atomic _____.

3 In the periodic table, what is a group?

4 Why is the periodic table called the periodic table?

5 List two problems Mendeleev noticed with his periodic table. Describe what he did to address these problems.

Exam tip   AQA

✓ In modern periodic tables, elements with similar properties are in the same vertical column – or group – of the periodic table.

Key words

law of octaves, periodic table

Learning objectives

After studying this topic, you should be able to:

- explain the links between an element's position in the periodic table, its atomic number, and its electron configuration

▲ The Wright brothers' aeroplane

A Name the sub-atomic particle discovered by J. J. Thomson.

B Describe Rutherford's two linked discoveries.

Tiny particles, big discoveries

The twentieth century got off to a flying start. In 1902, the Wright brothers made the first controlled, powered, heavier than air flight. In 1903, the Ford Car Company produced its first car.

The new century saw breakthroughs in chemistry, too. In 1897, Joseph John Thomson had experimented with cathode ray tubes and discovered electrons. In 1909, Ernest Rutherford bombarded gold foil with radioactive particles, and discovered that most of the mass of an atom is concentrated in a tiny, positively charged nucleus.

In 1911, Antonius van den Broek suggested that the amount of positive charge on the nucleus of an atom of an element might be linked to its position in the periodic table. This idea inspired British student Henry Moseley. Moseley carried out experiments that provided practical evidence to support van den Broek's theory.

In 1919, Rutherford made another vital breakthrough. He discovered the sub-atomic particle that gives nuclei their positive charge. He named this particle the proton.

Atomic number

The number of protons in an atom of an element is the **atomic number** of the element.

▼ The modern periodic table

Key

relative atomic mass
atomic symbol
name
atomic (proton) number

1	2											3	4	5	6	7	0
							1 **H** Hydrogen 1										4 **He** Helium 2
7 **Li** Lithium 3	9 **Be** Beryllium 4											11 **B** Boron 5	12 **C** Carbon 6	14 **N** Nitrogen 7	16 **O** Oxygen 8	19 **F** Fluorine 9	20 **Ne** Neon 10
23 **Na** Sodium 11	24 **Mg** Magnesium 12											27 **Al** Aluminium 13	28 **Si** Silicon 14	31 **P** Phosphorus 15	32 **S** Sulfur 16	35.5 **Cl** Chlorine 17	40 **Ar** Argon 18
39 **K** Potassium 19	40 **Ca** Calcium 20	45 **Sc** Scandium 21	48 **Ti** Titanium 22	51 **V** Vanadium 23	52 **Cr** Chromium 24	55 **Mn** Manganese 25	56 **Fe** Iron 26	59 **Co** Cobalt 27	59 **Ni** Nickel 28	63.5 **Cu** Copper 29	65 **Zn** Zinc 30	70 **Ga** Gallium 31	73 **Ge** Germanium 32	75 **As** Arsenic 33	79 **Se** Selenium 34	80 **Br** Bromine 35	84 **Kr** Krypton 36
85 **Rb** Rubidium 37	88 **Sr** Strontium 38	89 **Y** Yttrium 39	91 **Zr** Zirconium 40	93 **Nb** Niobium 41	96 **Mo** Molybdenum 42	[98] **Tc** Technetium 43	101 **Ru** Ruthenium 44	103 **Rh** Rhodium 45	106 **Pd** Palladium 46	108 **Ag** Silver 47	112 **Cd** Cadmium 48	115 **In** Indium 49	119 **Sn** Tin 50	122 **Sb** Antimony 51	128 **Te** Tellurium 52	127 **I** Iodine 53	131 **Xe** Xenon 54
133 **Cs** Caesium 55	137 **Ba** Barium 56	139 **La*** Lanthanum 57	178 **Hf** Hafnium 72	181 **Ta** Tantalum 73	184 **W** Tungsten 74	186 **Re** Rhenium 75	190 **Os** Osmium 76	192 **Ir** Iridium 77	195 **Pt** Platinum 78	197 **Au** Gold 79	201 **Hg** Mercury 80	204 **Tl** Thallium 81	207 **Pb** Lead 82	209 **Bi** Bismuth 83	[209] **Po** Polonium 84	[210] **At** Astatine 85	[222] **Rn** Radon 86
[223] **Fr** Francium 87	[226] **Ra** Radium 88	[227] **Ac*** Actinium 89	[261] **Rf** Rutherfordium 104	[262] **Db** Dubnium 105	[266] **Sg** Seaborgium 106	[264] **Bh** Bohrium 107	[277] **Hs** Hassium 108	[268] **Mt** Meitnerium 109	[271] **Ds** Darmstadtium 110	[272] **Rg** Roentgenium 111	Elements with atomic numbers 112–116 have been reported but not fully authenticated						

* The Lanthanides (atomic numbers 58–71) and the Actinides (atomic numbers 90–103) have been omitted.
Cu and **Cl** have not been rounded to the nearest whole number

Having discovered the proton, chemists tried arranging the elements in order of increasing atomic number. This placed all elements in appropriate groups. The problems of Mendeleev's periodic table, based on atomic weights, were solved.

Electrons matter too

Modern periodic tables still arrange the elements in order of increasing atomic number. The positions of the elements are also linked to their electronic structures. Elements in the same group have the same number of electrons in their highest occupied energy level. For example, the elements in Group 2 have the electronic structures shown below. There are two electrons in the highest occupied energy level of the atoms of each element.

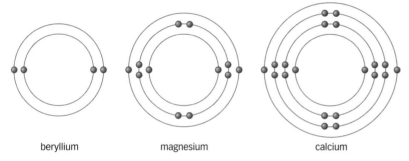

beryllium   magnesium   calcium

▲ The Group 2 elements all have two electrons in their highest occupied energy level

The periodic table started as a scientific curiosity. It became a useful tool. Today, chemists view it as an important summary of the structure of atoms.

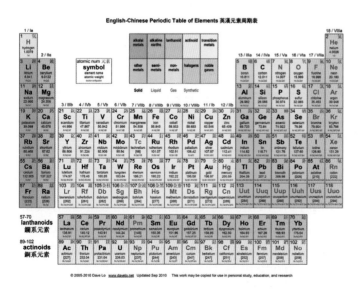

© 2005-2010 Dave Lo www.davelo.net Updated Sep 2010 This work may be copied for use in personal study, education, and research

▲ Chemists all over the world use the periodic table. This one is from China.

Key words

atomic number

Exam tip   AQA

✔ The number of electrons in the highest occupied energy level for the elements in the main groups of the periodic table is equal to the group number.

Questions

1 Give the meaning of the term atomic number.

2 Copy and complete: Modern periodic tables arrange the elements in order of increasing atomic _____.

 E

3 Name the first three elements in Group 1 of the periodic table.

4 Draw the electronic structures of the elements lithium, sodium, and potassium. How many electrons are in the highest occupied energy level of these elements?

 C

5 Predict the number of electrons in the highest occupied energy level of the elements fluorine, chlorine, and bromine.

 A*

3: Alkali metals – 1

Learning objectives

After studying this topic, you should be able to:

- ✔ describe some properties of the alkali metals

Key words

alkali metal

▲ Bolivia has huge reserves of lithium in salt flats like these

A The density of water is 1.00 g/cm³. Name the alkali metals that float on water.

B Draw a bar chart to show the densities of the alkali metals. Describe the overall pattern in density. Predict the density of caesium.

Lovely lithium

Lithium is in demand. Lithium batteries power mobile phones, personal music players, and artificial heart pacemakers. Electric cars have lithium batteries, too. As more and more people buy electric cars, so the demand for lithium will increase.

The South American country of Bolivia has huge reserves of lithium. In 2010, the Bolivian government was testing out ways of getting lithium from its vast salt flats. The government wants Bolivians, not foreign companies, to benefit from selling lithium.

Soft, light, and low

Group 1
the alkali metals

								H									He
Li	Be											B	C	N	O	F	Ne
Na	Mg											Al	Si	P	S	Cl	Ar
K	Ca	Sc	Ti	V	Cr	Mn	Fe	Co	Ni	Cu	Zn	Ga	Ge	As	Se	Br	Kr
Rb	Sr	Y	Zr	Nb	Mo	Tc	Ru	Rh	Pd	Ag	Cd	In	Sn	Sb	Te	I	Xe
Cs	Ba	La	Hf	Ta	W	Re	Os	Ir	Pt	Au	Hg	Tl	Pb	Bi	Po	At	Rn
Fr	Ra	Ac	Rf	Db	Sg	Bh	Hs	Mt	Ds	Rg							

▲ Group 1 elements are on the left of the periodic table

Lithium is in Group 1 of the periodic table, called the **alkali metals**. Lithium has the lowest density of all the metals. The other Group 1 elements also have low densities.

Element	Density (g/cm³)
lithium	0.53
sodium	0.97
potassium	0.86
rubidium	1.53

The Group 1 elements are very soft – you can easily cut them with a knife. They have lower melting points and boiling points than most other metals. In Group 1, the further down the group an element is, the lower its melting point and boiling point.

Reactions with non-metals

The alkali metals react vigorously with chlorine. Sodium, for example, burns with a bright orange flame in the pale green gas. The product is a white solid, sodium chloride.

$$\text{sodium} + \text{chlorine} \rightarrow \text{sodium chloride}$$
$$2Na(s) + Cl_2(g) \rightarrow 2NaCl(s)$$

Sodium reacts with chlorine in a similar way. So does lithium.

Potassium chloride, sodium chloride, and lithium chloride are white solids. They dissolve in water to form colourless solutions.

The alkali metal chlorides are ionic compounds. The atoms of all Group 1 elements have one electron in their highest occupied energy level. So when potassium reacts with chlorine, each potassium atom transfers one electron to a chlorine atom. This forms positive potassium ions, K^+, and negative chloride ions, Cl^-. Both types of ion have eight electrons in their highest occupied energy level.

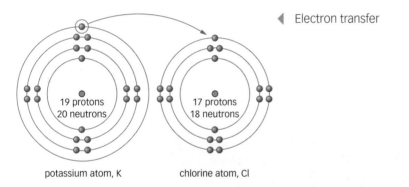

◀ Electron transfer

19 protons
20 neutrons

17 protons
18 neutrons

potassium atom, K   chlorine atom, Cl

▲ Potassium burns vigorously in chlorine

Questions

1　Describe three properties of the alkali metals.

2　Name the alkali metal with the lowest density.

3　Write a word equation for the reaction of potassium with chlorine.

4　Name the type of bonding in lithium chloride. Give one property of this solid.

5　Lithium reacts with bromine to form lithium bromide. Write a balanced symbol equation for the reaction.

↓ E

↓ C

↓ A*

Did you know...?

Lithium chloride can absorb huge amounts of water. It is used to dry the gases in submarine air conditioners.

Exam tip   AQA

✔ Remember, alkali metals react with chlorine to form ionic compounds in which the metal ion has a charge of +1.

Learning objectives

After studying this topic, you should be able to:

✔ describe the reactions of the alkali metals with oxygen and water

✔ explain the trend in reactivity of the alkali metals

▲ Physicists adjusting the settings of an atomic clock

Did you know...?

Streams of caesium ions ejected through the nozzle of a 'thruster' are used to steer satellites.

A Name the product of the reaction of lithium with oxygen.

B Write a symbol equation for the reaction of potassium with oxygen.

Keeping time

Does your watch, computer, or mobile phone keep accurate time? It will if it includes a radio clock. In the UK, radio clocks receive signals from three atomic clocks in Cumbria. Atomic clocks are based on electron movements in caesium atoms. They can be accurate to 1 second in 30 million years.

Caesium fluoride and caesium iodide absorb gamma rays (from radioactive material) and X-rays. As they absorb this radiation, they give out light. This property makes caesium fluoride and caesium iodide useful for monitoring radiation.

Caesium is in Group 1 of the periodic table, along with lithium, sodium, potassium, and rubidium. It is an alkali metal.

Reactions with oxygen

We saw on the previous spread that the alkali metals react vigorously with chlorine. They also react quickly with oxygen, another non-metal. At room temperature, their surfaces quickly tarnish when exposed to air. This is why they are stored under oil or grease.

The alkali metals burn in air and oxygen. For example:

$$\text{sodium} \quad + \quad \text{oxygen} \quad \rightarrow \quad \text{sodium oxide}$$
$$4Na(s) \quad + \quad O_2(g) \quad \rightarrow \quad 2Na_2O(s)$$

◀ Sodium burns brightly in oxygen

Sodium oxide is a white solid. It dissolves in water to make a colourless solution.

Alkali metal oxides are ionic compounds. They are made up of:

*   oxide ions, O^{2-}
*   metal ions with a charge of +1, for example Na^+ or Li^+.

Reactions with water

The alkali metals react vigorously with water. As they react, they zoom around on the water surface, propelled by the bubbles of hydrogen gas produced in the reaction. The other product of these reactions is a metal hydroxide. This dissolves in water to give an alkaline solution. For example:

sodium + water → sodium hydroxide + hydrogen

$2Na(s) + 2H_2O(l) \rightarrow 2NaOH(aq) + H_2(g)$

Group trend

Alkali metal reactions get more vigorous going down the group.

Going down the group, alkali metal reactions get more vigorous because the electrons involved in the reaction are further from the nucleus. This makes them less strongly attracted to the nucleus. So, in a reaction, an atom of an element at the bottom of the group gives away an electron more easily than an atom of an element at the top of the group.

▲ Sodium reacts vigorously with water

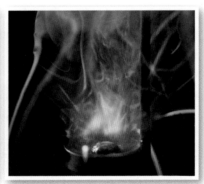

▲ Potassium is below sodium in Group 1. It reacts more vigorously with water than sodium does.

◀ Caesium is below both sodium and potassium in Group 1. It reacts violently with water.

Questions

1 Name the product of the reaction of sodium with oxygen.

2 Name the products of the reaction of potassium with water. E

3 Write a word equation for the reaction of caesium with water.

4 Suggest why the Group 1 elements are called the alkali metals. C

5 Write a balanced symbol equation for the reaction of rubidium (Rb) with water.

6 Describe and explain the trend in reactivity of the alkali metals. A*

Learning objectives

After studying this topic, you should be able to:

✔ compare the properties of transition metals and alkali metals

Key words

transition element

Catalysts, coins, and batteries

What links the pictures?

The answer is nickel. The coin is an alloy of copper and nickel. Nickel catalyses the reaction of hydrogen with vegetable oils to make margarine. Nickel–cadmium batteries can be recharged more than a thousand times.

Physical properties

Nickel is in the central block of the periodic table. It is a **transition element**. The transition elements are metals. Their properties have some similarities to those of the alkali metals. They conduct electricity, for example, and have shiny surfaces when freshly cut. But there are differences, too. Compared to the alkali metals, the transition elements

- are stronger and harder
- have higher densities
- have higher melting points (except for mercury, which is liquid at room temperature).

A Describe three differences between a typical alkali metal and a typical transition element.

B Predict whether metal X in the table is an alkali metal or a transition element. Give a reason for your decision.

Name of metal	Melting point (°C)	Density (g/cm³)
lithium	180	0.53
sodium	98	0.97
nickel	1453	8.9
palladium	1550	12.0
X	1769	21.4

Chemical reactions

The transition elements are less reactive than the alkali metals. For example, at room temperature the alkali metals react quickly with water and oxygen. The transition elements react slowly, if at all:

- Platinum and gold do not react with water or oxygen – that's why they make good jewellery, and why gold is used for electrical connections.
- Iron reacts with water and oxygen at room temperature, but slowly. The product is hydrated iron oxide, or rust.

Colours, catalysts, and ions

Many transition elements form more than one type of ion. For example, iron has two main oxides, FeO and Fe_2O_3. The oxide ion has a charge of –2 in both oxides. So FeO includes Fe^{2+} ions and Fe_2O_3 includes Fe^{3+} ions.

Many transition elements form coloured compounds.

▲ Iron(II) oxide, FeO, is green

▲ Iron(III) oxide, Fe_2O_3, is brown

◀ Vanadium compounds come in several colours. The colour of a compound depends on the charge of its vanadium ion.

Transition elements are important catalysts. For example, in catalytic convertors, platinum, palladium, and rhodium convert dangerous exhaust gases to ones that are less harmful.

▲ Compounds containing Cu^{2+} ions are blue or green

Questions

1 Describe one way in which transition metals are used.

2 Describe one difference between the reactions of alkali metals and the reactions of transition metals. ↓E

3 Explain why different vanadium compounds come in different colours. ↓C

4 Work out the charge on the vanadium ion in the compound V_2O_5. ↓A*

A Describe the pattern in boiling points as you go down the halogen group.

B Give the states of bromine and iodine at room temperature (20 °C).

◀ Chlorine reacts with iron to make iron(III) chloride

Deadly ... but vital

Group 7 is home to five deadly non-metal elements, the **halogens**.

▲ Group 7 elements are towards the right of the periodic table

But the halogens are not all bad. Chlorine destroys bacteria and viruses, so it is added to water to make it safe to drink. Fluoride compounds strengthen teeth. Iodine-containing hormones are vital for normal growth and development. They also keep your body temperature constant.

Physical properties

The halogens exist as two-atom molecules, such as F_2 and Br_2. The table shows some of their properties.

Element	Colour	Melting point (°C)	Boiling point (°C)
fluorine	pale yellow	−220	−188
chlorine	green	−101	−34.7
bromine	orange/brown	−7.2	58.8
iodine	grey/black with violet vapour	114	184

Comparing reactivity

A teacher reacts chlorine gas with iron wool.

The reaction is fast and fierce. Reddish-brown iron(III) chloride forms.

$$iron \quad + \quad chlorine \quad \rightarrow \quad iron(III)\ chloride$$
$$2Fe(s) \quad + \quad 3Cl_2(g) \quad \rightarrow \quad 2FeCl_3(s)$$

The other halogens also react with iron:
- Bromine forms iron(III) bromide. The reaction is slower than that of chlorine with iron.
- Iodine forms iron(III) iodide. The reaction is even slower than that of bromide with iron.

These reactions show that the halogens get less reactive as you go down the group.

Explaining reactivity

In the reactions of iron with the halogens, iron atoms give electrons to halogen atoms. This forms **halide ions**, such as Cl^- and Br^-. The smaller atoms at the top of the group gain electrons more easily. This is because the negatively charged electrons are added to an energy level that is closer to the positively charged nucleus. So the attraction between the nucleus and electrons is stronger. Overall, the higher the energy level, the less easily electrons are gained.

Displacement reactions

You can compare the reactivity of halogens in **displacement reactions**.

Miranda adds a solution of chlorine gas to potassium bromide solution. Yellow-orange bromine forms. Chlorine has 'pushed', or displaced, the bromide ion out of its compound. This shows that chlorine is more reactive than bromine.

$$\text{chlorine} + \begin{array}{c}\text{potassium}\\\text{bromide}\end{array} \rightarrow \begin{array}{c}\text{potassium}\\\text{chloride}\end{array} + \text{bromine}$$

$$Cl_2(aq) + 2KBr(aq) \rightarrow 2KCl(aq) + Br_2(aq)$$

Chlorine is also more reactive than iodine. So chlorine displaces iodine from its compounds.

$$\text{chlorine} + \begin{array}{c}\text{potassium}\\\text{iodide}\end{array} \rightarrow \begin{array}{c}\text{potassium}\\\text{chloride}\end{array} + \text{iodine}$$

$$Cl_2(aq) + 2KI(aq) \rightarrow 2KCl(aq) + I_2(aq)$$

Bromine displaces iodine from its compounds, too.

$$Br_2(aq) + 2KI(aq) \rightarrow 2KBr(aq) + I_2(aq)$$

Questions

1 Describe the pattern in melting points as you go down the group of halogens.

2 Give the formulae of fluorine gas and chlorine gas.

3 Write a word equation for the displacement reaction of bromine with potassium iodide.

4 Explain why the halogens get less reactive going down the group.

5 Miranda adds bromine solution to potassium chloride solution. Explain why there is no reaction.

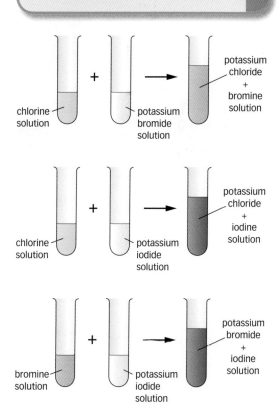

▲ Displacement reactions

Learning objectives

After studying this topic, you should be able to:

✔ explain what makes water hard or soft

✔ describe how to measure hardness

Key words

hard water, soft water, permanent hard water, temporary hard water

▲ Getting used to soft water

Did you know...?

Tea made from hard water tastes different from the same tea made with soft water. Some British tea companies blend teas especially for hard water areas.

New water

Ben moves from Wiltshire to Cheshire. He quickly settles into his new home and new school. But nothing will persuade him to drink the water in Cheshire. 'It tastes disgusting,' he says. Ben's neighbour can't see the problem. 'I've been drinking it all my life,' she says. 'It's delicious!' What makes the water in different areas taste so different?

Hard or soft?

The water Ben drank in Wiltshire is **hard water**. Hard water contains dissolved compounds, usually of calcium or magnesium. Water becomes hard when it flows through chalk or limestone rocks. Here's how:

- As rain falls, carbon dioxide from the air dissolves in it. Carbonic acid forms. So rainwater is weakly acidic.

$$\text{water} + \text{carbon dioxide} \rightarrow \text{carbonic acid}$$
$$H_2O(l) + CO_2(g) \rightarrow H_2CO_3(aq)$$

- As rainwater flows through chalk or limestone, its carbonic acid reacts with calcium carbonate in the rock. The product of the reaction is calcium hydrogencarbonate. Calcium hydrogencarbonate is soluble in water. Its calcium ions make water hard.

$$\begin{array}{ccc}\text{carbonic} \\ \text{acid}\end{array} + \begin{array}{c}\text{calcium} \\ \text{carbonate}\end{array} \rightarrow \begin{array}{c}\text{calcium} \\ \text{hydrogencarbonate}\end{array}$$
$$H_2CO_3(aq) + CaCO_3(s) \rightarrow Ca(HCO_3)_2(aq)$$

▲ Water from chalky areas is hard

Gypsum rock (mainly calcium sulfate) also makes water hard. When a river flows over gypsum, calcium sulfate dissolves in the water. The water now contains dissolved calcium ions.

Soft water does not contain dissolved calcium or magnesium ions.

Measuring hardness

Soft water lathers easily with soap. Calcium and magnesium ions in hard water react with soap to form scum. So hard water needs more soap to form a lather.

Samia wants to compare the hardness of different water samples. She adds soap solution to 10 cm³ of each water sample. The more soap solution needed to form a permanent lather, the harder the water. The table shows her results.

Water sample	Volume of soap solution needed to make a lather (cm³)	Volume of soapless detergent needed to make a lather (cm³)
rainwater	1	1
tap water from town A	1	1
tap water from town B	9	1

Hard forever?

There are two types of hard water:

- **Permanent hard water** remains hard, even when it is boiled. Water that has flowed over gypsum is permanent hard water.
- **Temporary hard water** is softened when it boils. Water that has flowed over chalk or limestone is temporary hard water.

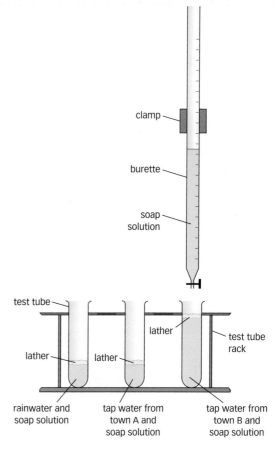

▲ Samia adds soap solution from the burette to test the hardness of the water samples

> **A** Which town has hard water?
> **B** Is rainwater hard or soft?

Questions

1 What is hard water?
2 Name three types of rock that make water hard.
3 Explain how water becomes hard. Include an equation to help you explain.
4 Describe the difference between temporary hard water and permanent hard water.
5 Use the data in the table to predict whether or not soapless detergents react with hard water to form scum. Explain your answer.

↓ E

↓ C

↓ A*

Hard or soft – pros and cons

I hate our hard water. It costs me a fortune in soap and washing powder.

Hard water is a nuisance. It makes scale in our kettles and central heating boiler. Scale makes our electric kettle and gas boiler less efficient than they should be. My electricity and gas bills are huge.

We have hard water. Its calcium compounds help my children's bones and teeth to grow. It tastes great too.

I read an article about hard and soft water in a scientific journal. The ions dissolved in hard water may help to reduce the chance of getting heart disease.

Softening hard water

There is money to be made in water softening. Many companies supply water-softening materials and equipment to UK homes and factories. All softening methods have the same aim – to remove the dissolved calcium ions (Ca^{2+}) and magnesium ions (Mg^{2+}) that make water hard.

Washing soda

A cheap and simple way of softening hard water is to add sodium carbonate, or **washing soda**. Most washing powders include washing soda.

Sodium carbonate is soluble in water. When you add it to hard water, its carbonate ions react with dissolved calcium and magnesium ions. Calcium carbonate and magnesium carbonate form as precipitates.

A Give the chemical name for washing soda.

B Explain how washing soda softens water.

The ionic equation below summarises the reaction that removes calcium ions. Only the ions that take part in the reaction are included.

$$\text{calcium ions} + \text{carbonate ions} \rightarrow \text{calcium carbonate}$$
$$\text{Ca}^{2+}\text{(aq)} + \text{CO}_3{}^{2-}\text{(aq)} \rightarrow \text{CaCO}_3\text{(s)}$$

Ion exchange columns

Some people buy **ion exchange columns** to soften their water. Ion exchange columns swap calcium and magnesium ions from hard water with sodium or hydrogen ions.

In this ion exchange resin, sodium ions are attached to the resin. Hard water flows in at the top. It trickles through the resin. On its way down, its calcium and magnesium ions swap with sodium ions and stick to the resin. The water that comes out of the bottom has sodium ions dissolved in it. It is no longer hard.

After a while, the column becomes saturated with calcium and magnesium ions. It no longer works. You need to pour sodium chloride solution through the column to flush out the calcium and magnesium ions and replace them with sodium ions. The column is now ready to use again.

An ion exchange column can supply a whole house with softened water. Scale no longer forms in kettles and boilers, so energy costs are reduced.

However, ion exchange columns increase the amount of sodium in the water. Dissolved sodium is not good for heart health, or for babies. So it is best not to use softened water for drinking, cooking, or babies' bottles.

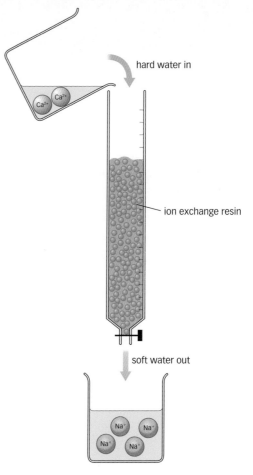

▲ An ion exchange column. Ions are not drawn to scale.

Removing temporary hardness

You can remove temporary hardness by boiling. The dissolved hydrogencarbonate ions decompose on heating to produce carbonate ions. The carbonate ions react with calcium or magnesium ions in the water to form a precipitate. The precipitate is the scale you see in kettles. Of course, it does not make economic sense to soften water by boiling on a large scale.

$$\begin{array}{ccccc}\text{calcium} & \rightarrow & \text{calcium} + & \text{carbon} + & \text{water}\\ \text{hydrogencarbonate} & & \text{carbonate} & \text{dioxide} & \end{array}$$
$$\text{Ca(HCO}_3)_2\text{(aq)} \rightarrow \text{CaCO}_3\text{(s)} + \text{CO}_2\text{(g)} + \text{H}_2\text{O(l)}$$

Questions

1. Describe two problems of hard water.
2. Describe two benefits of hard water.
3. Describe an economic benefit of softening hard water.
4. Write a balanced ionic equation to summarise how washing soda removes dissolved magnesium ions from solution.
5. Explain how an ion exchange resin makes hard water soft.

↓ E

↓ C

↓ A*

Key words

microstrainers, sand filters, sterilise

▲ Baths use lots of water

A Explain what makes UK tap water safe to drink.

B How much more water does an average European person use than an average person in a poorer part of the world?

How much?

How much water do you use each day? If you live in Europe, the answer is probably around 200 litres. That's enough to fill 16 big buckets. A typical north American uses around 400 litres a day for drinking, cooking, and washing. In poorer parts of the world, an average person uses just 10 litres of water a day.

How safe?

Dirty water is a killer. Worldwide, around 4000 children die every day from diarrhoea caused by unclean water and poor sanitation.

Water companies supply water to most UK homes. All this water is safe to drink. It has low levels of microbes, including disease-causing bacteria. It also has low levels of dissolved salts, such as nitrates, which are harmful to health.

Making water safe to drink

In the UK, water companies supply water of the correct quality by

- choosing appropriate water sources
- filtering the water to remove solids
- sterilising the water with chlorine or ozone.

Filtering

Water companies use many types of filtration, including:

- **Microstrainers** – large rotating sieves which remove solids, including algae, from the water.
- **Sand filters** – football-pitch-sized beds of sand about a metre deep. As the water trickles through the sand, solids and harmful bacteria are removed from the water.

Sterilising

Two gases are used to **sterilise** (kill bacteria) in water:

- Chlorine kills bacteria. The chlorine remains dissolved in the water until it comes out of the taps in our homes, so it also kills any bacteria that get into the water on its journey through the pipes from the water treatment works.
- Ozone, O_3, kills bacteria and destroys pesticides.

Water sources

Water companies take water from a variety of sources. Water from different sources needs different treatments.

Water from this borehole has been filtered by underground rocks for many years. It occasionally contains bacteria, so is sterilised with chlorine.

Water from streams fills this storage reservoir. The water is contaminated by tiny bits of soil, algae, viruses, and bacteria. It passes through microstrainers and sand filters. Then chlorine is added, to destroy bacteria and viruses.

Water from this canal is of poor quality. It contains algae, viruses, bacteria, and foul-smelling ammonia, and is a brown colour. It is filtered to remove solids. Activated carbon removes pesticides and ammonia from the water. Ozone is bubbled through the water to kill bacteria and destroy pesticides. Chlorine is added to keep the water clean on its journey to the user.

Questions

1 List the three stages by which UK water companies produce water of the correct quality.

2 Give the purpose of filtering water through a sand filter.

3 Explain why water from a borehole often needs only little treatment to make it safe to drink.

4 Explain why chlorine can keep water safe to drink throughout its journey from the water treatment works to people's homes.

5 Describe and explain all the stages in making poor quality canal water safe to drink.

↓ E

↓ C

↓ A*

Did you know...?

The weight of water that women in Africa and Asia carry on their heads is commonly 20 kg, the same as a typical UK airline luggage allowance.

Key words

fluoridated water, activated carbon, adsorption

Did you know...?

In one British city, one in five five-year-olds has had a tooth extracted, and more than half have some tooth decay.

Fluoride fracas

In the USA and Australia, about 70% of homes are supplied with **fluoridated water** – water that has had sodium fluoride, or another fluoride compound, added to it. In the UK, the figure is closer to 10%. Only people living in Yorkshire, Tyneside, and parts of the West Midlands have fluoridated water. There are arguments for and against adding fluoride to water.

I am a dentist. Fluoride water helps prevent tooth decay. It means fewer children have toothache. I think every UK home should have fluoridated water.

I compared dental health in the Irish Republic and Northern Ireland. In the Irish Republic, 70% of water is fluoridated. The average number of decayed, missing, and filled teeth per child is 1.3. In Northern Ireland, there is no fluoridation. The average number of decayed, missing, and filled teeth per child is 2.3.

I think that adding fluoride to water is an expensive way of improving the dental health of just a few people. If everyone cleaned their teeth properly, and didn't eat sweets, there would be no need for water fluoridation.

I don't think water should be fluoridated. When I was a little girl, my teeth were discoloured. The dentist said I had consumed too much fluoride. I know this was because I used to swallow my toothpaste, but the fluoride in water surely didn't help.

I am a health worker in a poor area of the UK. I think we should add fluoride to the water just in areas where a high percentage of people have decayed teeth. This would be less expensive than adding fluoride to all water, but would still improve dental health.

A Describe one benefit of adding sodium fluoride to water.

B Suggest an economic reason for not supplying fluoridated water to all UK homes.

Home water filters

All UK mains water is safe to drink. But some people want to improve the taste or quality of their tap water. They do this by using special filters or ion exchange resins.

Carbon filters

Carbon water filters contain **activated carbon**. Activated carbon is produced from materials such as coconut shells. It has been processed to give it lots of tiny holes. This means it has a very large surface area. One gram of activated carbon can have a surface area of up to 1500 m². As tap water passes through a carbon filter, molecules of unwanted substances stick to the surface of the carbon. The process is called **adsorption** and the molecules are described as being adsorbed. Carbon filters remove chlorine from water, as well as some compounds with bad tastes or smells.

Silver filters

Silver has long been known to help make water safe to drink. More than two thousand years ago, Cyrus the Great of Persia kept his drinking water in silver containers. In the 1960s, NASA used silver to help produce drinking water aboard the Apollo spacecraft. Today, some types of home water filters include a source of silver ions, Ag⁺. The ions destroy many types of bacteria.

▲ Activated carbon, as viewed under an electron microscope

Exam tip

✔ You do not need detailed knowledge of different water filters, but in the exam you may be given information about different water filters so that you can make comparisons.

▲ This home water filter contains silver nanoparticles to destroy dangerous bacteria

Ion exchange resins

Some home water treatment systems include an ion exchange resin. These are similar to ion exchange resins used to remove water hardness (see spread C3.8). They replace undesirable metal ions such as lead, copper, or cadmium ions that may be in the water with hydrogen, sodium, or potassium ions.

Questions

1   What do activated carbon filters remove from tap water?

2   Identify one benefit of a water filter that contains a source of silver ions. E

3   Draw up a table to summarise the substances removed from water by activated carbon filters, silver filters, and ion exchange columns. C

4   Write a paragraph to describe and evaluate the economic and social arguments for and against supplying all UK homes with fluoridated water. A*

11: Drinking seawater

Learning objectives

After studying this topic, you should be able to:

✔ describe and evaluate the production of pure water by distillation

Key words

desalination, distillation

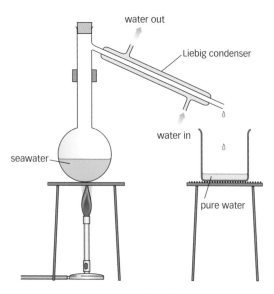

You can use apparatus like this to produce pure water from seawater in the lab

- **A** Write these stages of distillation in the order in which they happen: condense, evaporate, boil.

- **B** What will remain in the round-bottomed flask at the end of the distillation process?

Water shortage

The United Arab Emirates (UAE) has huge oil reserves. It is home to the world's tallest building, in Dubai. Many of its people have a lot of money to spend.

The demand for water in the UAE is high – average use in one region is 550 litres per person per day. But there are no permanent rivers or lakes in the United Arab Emirates, and rainfall is low in coastal areas. So where do people get their water from?

▲ Dubai at night

Drinking seawater

Around 98% of water in the UAE comes from the sea. **Desalination** removes all the dissolved salts from the water, making it safe to drink.

There are several methods of desalination. The most important is **distillation**. In the laboratory, you can use the apparatus on the left to distil seawater.

Distillation happens on a huge scale in the largest desalination plant in the world, at Jebel Ali in the UAE. The process is similar to laboratory distillation, but at Jebel Ali the pressure of the system is reduced so that the water boils at a lower temperature. This reduces the energy costs of the process.

▲ The largest desalination plant in the world, at Jebel Ali

Pros and cons

Distillation is a vital source of water for many, but it has its disadvantages:

- The water produced is completely pure. It contains no dissolved salts. So people drinking it do not experience the health benefits of dissolved calcium and magnesium ions.
- Many people dislike the taste of completely pure water.
- Distillation requires huge energy inputs, so the economic and environmental costs of distillation plants can be high.
- Sea life may be damaged at the water intake, and where highly concentrated salty water is returned to the sea.

▲ Ships and submarines produce pure water by distillation, too

Questions

1 What is desalination?

2 Describe and explain the processes that happen in the distillation of seawater to produce pure water.

3 Draw up a table to summarise the environmental and economic disadvantages of producing drinking water from seawater.

4 Imagine that the government of a country on the coast of South America is considering building a desalination plant to supply its people with water. Write a paragraph to help the government weigh up the pros and cons of this proposal.

E ↓ C

↓ A*

Exam tip **AQA**

✔ Remember – distillation requires huge amounts of energy. This makes it very expensive as a means of supplying drinking water on a large scale.

12: Measuring food and fuel energy

Learning objectives

After studying this topic, you should be able to:

✔ describe how to measure the energy transferred when foods and fuels burn

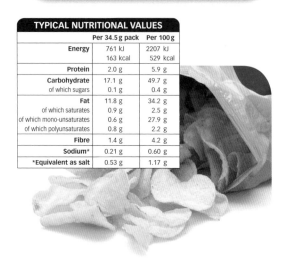

TYPICAL NUTRITIONAL VALUES		
	Per 34.5 g pack	Per 100 g
Energy	761 kJ	2207 kJ
	163 kcal	529 kcal
Protein	2.0 g	5.9 g
Carbohydrate	17.1 g	49.7 g
of which sugars	0.1 g	0.4 g
Fat	11.8 g	34.2 g
of which saturates	0.9 g	2.5 g
of which mono-unsaturates	0.6 g	27.9 g
of which polyunsaturates	0.8 g	2.2 g
Fibre	1.4 g	4.2 g
Sodium*	0.21 g	0.60 g
*Equivalent as salt	0.53 g	1.17 g

A A **joule** is the unit of energy. Give the number of joules in one **kilojoule**, 1 kJ.

B Which stores more energy – 100 g of crisps or 100 g of cashews?

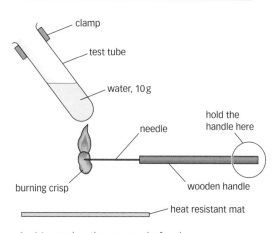

clamp

test tube

water, 10 g

needle

hold the handle here

burning crisp

wooden handle

heat resistant mat

▲ Measuring the energy in food

Behind the label

Which do you prefer – crisps or cashew nuts? Which provide more energy?

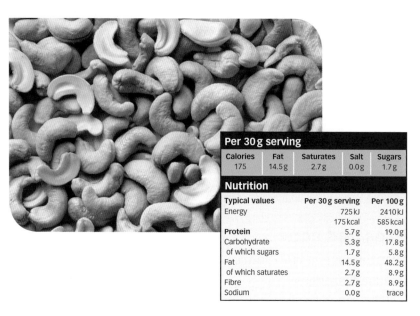

Per 30 g serving				
Calories	Fat	Saturates	Salt	Sugars
175	14.5 g	2.7 g	0.0 g	1.7 g

Nutrition		
Typical values	Per 30 g serving	Per 100 g
Energy	725 kJ	2410 kJ
	175 kcal	585 kcal
Protein	5.7 g	19.0 g
Carbohydrate	5.3 g	17.8 g
of which sugars	1.7 g	5.8 g
Fat	14.5 g	48.2 g
of which saturates	2.7 g	8.9 g
Fibre	2.7 g	8.9 g
Sodium	0.0 g	trace

Food labels tell us how much energy foods provide. Eating 100 g of cashew nuts provides 2410 kJ of energy, and 100 g of crisps provides 2207 kJ.

Of course, energy values are not the full story. Cashew nuts and crisps provide similar amounts of energy, but the nuts are more nutritious.

How do food companies know what numbers to write on the labels? Today, they use data tables to work out the energy values of processed foods. Before these data were available, scientists compared food energy values by using burning foods to heat water. The energy transferred on burning is similar to that available to the person eating the food.

Measuring food energy

Freya pours 100 g of water into a metal container. She measures its temperature. She heats the water with a burning crisp. She measures the temperature again.

Here is a summary of Freya's results.

Mass of crisp (g)	1
Increase in water temperature (°C)	40

Freya uses an equation to calculate the heat energy, Q, transferred to the water:

$$Q = mc\Delta T$$

- m is the mass of water, in grams.
- c is the **specific heat capacity** of the water. It is the energy needed to make 1 g of water 1 °C hotter. Its value is 4.2 J/g°C.
- ΔT is the temperature change of the water, in °C.

So for Freya's experiment, the heat, Q, transferred to 100 g of water by 1 g of crisps:

$$= 100\,g \times 4.2\,J/g°C \times 40\,°C$$
$$= 16\,800\,J$$
$$= 16.8\,kJ$$

This gives a value of –1680 kJ for burning 100 g of crisps. The negative sign shows that the burning reaction is exothermic. It transfers energy to the surroundings. In other words, it gives out energy.

Freya's value is different from that on the crisp packet. There are two reasons for this:

- Not all the heat from the burning crisp was transferred to the water – some was transferred to the surroundings and the apparatus.
- Some of the energy in crisps – that in the fibre – cannot be absorbed by the body. This energy is not included in the energy value on the crisp packet.

Comparing fuels

You can use a similar experiment to compare the heat produced by burning fuels. The diagram shows how.

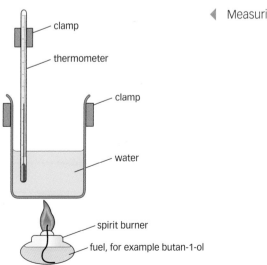

◀ Measuring the energy in a fuel

- clamp
- thermometer
- clamp
- water
- spirit burner
- fuel, for example butan-1-ol

Did you know...?

100 g of crisps provides 10 times more energy than an apple of the same mass, but the apple is much richer in vitamins and minerals.

Exam tip   AQA

✔ Take care with units, and note whether energy values are given in joules (J) or kilojoules (kJ). You may even be given energy data in calories.

Questions

1 Give the symbol for the scientific unit of energy. ↓E

2 Eva burns 1 g of butan-1-ol fuel in the apparatus shown. It makes 100 g of water 55 °C hotter. Calculate the amount of heat energy transferred to the water from the butan-1-ol. The specific heat capacity of water is 4.2 J/g°C. ↓C

3 Eva checks her result in a data book. This states that burning 1 g of butan-1-ol releases 36 122 J of heat energy. Suggest why Eva's value is different from that in the data book. ↓A*

13: Energy changes

Learning objectives

After studying this topic, you should be able to:

✔ calculate energy transfers for reactions in solution

Key words

exothermic, endothermic

How hot?

Combustion reactions can transfer huge amounts of energy to the surroundings.

▲ Forest fires give out huge amounts of energy

Other types of reaction give out heat energy too. They are **exothermic**. Barney adds magnesium powder to dilute hydrochloric acid. After a few minutes, the beaker feels warmer. So Barney knows the reaction is exothermic. But how much energy has the reaction transferred to the surroundings? Barney does an experiment to find out. He

- pours 20 cm³ of hydrochloric acid into an insulated container
- measures the temperature of the acid
- adds the magnesium powder, with stirring
- observes the temperature change for a few minutes and records the maximum temperature reached.

Here are Barney's results:

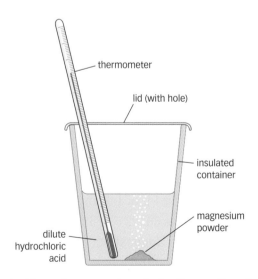

▲ Measuring energy transfer for the reaction of magnesium with dilute hydrochloric acid

volume of acid (cm³)	20
temperature at start (°C)	19
highest temperature reached (°C)	78
temperature change (°C)	59

Barney uses the equation $Q = mc\Delta T$ to calculate the energy transfer. He assumes that it is only the water in the solution that is being heated. So 4.2 J will raise the temperature of 1 g of the solution by 1 °C. He also assumes that the density of the solution is 1 g/cm³, so the mass of 20 cm³ of acid is 20 g.

$$Q = m \times c \times \Delta T$$
$$Q = 20 \text{ g} \times 4.2 \text{ J/g °C} \times 59 \text{ °C}$$
$$Q = 4956 \text{ J}$$

The energy change for the reaction is –4956 J for the amounts used in the experiment. The negative sign shows that the reaction is exothermic.

How cold?

If you add citric acid powder to sodium hydrogencarbonate solution, the reacting mixtures cools down. Then, slowly, the mixture warms up until it reaches room temperature. The reaction has taken in heat energy from the surroundings. It is **endothermic**.

You can use the equation $Q = mc\Delta T$ to calculate how much energy the reaction mixture takes in from the surroundings. For endothermic reactions, the value of Q is positive.

Questions

1 Suggest why Barney uses an insulated container in his experiment.

2 Describe the difference between an exothermic reaction and an endothermic reaction.

3 Calculate the energy transferred by the reaction of aluminium powder with 20 cm³ of hydrochloric acid. The temperature increase was 76 °C.

4 Calculate the energy transferred by the reaction of citric acid with 20 cm³ of sodium hydrogencarbonate solution. The temperature decrease was 11 °C.

5 Suggest why the temperature of a reacting mixture in an endothermic reaction decreases at first, and then later returns to room temperature.

A Calculate the energy transferred by the reaction of zinc powder with 20 cm³ of hydrochloric acid. The temperature increase was 9 °C.

B Calculate the energy transferred by the reaction of 100 cm³ of 1 mol/dm³ hydrochloric acid with 100 cm³ of 1 mol/dm³ sodium hydroxide solution. The temperature increase was 6 °C.

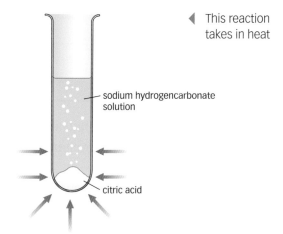

◀ This reaction takes in heat

sodium hydrogencarbonate solution

citric acid

Did you know...?

Photosynthesis is endothermic. Plants absorb energy in the form of light. They can then convert carbon dioxide and water into glucose and oxygen.

Exam tip   AQA

✓ To remember the difference between exothermic and endothermic reactions, think of *entering* – or going *in* to – a room. *End*othermic reactions take *in* energy.

Key words

energy level diagram, activation energy

A Use the energy level diagram to work out the energy change for reaction 2.

B Use the two energy level diagrams to decide which of the two reactions transfers more energy to the surroundings.

New hand warmer

Carmella is a chemist. She is developing a new type of hand warmer. She tries reacting different pairs of substances. Which would transfer most energy to a person's hands? The chemist draws **energy level diagrams** to represent her results. An energy level diagram shows the relative energies of the reactants and products in a reaction.

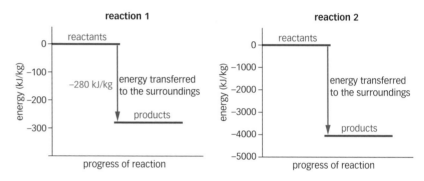

▲ Energy level diagrams for two reactions. The two diagrams are drawn to different scales.

The energy level diagrams show that reactions 1 and 2 are exothermic. In both reactions, the energy stored in the products is less than the energy stored in the reactants. The extra energy first heats up the reaction mixture. Then it is transferred to the surroundings, as heat. Energy changes for exothermic reactions are negative. The energy change for reaction 1 is –280 kJ/kg.

Sports injury pack?

The reaction represented by the energy level diagram on the left would be no good for a hand warmer. It would be better for a sports injury pack, to cool an injured arm or leg.

▲ An energy level diagram for an endothermic reaction

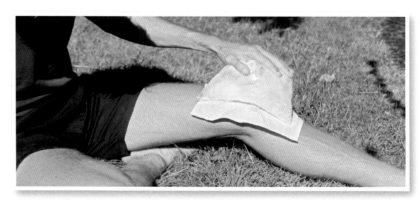

▲ Sports injury packs cool injured limbs

The energy level diagram for the sports injury pack shows that the energy stored in the products is more than the energy stored in the reactants. The extra energy was taken from the reaction mixture. So its temperature fell. Then the mixture took in energy from the surroundings. Its temperature increased, back to room temperature. The reaction is endothermic. Energy changes for endothermic reactions have positive values.

The energy change for the reaction in the diagram is +450 kJ/kg.

Exam tip AQA

✔ In energy level diagrams, the reactants are above the products for exothermic reactions. The products are above the reactants for endothermic reactions.

Getting going

All chemical reactions need energy to get them going. Reactions can only happen when reactant particles collide. Only those particles with enough energy are able to react when they do collide. The minimum energy needed for a reaction to start is the **activation energy**.

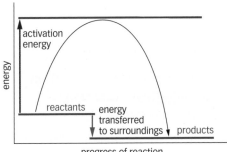

◄ Energy level diagram with activation energy. The curved arrow shows the energy as the reaction proceeds.

Catalysts and activation energy

Catalysts speed up reactions without themselves being used up. Catalysts provide a different pathway for a reaction, with a lower activation energy.

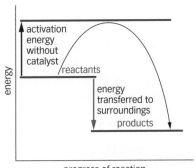
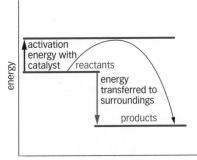

▲ The two energy level diagrams are for the same reaction. The diagram on the right shows that the activation energy is lower when a catalyst is used.

Questions

1 What is a catalyst?

2 Explain the meaning of the term activation energy.

3 Sketch an energy level diagram that represents an exothermic reaction.

4 Draw an energy level diagram to represent the endothermic reaction in which nitrogen dioxide gas is formed from its elements. During the reaction, 34 kJ/mol is absorbed from the surroundings.

5 Use the diagram on the left to help you explain how catalysts reduce activation energy.

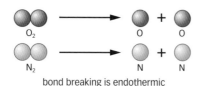

bond breaking is endothermic

bond making is exothermic

▲ Bond breaking in N_2 and O_2 and bond making in NO

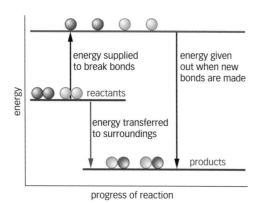

▲ Bond breaking is endothermic. Bond making is exothermic.

> **A** Is bond breaking exothermic or endothermic?

Nasty NO$_x$

Every year, UK cars must pass an exhaust emissions test. There are strict limits on amounts of exhaust pollutants, including oxides of nitrogen, NO$_x$. Oxides of nitrogen form when nitrogen and oxygen from the air react together. At normal temperatures, there is no reaction. But inside a hot car engine, the gases react rapidly.

Bond breaking, bond making

A minimum energy, the activation energy, is needed to start the reaction. Heat from the car engine supplies this energy. It is used to break bonds in nitrogen molecules, N_2, and oxygen molecules, O_2. Bond breaking is endothermic.

New bonds are made as products such as nitrogen monoxide, NO, are formed. Bond making releases energy. It is an exothermic process.

Exothermic or endothermic?

The difference between the energy supplied to break bonds in reactants and the energy released on forming bonds in products determines whether a reaction is exothermic or endothermic.

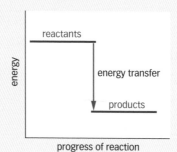

▲ The energy released in forming new bonds is greater than the energy needed to break existing bonds. The reaction is exothermic.

▲ The energy needed to break existing bonds is greater than the energy released from forming new bonds. The reaction is endothermic.

> **B** Explain how the difference between the energy supplied to break bonds and the energy released on forming bonds determines whether a reaction is endothermic or exothermic.

◀ Bonds are made as nitrogen oxides form in car exhaust

Exam tip

✓ Energy must be supplied to break bonds. Energy is released when bonds are formed.

Using bond energies

Every type of bond needs a certain amount of energy in order to break. This is the **bond energy**. You can use bond energy data to calculate energy transfers in reactions.

Bond	Bond energy (kJ/mol)
H–H	436
Cl–Cl	243
F–F	158
H–Cl	432
H–F	562

Worked example

Calculate the energy change for the reaction

$$H_2(g) + Cl_2(g) \rightarrow 2HCl(g)$$

One mole of H–H bonds and one mole of Cl–Cl bonds break in the reaction.

The energy needed to break these bonds is

$(436 + 243) = 679$ kJ.

Two moles of H–Cl bonds form in the reaction. The energy released by this process is $(2 \times 432) = 864$ kJ.

The overall energy transfer

= the energy supplied to break bonds – the energy released on making bonds

= 679 – 864

= –185 kJ

The negative sign shows that, overall, the reaction is exothermic.

Questions

1 Is bond making endothermic or exothermic?

2 An ozone molecule, O_3, splits up to make an oxygen molecule, O_2, and an oxygen atom, O. Predict whether the process is endothermic or exothermic. Give a reason for your answer.

3 Use bond energy data to calculate the energy change for the reaction
$H_2(g) + F_2(g) \rightarrow 2HF(g)$

4 Which process is more exothermic – the formation of hydrogen chloride gas from its elements, or the formation of hydrogen fluoride gas from its elements?

Learning objectives

After studying this topic, you should be able to:

✔ evaluate the use of hydrogen as a fuel for cars

Key words

particulate, internal combustion engine, fuel cell

Problems with petrol

Loretta loves her car. She says it makes travel quick and convenient. But her son, Seth, thinks his mum should cycle everywhere, like he does. Burning petrol and diesel in car engines produces damaging exhaust products:

- Carbon dioxide – causes climate change.
- **Particulates** (tiny particles of soot and unburned fuel) – may lead to asthma, lung cancer, and heart disease. They are created by burning diesel.
- Oxides of nitrogen – cause acid rain. They also destroy the ozone in the upper atmosphere that protects us from cancer-causing ultraviolet radiation.

Alternatives to oil

We cannot fuel cars with petrol and diesel forever. Petrol and diesel are produced from crude oil. Supplies of crude oil are finite – they will one day run out.

One alternative to fossil fuel is hydrogen. Hydrogen cars produce mainly one exhaust product:

$$\text{hydrogen} + \text{oxygen} \rightarrow \text{water}$$
$$2H_2(g) + O_2(g) \rightarrow 2H_2O(g)$$

Two types of hydrogen vehicle

Hydrogen-fuelled cars are in an early stage of development. There are two types:

- Some burn hydrogen in their **internal combustion engines**, such as Arnold Schwarzenegger's Hydrogen Hummer.
- Others, such as Honda's FC Sport, have hydrogen **fuel cells**. Hydrogen gas flows into the fuel cell. There, it reacts with oxygen. The process generates electricity to move the car.

A List three disadvantages of fuelling cars with petrol and diesel.

B Name the main exhaust product of hydrogen cars.

Did you know...?

Arnold Schwarzenegger's Hydrogen Hummer needs refuelling every 60 miles.

▲ Schwarzenegger's Hydrogen Hummer

▲ The Honda FC Sport

Sources of hydrogen

There is no naturally occurring hydrogen gas on Earth. So hydrogen fuel must be manufactured. Most hydrogen is made by reacting methane with water:

methane + water → hydrogen + carbon monoxide

$$CH_4(g) + H_2O(l) \rightarrow 3H_2(g) + CO(g)$$

Carbon monoxide is poisonous, so it is reacted with oxygen as it is made. The product is carbon dioxide, a greenhouse gas.

carbon monoxide + oxygen → carbon dioxide

$$2CO(g) + O_2(g) \rightarrow 2CO_2(g)$$

Fuel cell versus internal combustion engine

Both types of hydrogen-powered vehicles have pros and cons.

Fuel cells	Hydrogen-fuelled internal combustion engine (ICE)
more efficient than ICEs	less efficient than fuel cells
batteries expensive to produce, but getting cheaper as the process is automated	technology well understood, since most cars have them
include an expensive platinum catalyst, but new battery designs require less platinum	nitrogen and oxygen react in the engine to produce oxides of nitrogen as an exhaust gas, as well as water
few fuel stations currently supply hydrogen gas for refuelling	
methane, from which hydrogen is made, can be a renewable resource	

Questions

1 Name the two types of hydrogen car.

2 Give two advantages of hydrogen cars compared to petrol and diesel cars.

3 Describe how hydrogen is manufactured from methane gas.

4 Write a paragraph to compare the advantages and disadvantages of the combustion of hydrogen in car engines with the use of hydrogen fuel cells.

E

↓ C

↓ A*

Exam tip

✔ In the exam, you may be given information about the two types of hydrogen car, and asked to compare their advantages and disadvantages.

Course catch-up

Revision checklist ✔

- ○ Newlands listed elements in order of atomic weights. Mendeleev arranged elements into groups and periods to fit repeating patterns in properties.
- ○ Modern periodic tables arrange elements by atomic number.
- ○ Number of electrons in the highest energy level indicates group number.
- ○ Elements in Group 1 (alkali metals) are soft, low-density metals. Alkali metals react rapidly with water, forming alkalis and hydrogen. Alkali metals form ionic compounds with non-metals.
- ○ Group 1 ions have a charge of 1+.
- ○ Group 1 elements become more reactive further down the group.
- ○ Transition elements are denser, stronger, harder, and less reactive than alkali metals. They form coloured compounds and may act as catalysts. Transition metals have ions with different charges.
- ○ Elements in Group 7 (halogens) are coloured non-metals.
- ○ Reactive halogens displace less reactive halogens from solutions of halide ions.
- ○ Group 7 ions have a charge of 1−.
- ○ Group 7 elements become less reactive further down the group.
- ○ Hard water is caused by calcium and magnesium ions dissolving when acidic rainwater flows through rocks.
- ○ Temporary water hardness (caused by calcium hydrogencarbonate) can be removed by boiling. Permanent hardness (caused by calcium sulfate) isn't removed by boiling.
- ○ Washing soda or ion-exchange resins also soften water.
- ○ Water is filtered to remove solids and sterilised with chlorine to kill microbes. Dissolved substances are removed by specialised filters or ion exchange.
- ○ Seawater can be desalinated by distillation, which needs a lot of energy.
- ○ In calorimetry, the energy released from a chemical reaction is transferred to water. Energy transferred = $mc\Delta T$.
- ○ Energy level diagrams show how the energies of chemicals change during a reaction. Energy is released when chemical bonds form and is required to break bonds.
- ○ Catalysts reduce the minimum amount of energy needed to start a reaction (the activation energy).
- ○ Hydrogen releases energy when it reacts with oxygen in combustion or in fuel cells.

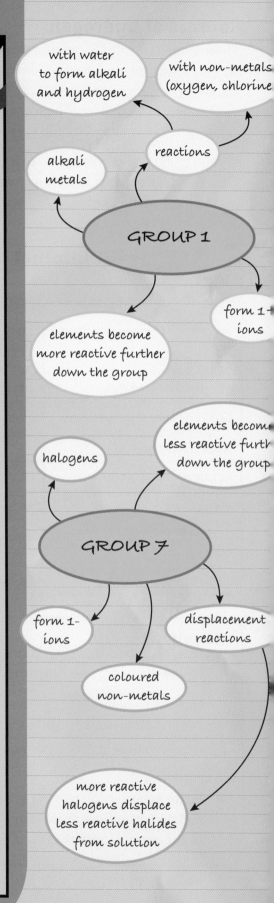

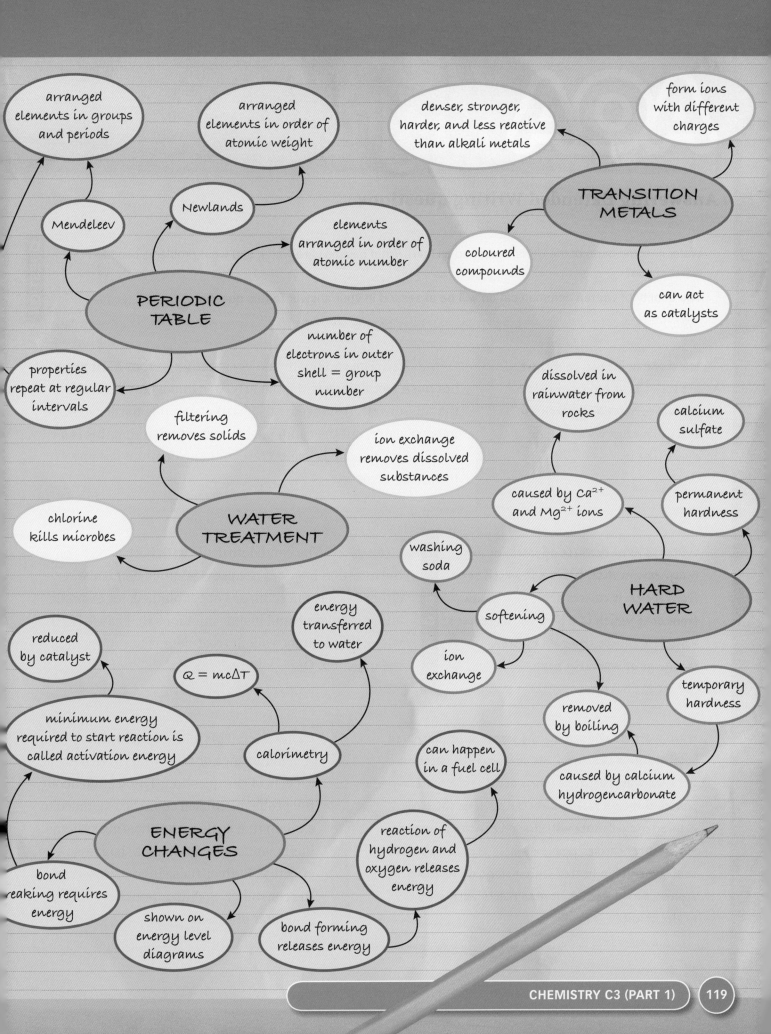

arranged elements in groups and periods

arranged elements in order of atomic weight

denser, stronger, harder, and less reactive than alkali metals

form ions with different charges

Newlands

Mendeleev

elements arranged in order of atomic number

TRANSITION METALS

coloured compounds

PERIODIC TABLE

can act as catalysts

properties repeat at regular intervals

number of electrons in outer shell = group number

dissolved in rainwater from rocks

calcium sulfate

filtering removes solids

ion exchange removes dissolved substances

caused by Ca^{2+} and Mg^{2+} ions

permanent hardness

chlorine kills microbes

WATER TREATMENT

washing soda

HARD WATER

energy transferred to water

softening

reduced by catalyst

$Q = mc\Delta T$

ion exchange

temporary hardness

minimum energy required to start reaction is called activation energy

calorimetry

can happen in a fuel cell

removed by boiling

caused by calcium hydrogencarbonate

bond breaking requires energy

ENERGY CHANGES

reaction of hydrogen and oxygen releases energy

shown on energy level diagrams

bond forming releases energy

AQA Upgrade

Answering Extended Writing questions

Water in some parts of the UK is described as hard. What causes hard water, and what problems can hard water cause?

The quality of written communication will be assessed in your answer to this question.

G–E

Hard water means that there are rocks that have got into the water. You can't wash so easily in hard water so people don't like it.

Examiner: The candidate knows something about hard water, but hasn't explained it very clearly. It is important to mention that dissolved substances cause hard water. It is harder to wash in hard water, but the candidate should mention that this is a problem when soap is used. The candidate does not use any technical terms.

D–C

Water is hard because of calcium and magnesium dissolved in it which come from rocks. It causes scale and scum from soap which is a problem in people's homes. It can be removed by iron-exchange or washing soda.

Examiner: The candidate deals with both aspects of the question but does not provide much detail about either – scale and scum are not explained, for example, and it is calcium and magnesium ions that cause hard water. The sentence about treatment is not relevant to the question. One spelling error.

B–A*

Hard water is caused by the presence of dissolved calcium and magnesium compounds. These can get into water because when acidic rain water passes through rocks, substances like calcium hydrogencarbonate will dissolve into the water. Hard water causes problems because it can make scale when it is heated which clogs up heating systems and kettles. It also reacts with soap to make scum.

Examiner: This answer includes an excellent range of facts that cover both aspects of the question. The section about the problems caused could be expanded to explain that scale makes heating systems inefficient and scum makes soap less effective. Both of these increase costs to the consumer. Spelling, punctuation, and grammar are good.

Exam-style questions

1 a Complete the following description of the periodic table, using the words below.

> masses   numbers   groups
> periods   properties

The periodic table contains elements arranged in order of their atomic _____. It contains vertical columns called _____ and horizontal rows called _____. Elements in the same group have similar _____.

b Name an element from:

i Group 1   **ii** Group 7

iii the transition elements.

2 Kate adds 1 g of zinc to 100 cm³ of dilute sulfuric acid in an insulated cup. She measures a temperature rise of 23.6 °C.

a Use the equation $Q = mc\Delta T$ to calculate the amount of energy in J released in this experiment ($c = 4.2$ J/g°C).

b i Copy and complete this energy level diagram to show the relative energies of the reactants and products.

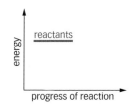

reactants

energy

progress of reaction

ii Label the diagram to show the energy change and the activation energy of the reaction.

c The reaction is faster with a copper sulfate catalyst. Explain why.

3 Elements in Group 7 have similar properties. However, their reactivity increases going down the group.

a Halogen elements react by gaining electrons to form a halide ion.

i Complete this equation to show how chlorine forms chloride ions: $Cl_2 + \_\_e– \rightarrow \_\_Cl–$

ii What name is given to reactions in which electrons are gained?

iii Bromine is less reactive than chlorine. Use ideas about electronic structure to explain why.

b When chlorine is added to a solution of potassium bromide, an orange solution is formed.

i Name the orange product.

ii What type of reaction has occurred?

iii Complete and balance this symbol equation for the reaction: $Cl_2 + 2KBr \rightarrow \_\_$

Extended Writing

4 Water must be treated before it is suitable for drinking. Describe the treatments used in the UK water supply.

5 Stefan lives in a part of the country with hard water. Describe how the water becomes hard and discuss the ways in which hard water may be softened.

6 The work of Dmitri Mendeleev was important in developing the modern periodic table. Describe his contribution.

C3 Part 2

Analysis, ammonia, and organic chemistry

Why study this unit?

Every year, UK factories make more than one million tonnes of ammonia. The gas makes vital fertilisers, explosives, and cleaning materials. We also use large amounts of carbon-based organic compounds, such as alcohols, carboxylic acids, and esters. Their properties make them ideal for many purposes. Health and environment workers and forensic scientists use chemistry to identify substances.

In this unit you will discover how to identify positive and negative ions in salts, and how to measure the amounts of substances in solution. You will also learn about the manufacture of ammonia, and how chemical engineers choose optimal conditions for the process. Finally, you will study patterns in the properties of three groups of organic compounds, and discover how their uses depend on their properties.

You should remember

1 A salt is a compound that contains metal ions, and that can be made from an acid.

2 Concentration is the amount of a substance in a certain volume of solution.

3 A reversible reaction is one in which the products of a reaction can react to produce the original reactants.

4 Compounds of carbon are called organic compounds.

5 Organic compounds are classified into groups with similar properties, such as alkanes and alkenes.

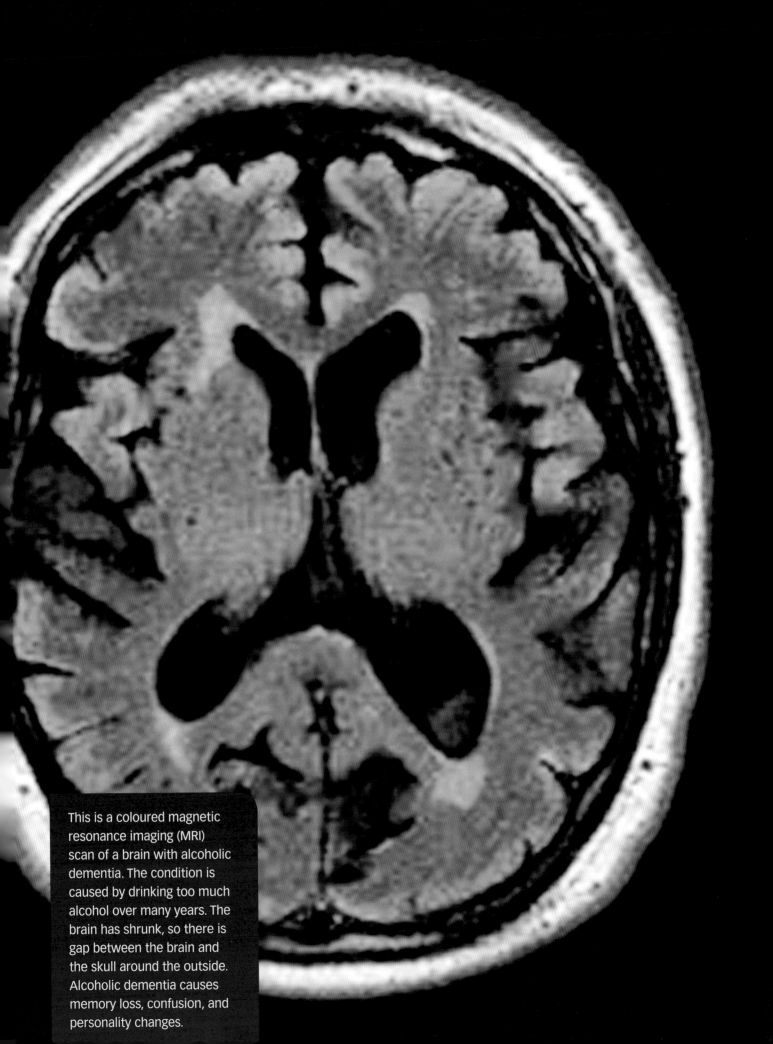

This is a coloured magnetic resonance imaging (MRI) scan of a brain with alcoholic dementia. The condition is caused by drinking too much alcohol over many years. The brain has shrunk, so there is gap between the brain and the skull around the outside. Alcoholic dementia causes memory loss, confusion, and personality changes.

▲ Firework colours come from burning metal compounds

A Draw a table showing the flame colours given by lithium, sodium, potassium, calcium, and barium compounds.

▲ Iron(II) ions (Fe^{2+}) form a green precipitate. Iron(III) ions (Fe^{3+}) form a brown precipitate. Copper(II) ions (Cu^{2+}) form a blue precipitate.

Firework fantasy

It's 5th November. Fireworks light up the sky. But how do chemists give fireworks their colours?

Firework colours come from burning metal compounds. Different metal ions give different coloured flames.

Flame tests

Flame colours are not just useful for fireworks. They also help to identify metal ions. Several metal ions produce distinctive colours in **flame tests**. You can do a flame test by dipping the end of clean nichrome wire in a sample of a salt. Hold the end of the wire in a Bunsen flame, and observe the flame colour.

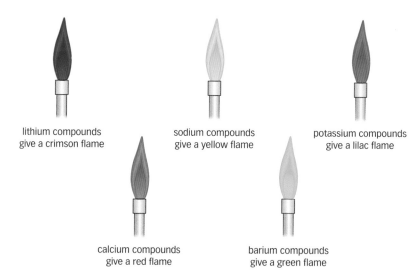

lithium compounds give a crimson flame

sodium compounds give a yellow flame

potassium compounds give a lilac flame

calcium compounds give a red flame

barium compounds give a green flame

B Apart from identifying metal ions, how else are flame colours useful?

Identifying other metal ions

You can use sodium hydroxide to identify some metal ions. Here's how:

- Dissolve a sample of the compound in pure water to make a solution.
- Add a few drops of dilute sodium hydroxide to the solution.
- If a precipitate forms, observe its colour.

Different metal ions form precipitates of different colours.

The precipitates are all metal hydroxides. The equations show how copper(II) hydroxide is formed in a precipitation reaction:

| copper(II) chloride | + | sodium hydroxide | | copper(II) hydroxide | + | sodium chloride |

$$CuCl_2(aq) + 2NaOH(aq) \rightarrow Cu(OH)_2(s) + 2NaCl(aq)$$

An ionic equation summarises the reaction. It shows only the ions involved in the reaction:

$$Cu^{2+}(aq) + 2OH^-(aq) \rightarrow Cu(OH)_2(s)$$

Aluminium hydroxide, calcium hydroxide, and magnesium hydroxide are all white precipitates. You can distinguish aluminium from the other two hydroxides by adding extra sodium hydroxide solution. Aluminium hydroxide dissolves in the excess sodium hydroxide:

$$Al(OH)_3(s) + OH^-(aq) \rightarrow Al(OH)_4^-(aq)$$

Precipitates of calcium hydroxide and magnesium hydroxide do not dissolve in excess sodium hydroxide.

▲ Aluminium ions (Al^{3+}), calcium ions (Ca^{2+}), and magnesium ions (Mg^{2+}) form white precipitates with sodium hydroxide solution

Questions

1 Name the flame colours given by burning calcium and barium compounds.

2 Draw a table to show the results of adding dilute sodium hydroxide to solutions containing these ions:

Cu^{2+} Fe^{2+} Fe^{3+} Mg^{2+} Ca^{2+} Al^{3+}

3 Write an ionic equation to summarise the reaction of sodium hydroxide solution with iron(III) chloride solution.

4 You have a white solid. You dissolve some of it in pure water to make a colourless solution. Adding dilute sodium hydroxide gives a white precipitate. Describe how to find out whether the original solid is magnesium chloride, calcium chloride, or aluminium chloride. Give the results you would expect for each salt.

Key words

flame test

Did you know...?

Bunsen and Kirchhoff discovered the elements caesium and rubidium by examining flame colours carefully.

Exam tip   AQA

✓ In the exam, you may be asked to interpret flame test results and sodium hydroxide test results.

Did you know...?

In 1949, an American woman murdered her neighbour, and rival in love, by adding sodium fluoride-based insecticide to her coffee.

Fluoride fatalities

Have you ever put salt in your tea, or sugar on your chips? These mistakes don't taste good, but are unlikely to harm you. However, some kitchen mix-ups can be fatal. In 1942, an American hospital cook added sodium fluoride – a cockroach killer – to scrambled eggs, instead of milk powder. Hours later, 47 patients were dead.

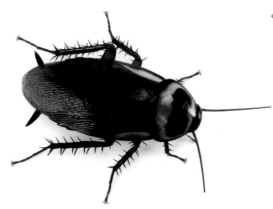

◀ Sodium fluoride kills cockroaches

You cannot identify a compound by looking at it. So chemists have devised tests and instrumental methods to identify chemicals. The previous spread describes tests for metal ions. This spread describes tests for negative ions.

Testing for carbonates

To find out if a solid contains carbonate ions (CO_3^{2-}):

- Add a few drops of dilute hydrochloric acid to the surface of the solid.
- Watch carefully. If you notice fizzing, a gas is being produced.
- Use limewater to test the gas. If the limewater goes cloudy, the gas is carbon dioxide, and the solid is a carbonate.

For example:

calcium carbonate + hydrochloric acid → calcium chloride + carbon dioxide + water

$$CaCO_3(s) + 2HCl(aq) \rightarrow CaCl_2(aq) + CO_2(g) + H_2O(l)$$

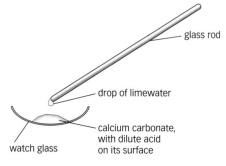

glass rod

drop of limewater

calcium carbonate, with dilute acid on its surface

watch glass

▲ Carbonates react with dilute acids to form carbon dioxide gas

---

A Name the products of the reaction of magnesium carbonate with hydrochloric acid.

B Describe how to test for carbon dioxide gas.

Testing for halide ions

You can use silver nitrate solution to test for compounds containing chloride, bromide, and iodide ions. Here's how:

- Dissolve a sample of the solid in dilute nitric acid.
- Add silver nitrate solution.

Different halide ions form precipitates of different colours. The precipitates are silver halides. The equations below summarise the reaction of sodium chloride with silver nitrate:

$$\begin{array}{ccccccc} \text{sodium} & + & \text{silver} & \rightarrow & \text{silver} & + & \text{sodium} \\ \text{chloride} & & \text{nitrate} & & \text{chloride} & & \text{nitrate} \end{array}$$

$$NaCl(aq) + AgNO_3(aq) \rightarrow AgCl(s) + NaNO_3(aq)$$

This ionic equation summarises the reaction:

$$Ag^+(aq) + Cl^-(aq) \rightarrow AgCl(s)$$

Testing for sulfates

To find out whether a compound includes sulfate ions (SO_4^{2-}):

- Dissolve a sample of the solid in dilute hydrochloric acid.
- Add barium chloride solution.

Sulfate compounds react with barium chloride solution to form a white precipitate of barium sulfate. The ionic equation for the reaction is:

$$Ba^{2+}(aq) + SO_4^{2-}(aq) \rightarrow BaSO_4(s)$$

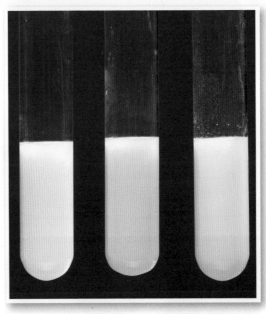

▲ Silver chloride (AgCl) is white. Silver bromide (AgBr) is cream. Silver iodide (AgI) is yellow.

Exam tip

✔ Remember the precipitate colours – they will help you interpret the results of chemical analysis tests in the exam.

Questions

1 Give the colour of the precipitate formed by reacting sodium chloride with acidified silver nitrate solution. ↓ E

2 Draw a table to show how to test for these ions: CO_3^{2-}, SO_4^{2-}, Cl^-, Br^-, I^-. In your table, include the names of the chemicals you add for each test, and the expected results. ↓ C

3 Write a balanced symbol equation for the reaction of magnesium sulfate with barium chloride in the presence of dilute hydrochloric acid.

4 Write an ionic equation for the reaction of sodium bromide with silver nitrate in the presence of dilute nitric acid. ↓ A*

▲ Environment workers collect and test water samples from rivers

Health, the environment, and forensics

Paula is pregnant. She gives her midwife a urine sample. The midwife places a dipstick in the urine to test for protein. The dipstick changes colour if protein is present. Protein in the urine of a pregnant woman shows that she may have a serious condition that needs urgent treatment.

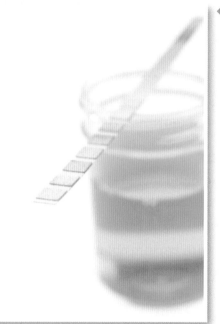

◀ Urine dipstick

Sophie works for an environment organisation. She collects river water samples. She takes the samples to a laboratory. There, scientists use instrumental methods to test the water for various substances, including lead ions. Lead ions may affect brain development in children. Lead ions in river water damage plants and animals, including fish.

Phil is a forensic scientist. He analyses drugs, such as heroin and cocaine, seized by the police. He uses instrumental methods to find out whether the drugs are pure, or mixed with other substances.

A Name three types of work that may involve identifying substances.

B Explain why it is important to measure the concentration of lead ions entering river water from a sewage treatment works.

Identifying the substances in a mixture

Clare has a sample of small white crystals. She knows the sample is a mixture of two substances. She divides her sample in half. She dissolves one half in water, and leaves the other half as it is. Clare uses chemical tests to identify the ions in the mixture. The tables show the tests she does, and their results.

Tests on the solid

Description of test	Observations
flame test	bright yellow flame
add drops of dilute hydrochloric acid to the solid	no bubbles

Tests on the solution

Description of test	Observations
add dilute nitric acid and silver nitrate solution	white precipitate
add dilute hydrochloric acid and barium chloride solution	white precipitate
add sodium hydroxide solution	white precipitate that dissolves in excess sodium hydroxide solution

◀ A solution of Clare's sample produced a white precipitate when dilute hydrochloric acid and barium chloride were added to it

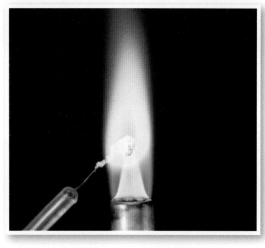

▲ Clare's sample produced a yellow flame

Questions

Use the two results tables above to help you answer the questions.

1 What does the flame test result show?

2 Explain how the test results show that the mixture includes no carbonate ions.

3 What do the results of the silver nitrate and barium chloride tests show?

4 Give the formulae of the four ions present in Clare's mixture.

5 Use ionic equations to help you explain the results of the silver nitrate, barium chloride, and sodium hydroxide tests.

Learning objectives

After studying this topic, you should be able to:

✔ use titrations to find out the volumes of solutions that react together

Key words

burette, end point, pipette, rough titration, titration

▲ Is it safe for these boys to swim?

1. Use a pipette to measure accurately 25.00 cm³ of sodium hydroxide solution.

2. Allow the sodium hydroxide solution to run into a conical flask. Add a few drops of phenopthalein.

3. Pour hydrochloric acid into a burette. Read the scale. Add hydrochloric acid from the burette to the conical flask until the indicator just turns colourless. Read the scale. Calculate the amount of acid added. This rough titration gives an idea of how much acid is needed to neutralise the sodium hydroxide, or reach the end point.

4. Repeat steps 1–3, burette the acid one drop at a time as you near the end point. Swirl after each addition. Repeat until you have three consistent values for the acid volume.

Acid spill

It's 7.25 a.m. A park worker notices a pungent smell near an open-air swimming lake. He struggles to breathe. Fire crews arrive at the scene. They discover an acid spill. More than 150 litres of hydrochloric acid has leaked from the chlorination system that treats the lake water. The fire fighters close the swimming lake.

Later, public health officials turn up. They measure the concentration of acid in the lake water. It is safe for swimming. There is no need to add a base to neutralise extra acid in the water. Most of the acid must have soaked into the soil around the chlorination equipment.

Measuring acids and alkalis

Environment workers sometimes add bases to lakes that have been acidified by acid rain. Beforehand, they use instrumental techniques to measure the concentration of acid in the lake water. They do calculations to work out how much base to add.

In the laboratory, you can do **titrations** to measure the volumes of acid and alkali solutions that react with each other. The diagrams show how to measure the volume of dilute hydrochloric acid that reacts with a 25.00 cm³ sample of dilute sodium hydroxide solution.

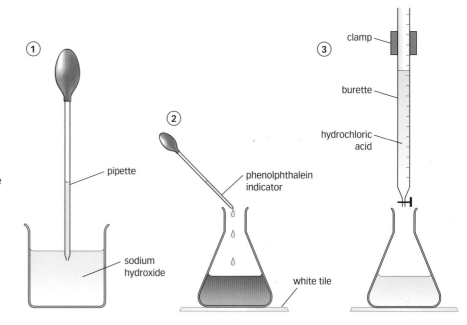

A What is the purpose of a rough titration?

B In a titration, what is the meaning of the term end point?

Calculating titration volumes

The table gives titration results for neutralising 25.00 cm³ of 1.0 mol/dm³ sodium hydroxide solution with approximately 1 mol/dm³ hydrochloric acid.

	Rough	Run 1	Run 2	Run 3
initial burette reading (cm³)	0.25	25.15	0.05	24.25
final burette reading (cm³)	25.15	49.25	24.25	48.40
volume of acid added (cm³)	24.90	24.10	24.20	24.15

You can use the results to calculate the mean volume of acid added. The result of the rough titration is not included in the calculation.

Mean volume = (24.10 + 24.20 + 24.15) ÷ 3 = 24.15 cm³.

Questions

1 Describe one purpose of doing titrations.

2 Name the piece of titration apparatus that has a tap and a graduated scale.

↓ E

3 Rafat adds dilute sulfuric acid to a mixture of sodium hydroxide solution and litmus. What colour change will he see?

↓ C

4 In a titration, if the initial burette reading is 0.75 cm³, and the final burette reading is 26.10 cm³, what volume of solution has been added?

5 Use the data below to calculate the mean volume of solution added from a burette.
Rough volume = 15.70 cm³
Run 1 volume = 15.30 cm³
Run 2 volume = 15.25 cm³
Run 3 volume = 15.30 cm³.

↓ A*

Exam tip

✓ Do not include rough titration results when calculating mean volumes in titrations.

Learning objectives

After studying this topic, you should be able to:

✔ use titration results to calculate the concentrations of solutions

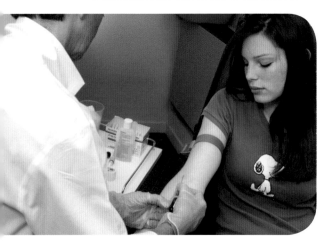

▲ Blood tests help health workers diagnose disease

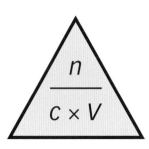

▲ *n* is the number of moles, or the mass, of the solute

A Calculate the concentration, in mol/dm³, of a solution that has 0.5 mol of an alkali in 2 dm³ of solution.

B Calculate the concentration, in mol/dm³, of a solution that has 2 mol of an acid in 250 cm³ of solution.

Amounts matter

Lilya is ill. She has sickness and diarrhoea, and sweats at night. Her doctor orders blood tests. The test results show that the **concentration** of sodium ions in Lilya's blood is higher than normal. The concentration of potassium ions is lower than normal. The doctor uses these results to help him work out what is wrong with Lilya.

Calculating concentration

The concentration of a solution is the amount of solute per unit volume of solution. A **solute** is a substance that is dissolved in solvent. Chemists measure concentration in grams per cubic decimetre (g/dm³), or in moles per cubic decimetre (mol/dm³). One dm³ is the same as one litre, or 1000 cm³. One mole (1 mol) of a substance is its formula mass in grams.

Use this equation to calculate concentration in g/dm³:

$$\text{concentration} = \frac{\text{mass of solute (in g)}}{\text{volume of solution (in dm}^3)}$$

Use this equation to calculate concentration in mol/dm³:

$$\text{concentration} = \frac{\text{number of moles of solute (in mol)}}{\text{volume of solution (in dm}^3)}$$

Worked example 1

What is the concentration of a solution that has 36.5 g of solute in 500 cm³ of solution?

$$\text{volume of the solution in dm}^3 = \frac{500 \text{ cm}^3}{1000 \text{ cm}^3}$$

$$= 0.5 \text{ dm}^3$$

$$\text{concentration in g/dm}^3 = \frac{\text{mass}}{\text{volume}}$$

$$= \frac{36.5 \text{ g}}{0.5 \text{ dm}^3}$$

$$= 73 \text{ g/dm}^3$$

Calculating masses and moles

If you know the concentration of a solution and its volume, you can calculate the number of moles of solute, or the mass of solute, in a given volume of solution.

▲ Titration apparatus

Questions

1 What is the concentration of a solution that has 40 g of solute in 2 dm^3 of solution?

2 What is the concentration of a solution that has 0.25 mol of solute in 125 cm^3 of solution?

3 How many moles of copper sulfate are there in 25 cm^3 of a 0.1 mol/dm^3 solution?

4 What mass of magnesium chloride is there in 1 dm^3 of a 1 mol/dm^3 solution? The formula of magnesium chloride is $MgCl_2$.

5 What mass of sodium fluoride is in 500 cm^3 of a 2 mol/dm^3 solution? The formula of sodium fluoride is NaF.

↓ A*

Worked example 2

How many moles of sodium sulfate are there in 250 cm^3 of a 2 mol/dm^3 solution?

volume of the solution (in dm^3) $= \dfrac{250\ cm^3}{1000\ cm^3}$

$= 0.25\ dm^3$

number of moles = concentration in mol/dm^3 × volume in dm^3

$= 2\ mol/dm^3 × 0.25\ dm^3$

$= 0.5\ mol$

Learning objectives

After studying this topic, you should be able to:

✔ use titrations to find the concentrations of acids and alkalis

A Describe two uses of titration reactions.

B Name two pieces of titration apparatus that measure volume accurately.

▲ Abdul doing titration

Using titrations to calculate concentrations

Titrations are useful for measuring the volumes of acid and alkali solutions that react with each other. But this is not the only use of titrations. In titrations, if you know the concentration of one reactant, you can use titration results to find the concentration of the other reactant.

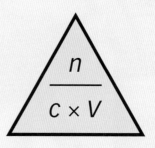

$$\frac{n}{c \times V}$$

▲ n is the number of moles, or the mass, of the solute

Worked example

Abdul places 25.00 cm³ of sodium hydroxide solution in a flask. Its concentration is 0.50 mol/dm³. Abdul does a titration. He finds that it takes 12.70 cm³ of sulfuric acid to neutralise the sodium hydroxide solution. Calculate the concentration of the sulfuric acid in g/dm³.

Calculate the number of moles of sodium hydroxide:

number of moles

= concentration in mol/dm³ × volume in dm³

= 0.5 mol/dm³ × (12.7 ÷ 1000) dm³

= 0.00635 mol

Write a balanced equation for the reaction. Use it to work out the number of moles of sulfuric acid in 12.7 cm³ of solution.

$$2NaOH(aq) + H_2SO_4(aq) \rightarrow Na_2SO_4(aq) + 2H_2O(l)$$

The equation shows that 2 mol of sodium hydroxide reacts with 1 mol of sulfuric acid. Abdul has 0.00635 mol of sodium hydroxide.

So the number of moles of sulfuric acid in 12.7 cm³ is

(0.00635 ÷ 2) = 0.00318 mol of sulfuric acid.

Calculate the concentration of the sulfuric acid in mol/dm³

$$\text{concentration} = \frac{\text{number of moles}}{\text{volume}}$$

$$= \frac{0.00318 \text{ mol}}{(12.7 \div 1000) \text{ dm}^3}$$

$$= 0.25 \text{ mol/dm}^3$$

Calculate the concentration of the sulfuric acid in g/dm³

Mass of 1 mol of sulfuric acid,

$H_2SO_4 = (2 \times 1) + 32 + (4 \times 16)$

$\qquad = 98$ g

So the mass of 0.25 mol of sulfuric acid

$= 0.25 \times 98$ g

$= 24.5$ g

So the concentration in g/dm³ = 24.5 g/dm³

Questions

1 Harry places 25.00 cm³ of sodium hydroxide solution in a flask. Its concentration is 1.0 mol/dm³. It takes 27.00 cm³ of hydrochloric acid to neutralise the solution. Calculate the concentration of the hydrochloric acid, HCl, in g/cm³.

2 Sabina places 25.00 cm³ of nitric acid in a flask. Its concentration is 0.50 mol/dm³. It takes 28.0 cm³ of potassium hydroxide solution to neutralise the acid. Calculate the concentration of the potassium hydroxide in mol/dm³.

↓
A*

3 Marcus places 10.00 cm³ of sulfuric acid in a flask. Its concentration is 0.20 mol/dm³. It takes 19.00 cm³ of sodium hydroxide solution to neutralise the acid. Calculate the concentration of the sodium hydroxide in g/dm³.

▲ Fertilisers made from ammonia hugely increase crop yields

▲ Ammonia gas is used in the refrigeration of some ice skating rinks

Amazing ammonia

Ammonia is a toxic gas with a penetrating, suffocating smell. It may cause serious burns, and is extremely harmful to the eyes. Its reactions can be violent. Even so, UK factories make more than 1 million tonnes of the gas each year. Worldwide, factories in China, India, Russia, and other countries produce around 3 million tonnes of ammonia every week. Why?

▲ Ammonia factory

Ammonia is a compound of nitrogen and hydrogen. Its formula is NH_3. Plants need nitrogen to grow properly, so nitrogen compounds are important fertilisers. More than 80% of the world's ammonia is used to make fertiliser compounds, for example ammonium nitrate, NH_4NO_3.

Chemical companies also convert huge amounts of ammonia into nitric acid. The acid is used to make more fertilisers, and explosives such as TNT (trinitrotoluene). Dilute ammonia solution reacts with grease, so it makes good glass and oven cleaners.

Raw materials

Ammonia is made from its elements, nitrogen and hydrogen:

- Nitrogen is separated from the air.
- There are several possible sources of hydrogen. One of these is natural gas. Methane from natural gas reacts with steam:

methane + steam → carbon monoxide + hydrogen
$$CH_4(aq) + H_2O(g) \rightarrow CO(g) + 3H_2(g)$$

A Give the formula of ammonia.

B Name the raw materials for making ammonia. Describe how they are obtained.

Making ammonia

Ammonia is made from its raw materials by the **Haber process**. The diagram on the right summarises the processes and conditions involved.

In the reaction vessel, hydrogen and nitrogen begin reacting to form ammonia. This is a **reversible reaction**. This means that, as some ammonia molecules are being made, others are breaking down to make hydrogen and nitrogen again. The $\rightleftharpoons$ sign shows that the reaction is reversible:

$$\text{nitrogen} + \text{hydrogen} \rightleftharpoons \text{ammonia}$$
$$N_2(g) + 3H_2(g) \rightleftharpoons 2NH_3(g)$$

There are three gases in the reaction vessel. They are cooled and separated in the condenser. The table shows their boiling points.

Substance	Boiling point (°C)
nitrogen	−196
hydrogen	−252
ammonia	−33

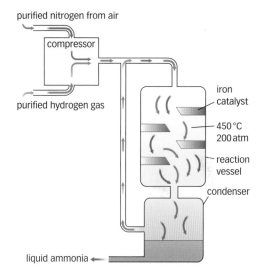

purified nitrogen from air

compressor

iron catalyst

450 °C
200 atm

reaction vessel

purified hydrogen gas

condenser

liquid ammonia

▲ This diagram summarises the Haber process

Questions

1 Describe two properties of ammonia.

2 Describe three uses of ammonia.

3 List the conditions for the Haber process. Include the temperature, pressure, and catalyst.

4 Explain the meaning of the term reversible reaction.

5 Study the boiling point data in the table. Use it to suggest how ammonia is separated from hydrogen and nitrogen in the condenser.

↓ E

↓ C

↓ A*

Exam tip

✓ Revise the Haber process carefully. It comes up in exams very often.

Key words

ammonia, Haber process, reversible reaction

24: Conditions for the Haber process

Learning objectives

After studying this topic, you should be able to:

✔ evaluate the conditions used in the Haber process in terms of yield, energy, and environmental impact

Key words

yield, heat exchanger

Money in ammonia

Making ammonia is big business. There is a huge demand for the gas. But the process is not cheap. To maximise profits, companies need to keep costs low. They also need to make as much product as possible, as quickly as possible.

▲ Most ammonia is used to make fertilisers, but some is used for making explosives

Choosing conditions

As we saw on the previous spread, the Haber process involves a reversible reaction:

$$N_2(g) \ + \ 3H_2(g) \ \rightleftharpoons \ 2NH_3(g)$$

Two reactions are happening at once:

- a forward reaction, in which nitrogen and hydrogen react to form ammonia
- a backward reaction, in which ammonia breaks down to form hydrogen and nitrogen.

The reaction vessel always contains a mixture of nitrogen, hydrogen, and ammonia. Companies want conditions that maximise the amount of ammonia made in the reaction, or its **yield**. They also want ammonia to form quickly.

Pressure

The higher the pressure, the higher the yield of ammonia. But the higher the pressure, the stronger the reaction vessel and pipes need to be. Strong vessels and pipes are expensive. The chemical engineers who design new Haber process plants compromise with a pressure of about 200 atmospheres.

A Suggest why chemical companies want to maximise yield.

B Explain why operating at high pressure is expensive.

Temperature

The lower the temperature, the higher the yield of ammonia. But the reaction is slow at low temperatures. So there will be only small amounts of ammonia to sell each day. The chosen temperature, 450 °C, is another compromise – this time between yield and speed.

Catalyst

Catalysts increase reaction speeds without being used up in the reaction. Using a catalyst increases the yield at a given temperature and pressure. Iron is the chosen catalyst in the Haber process. It works well, and is cheap and easy to obtain. It is important to look after the catalyst. Tiny amounts of impurities can stop it working properly. That's why the hydrogen and nitrogen entering the reaction vessel must be very pure.

▲ Magnetite, a form of iron oxide, can also be used as a catalyst in the Haber process

Energy costs

Keeping the reaction vessel at 450 °C requires energy inputs. Once the process has started, much of the heat is supplied within the process. As the gas mixture cools in the condenser, energy is transferred to a **heat exchanger**. The heat exchanger heats up the nitrogen and hydrogen before they enter the reaction vessel.

Minimising energy inputs helps to minimise the impacts of ammonia production on the environment. In the UK, there are strict rules to ensure that poisonous ammonia gas does not escape into the air or water.

Did you know...?

The production of ammonia uses 1% of the world's energy that is available for human use.

Exam tip   AQA

✔ In the exam, you may be asked to give reasons for Haber process conditions.

Questions

1 Explain what is meant by yield.

2 Explain the purpose of using iron in the Haber process.

3 Explain why a pressure of 200 atm is chosen for the Haber process.

4 Explain why a temperature of 450 °C is chosen for the Haber process.

5 Suggest why unreacted gases are recycled in the Haber process.

25: Equilibrium reactions

Learning objectives

After studying this topic, you should be able to:

✔ explain equilibrium reactions

▲ Reaction between hydrogen chloride and ammonia to form ammonium chloride

A What is a closed system?

B Explain the meaning of the term dynamic equilibrium.

Key words

closed system, dynamic equilibrium

Reversible reactions

What does the picture on the left show?

Ammonia gas and hydrogen chloride gas from the bottle stoppers are reacting together. The product of the reaction is ammonium chloride. It forms as fumes of white solid.

ammonia + hydrogen chloride → ammonium chloride

$$NH_3(g) + HCl(g) \rightarrow NH_4Cl(s)$$

The reaction happens in reverse, too. If you heat ammonium chloride, it decomposes:

$$NH_4Cl(s) \rightarrow NH_3(g) + HCl(g)$$

Because the reaction can go in both directions, it is reversible, like the Haber process reaction.

Dynamic equilibrium

Ammonia and hydrogen chloride can also react in a **closed system**. The picture shows a closed system – no materials can enter or leave the beaker in which the reaction takes place.

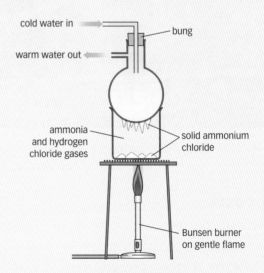

cold water in

bung

warm water out

ammonia and hydrogen chloride gases

solid ammonium chloride

Bunsen burner on gentle flame

▲ Hydrogen chloride and ammonia equilibrium apparatus

After a while, the system reaches **dynamic equilibrium**. The forward and backward reactions are both happening. The rate of reaction is the same in both directions. So the amount of each substance in the reaction mixture does not change.

$$NH_3(g) + HCl(g) \rightleftharpoons NH_4Cl(s)$$

Another equilibrium reaction

If you heat calcium carbonate strongly in an open container, it decomposes. There are two products:

- carbon dioxide gas, which escapes
- calcium oxide, used for neutralising acid soils and making cement.

▲ Calcium carbonate decomposes on heating to make calcium oxide and carbon dioxide. Here, a man is heating limestone in an open kiln in Turkey to make calcium oxide.

Calcium carbonate also decomposes in a closed container. You need to pump the air out first, and then heat a few grams of the solid to about 800°C. After a while, the amounts of substances in the container no longer change. Calcium carbonate is decomposing as fast as calcium oxide and carbon dioxide are reacting. The reactions occur at the same rate. Dynamic equilibrium has been reached.

calcium carbonate ⇋ calcium oxide + carbon dioxide

$$CaCO_3(s) \rightleftharpoons CaO(s) + CO_2(g)$$

Did you know...?

Carbon dioxide in the atmosphere is in equilibrium with carbon dioxide dissolved in seawater.

$$CO_2 \rightleftharpoons CO_2$$
(atmosphere)   (dissolved in seawater)

As more carbon dioxide enters the atmosphere from human activities, more carbon dioxide enters the oceans. The atmosphere–ocean system is not strictly a closed system.

Exam tip   AQA

✔ Any reversible reaction that happens in a closed system will reach equilibrium.

Questions

1. Write an equation to represent the dynamic equilibrium reaction of ammonia reacting with hydrogen chloride.

2. Explain why the amounts of substances in an equilibrium mixture do not change.

3. Suggest why companies that produce calcium oxide from limestone do the reaction in open kilns.

4. Describe how to establish a dynamic equilibrium between calcium carbonate, calcium oxide, and carbon dioxide.

A*

Learning objectives

After studying this topic, you should be able to:

✔ predict the effects of changing temperature on the amounts of substances in an equilibrium mixture.

A How does the chemist know when the reaction mixture has reached equilibrium?

B Predict what would happen if the chemist started by filling a glass tube with nitrogen dioxide, NO_2, instead of dinitrogen tetroxide, N_2O_4.

▲ The position of the equilibrium $N_2O_4(g) \rightleftharpoons 2NO_2(g)$ depends on the temperature

Equilibrium

A chemist fills a glass tube with a colourless gas, dinitrogen tetroxide, N_2O_4. He seals the end of the tube, and waits. Gradually, a brown colour appears in the tube. The colour gets darker and darker, until it no longer changes. What's going on?

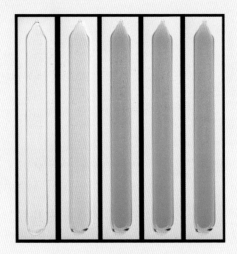

In the tube, dinitrogen tetroxide decomposes to form a brown gas, nitrogen dioxide, NO_2:

$$N_2O_4(g) \rightarrow 2NO_2(g)$$

As nitrogen dioxide forms, the reverse reaction starts to happen:

$$2NO_2(g) \rightarrow N_2O_4(g)$$

The brown colour gets darker until both reactions are happening at the same rate. The system is now in dynamic equilibrium.

$$N_2O_4(g) \rightleftharpoons 2NO_2(g)$$

Changing temperature

The amounts of substances in an equilibrium mixture depend on the conditions of the reaction. The picture shows what happens if you heat and cool the $N_2O_4(g) \rightleftharpoons 2NO_2(g)$ equilibrium mixture:

- The tube on the left has been warmed. There is more brown NO_2 in the equilibrium mixture. Warming shifts the equilibrium $N_2O_4(g) \rightleftharpoons 2NO_2(g)$ to the right.
- The tube on the right has been cooled. There is more colourless N_2O_4 in the equilibrium mixture. Cooling shifts the equilibrium to the left.

Explaining equilibrium shifts

Energy changes explain the different amounts of substances in the equilibrium mixture at different temperatures. For the equilibrium reaction below, the forward reaction is endothermic.

$$N_2O_4(g) \rightleftharpoons 2NO_2(g) \quad \Delta H = +58 \text{ kJ/mol}$$

Increasing the temperature shifts the equilibrium to the right, to absorb the extra heat. The yield of NO_2 from the endothermic reaction increases.

Decreasing the temperature shifts the equilibrium to the left, to give out more heat. The yield of N_2O_4 from the exothermic reaction increases.

For the Haber process reaction, the forward reaction is exothermic.

$$N_2(g) + 3H_2(g) \rightleftharpoons 2NH_3(g) \quad \Delta H = -92 \text{ kJ/mol}$$

At low temperatures, the position of the equilibrium shifts to the right. So the yield of ammonia is greater at low temperatures.

Exam tip AQA

For reversible reactions:
- ✔ Increasing the temperature increases the yield from an endothermic reaction and decreases the yield from the exothermic reaction.
- ✔ Decreasing the temperature decreases the yield from an endothermic reaction and increases the yield from the exothermic reaction.

Questions

1 Describe what happens to the yield of an exothermic equilibrium reaction as the temperature increases.

2 Describe what happens to the yield of an endothermic equilibrium reaction as the temperature decreases.

3 Use ideas about exothermic and endothermic reactions to explain why the yield of ammonia is greater at low temperatures.

A*

4 The equation below represents an important step in the production of sulfuric acid:

$$2SO_2(g) + O_2(g) \rightleftharpoons 2SO_3(g) \quad \Delta H = -197 \text{ kJ/mol}$$

Which would increase the yield of sulfur trioxide, SO_3 – increasing the temperature, or decreasing the temperature? Explain your answer.

Learning objectives

After studying this topic, you should be able to:

- ✔ predict the effects of changing pressure on the amounts of substances in an equilibrium mixture

Vital acid

Do you enjoy relaxing in a bubbly bath, eating delicious food, or travelling by car? One important chemical helps make these activities possible – sulfuric acid. Every year, chemical plants all over the world produce over 150 million tonnes of the acid.

▲ Car batteries use sulfuric acid

▲ Sulfuric acid helps make paints

▲ Sulfuric acid helps make detergents

▲ Sulfuric acid helps make phosphate fertilisers

Important equilibrium

Making sulfuric acid involves several stages, including this equilibrium reaction:

sulfur dioxide + oxygen ⇌ sulfur trioxide

$$2SO_2(g) + O_2(g) \rightleftharpoons 2SO_3(g) \qquad \Delta H = -197 \text{ kJ/mol}$$

The reaction is exothermic. So lowering the temperature increases the yield of sulfur trioxide, SO_3. The reaction is very slow at low temperatures, so a temperature of around 450 °C is chosen as a compromise.

A Explain why sulfuric acid is manufactured in huge quantities.

B Explain why a temperature of 450 °C is chosen for the equilibrium reaction shown on the right.

Pressure matters, too

Increasing the pressure also increases the yield of sulfur trioxide. This is because there are fewer molecules shown on the right of the symbol equation than on the left:

$$2SO_2(g) + O_2(g) \rightleftharpoons 2SO_3(g)$$

Number of molecules on left = $(2 + 1) = 3$
Number of molecules on right = 2

For all equilibrium gas reactions, an increase in pressure favours the reaction that produces the fewest molecules, as shown by the symbol equation for the reaction.

The Haber process reaction equation shows a total of four molecules on the left and two on the right:

$$N_2(g) + 3H_2(g) \rightleftharpoons 2NH_3(g)$$

So an increase in pressure shifts the equilibrium to the right, and increases the yield of ammonia. This explains why a high pressure is chosen for the Haber process.

Did you know...?

Sulfuric acid is produced in the upper atmosphere of Venus. Light energy from the Sun helps carbon dioxide, sulfur dioxide, and water vapour to react together to make the acid.

Questions

1 Copy and complete: For gaseous reactions, an increase in pressure favours the reaction that produces the _____ molecules, as shown by the symbol equation for the reaction.

2 Predict the effect of decreasing the pressure on an equilibrium reaction.

3 Predict whether a high or low pressure would maximise the yield of nitrogen monoxide, NO, in the reaction below. Give a reason for your prediction.

$$4NH_3(g) + 5O_2(g) \rightleftharpoons 4NO(g) + 6H_2O(g)$$

4 Predict the effect of increasing pressure on the equilibrium reaction below. Give a reason for your prediction.

$$H_2(g) + I_2(g) \rightleftharpoons 2HI(g)$$

↓
A*

Exam tip   AQA

✔ In equilibrium gas reactions, an increase in pressure will favour the reaction that produces the least number of molecules, as shown by the symbol equation for the reaction.

Depressant

Drugs alter normal bodily functions. Which recreational drug has the effects below?

- slows reaction times
- makes people forget things and feel confused
- causes vomiting, unconsciousness, and even death.

The answer is **ethanol**, the **alcohol** in alcoholic drinks. In the UK, heavy drinking is blamed for up to 33 000 deaths a year. A Swedish study found that up to 44% of deaths not caused by illness might be linked to ethanol, including those from falls, traffic accidents, suicide, and murder.

Drinking ethanol also has economic impacts. It makes huge profits for drinks companies. Its taxes bring income to the Government. But there are economic disadvantages, too. Ethanol costs the National Health Service an estimated £3 billion each year. The cost of policing alcohol-related crimes is also high.

A List three social disadvantages of drinking alcohol.

B List two economic advantages of alcohol, and two economic disadvantages.

Inside alcohols

Ethanol is a compound of carbon, so it is an **organic compound**. Its molecules include the reactive –OH group. A reactive group of atoms in an organic molecule is called a **functional group**. Ethanol is not the only alcohol. It is a member of the **homologous series** of alcohols. The compounds of a homologous series have the same functional group, but a different number of carbon atoms. The table shows the first three members of the homologous series of alcohols.

Name	Molecular formula	Structural formula
methanol	CH_3OH	H—C—O—H with H above and below C
ethanol	CH_3CH_2OH	H—C—C—O—H with H above and below each C
propanol	$CH_3CH_2CH_2OH$	H—C—C—C—O—H with H above and below each C

Useful solvent

What's your favourite perfume or deodorant? Many perfumes and deodorants include ethanol as a solvent. Medicines, marker pens, and food flavourings may also include an ethanol solvent. **Methanol** makes a useful solvent, too.

Methanol and ethanol dissolve well in water. This is because the –OH group of their molecules is similar to water, H_2O, so alcohol and water molecules mix easily. Solutions of alcohols with water are neutral – their pH is 7.

◀ Deodorant often contains ethanol

Questions

1 List three uses of ethanol.

2 What is an organic compound?

↓ E

3 Draw the functional group in methanol, ethanol, and propanol.

4 Name the homologous series of which methanol is a member.

↓ C

5 Draw up a table to summarise the economic and social advantages and disadvantages of the uses of alcohols.

6 Explain why ethanol dissolves well in water.

↓ A*

29: Alcohols – 2

Learning objectives

After studying this topic, you should be able to:

✔ describe some properties of alcohols

✔ describe and evaluate the use of alcohols as fuels

Key words

carbon neutral

A Write a word equation for the combustion reaction of propanol.

B Write a balanced symbol equation for the combustion reaction of methanol.

Alcohols burn

If you refuel your car in Brazil, you won't be adding just petrol to your tank. Brazilian car fuel is a mixture of petrol and ethanol, or even a mix of 95% ethanol with 5% water. In Brazil, ethanol is made by fermenting sugar cane.

Alcohols burn in air to make carbon dioxide and water. For example:

$$\text{ethanol} + \text{oxygen} \rightarrow \text{carbon dioxide} + \text{water}$$
$$CH_3CH_2OH(l) + 3O_2(g) \rightarrow 2CO_2(g) + 3H_2O(g)$$

▲ Drag racers often fuel their cars with methanol

Pros and cons

There are advantages and disadvantages of using ethanol as a vehicle fuel instead of fossil fuels such as petrol and diesel.

Advantages	Disadvantages
Made from a renewable resource, eg sugar cane or maize.	Crops from which ethanol is made are grown on land that could be used to grow food.
The plants from which the fuel is made remove carbon dioxide from the atmosphere are they grow. Some people say this means that ethanol fuel is **carbon neutral** – the plants remove the same amount of carbon dioxide from the atmosphere as burning the fuel later puts into the atmosphere.	Produces carbon dioxide, a greenhouse gas, as it burns. Carbon dioxide is also added to the atmosphere as a result of making fertilisers for the crops, and during the manufacture of ethanol from the crops. Some people say this means ethanol fuel is not carbon neutral.

Reaction with sodium

Alcohols react with sodium. The products are a salt and hydrogen. For example:

ethanol + sodium → sodium ethoxide + hydrogen

$$2CH_3CH_2OH(l) + 2Na(s) → 2CH_3CH_2ONa(aq) + H_2(g)$$

Exam tip **AQA**

✓ You may be asked to write balanced symbol equations for the combustion reactions of alcohols.

Water reacts with sodium more vigorously, but makes similar products:

water + sodium → sodium hydroxide + hydrogen

$$2H_2O(l) + 2Na(s) → 2NaOH(aq) + H_2(g)$$

The reactions of sodium with ethanol and with water are similar because both water and ethanol contain an –OH group. During the reaction, O–H bonds break.

Making vinegar

Francis leaves a bottle of wine open. A few days later, it tastes sour. The sour taste comes from ethanoic acid. Ethanoic acid forms when oxygen from the air oxidises some of the ethanol in the wine. Ethanoic acid is the main acid in vinegar.

You can also oxidise ethanol by
- the action of microbes
- reacting it with a chemical oxidising agent, such as acidified potassium dichromate(VI) solution.

▲ Orange acidified potassium dichromate(VI) solution oxidises ethanol to ethanoic acid. In the process, orange dichromate(VI) ions are reduced to green chromium ions, Cr^{3+}.

Questions

1 Describe one advantage and one disadvantage of using ethanol as a fuel.

2 Name the products made when methanol burns.

3 Write a word equation for the reaction of propanol with sodium. The name of the salt formed is sodium propoxide.

4 List two ways by which ethanol can be oxidised to ethanoic acid.

5 Write a paragraph to evaluate the advantages and disadvantages of using ethanol made by the fermentation of sugar cane as a vehicle fuel.

30: Carboxylic acids – 1

Learning objectives

After studying this topic, you should be able to:

✔ describe some properties and uses of carboxylic acids

▲ Dogs are better than humans at detecting the smells of carboxylic acids in sweat

Sweat

Everyone has their own unique smell. Why? The answer is in your sweat. Everyone has a slightly different mix of compounds in their sweat. So everyone smells slightly different.

Homologous series

The compounds that give sweat its smell are **carboxylic acids**. The carboxylic acids make up a homologous series. The series includes methanoic acid, ethanoic acid, and propanoic acid. All carboxylic acid molecules have the functional group –COOH, in which the atoms are arranged like this:

Following a trend

As you go up any homologous series, there is a gradual change in some properties, such as boiling point. The boiling points and densities of some carboxylic acids are given in the table.

Name of carboxylic acid	Molecular formula	Structural formula	Boiling point (°C)	Density (g/cm³)
methanoic acid	HCOOH		101	1.22
ethanoic acid	CH_3COOH		118	1.05
propanoic acid	CH_3CH_2COOH		141	0.99

A Describe the trends in density and boiling point from methanoic acid to propanoic acid.

B Draw the carboxylic acid functional group.

Typical acids

Every carboxylic acid has the same functional group, so they all have similar chemical properties:

- They dissolve in water to make acidic solutions, with pH less than 7.
- They react with carbonates to produce carbon dioxide gas. For example:

ethanoic acid + calcium carbonate → calcium ethanoate + water + carbon dioxide

Calcium ethanoate is a salt.

Using carboxylic acids

Carboxylic acids have many uses.

▲ Vinegar is a solution of ethanoic acid and other compounds in water

▲ Citric acid is added to many drinks to give them a sour taste

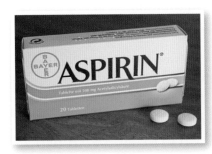

▲ Aspirin is an important carboxylic acid. It is used as a painkiller, and is also taken by people at risk of heart attack since it reduces blood clotting.

▲ Many fruits and vegetables contain ascorbic acid, vitamin C. Vitamin C is vital for health.

Key words

carboxylic acid, methanoic acid, ethanoic acid, propanoic acid

Did you know...?

When an ant stings, it injects its victim with methanoic acid.

Butanoic acid gives rancid butter its foul smell, and vomit its sour taste.

Exam tip

✔ You will not be expected to write balanced symbol equations for the reactions of carboxylic acids.

Questions

1 Name three carboxylic acids.

2 Describe two uses of carboxylic acids.

3 Describe two properties of carboxylic acids that are typical of all acids.

4 Write a word equation for the reaction of propanoic acid with sodium carbonate. The salt formed is sodium propanoate.

5 Write a paragraph to describe the patterns in the properties of carboxylic acids.

↓ E

↓ C

↓ A*

Learning objectives

After studying this topic, you should be able to:

- ✔ explain what makes carboxylic acids weak acids

Key words

ionise, strong acid, weak acid

Weak or strong?

It's the functional group that gives carboxylic acids their acid properties. When an ethanoic acid molecule dissolves in water, a hydrogen ion may leave its functional group. The acid molecule has split up to form ions. It has **ionised**.

Hydrochloric acid is almost completely ionised in solution. Every hydrogen chloride molecule has split up to make hydrogen ions and chloride ions. The acid is fully ionised.

$$HCl(g) + (aq) \rightarrow H^+(aq) + Cl^-(aq)$$

Acids that are fully ionised in solution are **strong acids**. Hydrochloric acid, sulfuric acid, and nitric acid are all strong acids.

◀ Strong acids

> **A** Explain the meaning of the sentence: Hydrogen chloride is fully ionised in solution.

Carboxylic acids are different. Fewer than 1% of their molecules ionise when they dissolve in water. This means they are **weak acids**. The equilibrium for the solution of ethanoic acid lies towards the left:

$$CH_3COOH(l) + (aq) \rightleftharpoons CH_3COO^-(aq) + H^+(aq)$$

> **B** Explain what is meant by the term weak acid.

Weak acids and pH

A solution is acidic if its pH is less than 7. The lower the pH, the more acidic the solution. pH is a measure of the concentration of hydrogen ions, H^+, in solution. The greater the concentration of hydrogen ions, the lower the pH.

Jack tests the pH of two acids of the same concentration. His results are in the table.

Name and concentration of acid	pH
hydrochloric acid, 0.1 mol/dm³	1.0
ethanoic acid, 0.1 mol/dm³	2.9

- The hydrochloric acid has a lower pH. It is more acidic. This is because all the hydrogen chloride molecules are ionised. The concentration of hydrogen ions is relatively high.
- The ethanoic acid has a higher pH. It is less acidic. This is because fewer than 1% of the ethanoic acid molecules are ionised. The concentration of hydrogen ions is relatively low.

 Universal indicator in a weak acid

Questions

1 What is the difference between a strong acid and a weak acid?

2 Predict which will have the lower pH – a 1 mol/dm³ solution of ethanoic acid, or a 2 mol/dm³ solution of ethanoic acid.

3 Predict which will have the lower pH – a 1 mol/dm³ solution of propanoic acid or a 1 mol/dm³ solution of sulfuric acid.

4 Explain the difference between a weak acid and a dilute acid.

A*

What gives an apple its smell?

Or a pear, or a strawberry, or an orange?

Complicated mixtures of chemicals give fruits their distinctive smells. But one group of compounds dominates fruit smells – the **esters**. Esters have the functional group –COO–, in which the atoms are arranged like this:

▲ The ester pentyl ethanoate contributes to the smell of pears

▲ The ester pentyl butanoate contributes to the smell of strawberries

Did you know...?

Pear drop sweets have no pear in them – just the ester 3-methylbutyl ethanoate.

A Draw the functional group that appears in all esters.

B Give one property of esters.

Ester properties

Most esters are liquids at room temperature. Liquid esters are **volatile** – they easily form vapours. And, of course, they all have distinctive smells.

Using esters

The properties of esters determine their uses. Their smells and tastes make them useful for

- making sweet-smelling perfumes, shampoos, and shower gels
- flavouring foods, including sweets and chocolates.

The ester ethyl ethanoate is a useful solvent, since it is cheap, not poisonous, and has a pleasant smell. As a solvent, it is useful for cleaning circuit boards and removing caffeine from tea and coffee to make decaffeinated drinks.

Making esters

Plants make a huge variety of natural esters. You can also make esters in the laboratory, by reacting a carboxylic acid with an alcohol. The diagrams show how to make ethyl ethanoate.

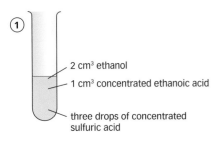

① 2 cm³ ethanol
1 cm³ concentrated ethanoic acid
three drops of concentrated sulfuric acid

② test tube holder
heat gently

③ pour onto water and smell carefully
ester
water
watch glass

▲ How to make ethyl ethanoate

The process of making an ester is called **esterification**. Concentrated sulfuric acid catalyses the reaction. The equation below summarises the reaction for making ethyl ethanoate from ethanol and ethanoic acid.

ethanoic acid   ethanol   ethyl ethanoate   water

Questions

1 Explain the meaning of the term volatile.
2 What is a natural ester?

3 List three uses of esters, and explain how their properties make them suitable for these uses.
4 Name the reactants in the esterification reaction above.

5 Write a balanced symbol equation for the formation of ethyl ethanoate from ethanoic acid and ethanol. Use the equation that includes structural formulae to help you.

↓ E
↓ C
↓ A*

Exam tip   AQA

✔ You could be given the formula of ethyl ethanoate and asked to name the ester. You also need to be able to recognise a compound as an ester from its name or structural formula. But you do not need to name – or draw structural formulae for – any ester other than ethyl ethanoate.

Course catch-up

Revision checklist

- Colours produced in flame tests are used to identify Group 1 ions. Precipitation reactions with sodium hydroxide identify other metal ions.
- Precipitation is used to identify Group 7 ions (halides) by reactions with silver nitrate, and to identify sulfate ions by reaction with barium chloride.
- Carbonate ions produce carbon dioxide when added to acids.
- In titrations, the volumes of acid and alkali reacting together are accurately measured. The results are used to calculate the concentration of solutions.
- Colour changes of indicators show the end point of titrations.
- Ammonia (NH_3) is manufactured when nitrogen and hydrogen are passed over an iron catalyst (Haber process). Nitrogen is obtained from air, and hydrogen from natural gas.
- The Haber process uses a temperature of 450°C and a pressure of 200 atmospheres. Conditions are chosen to make the yield as high as possible while keeping costs low. The Haber process is a reversible reaction.
- In closed systems, reversible reactions reach equilibrium when rate of forward reaction = rate of backward reaction.
- Increasing temperature makes the yield of an exothermic reaction lower.
- Increasing pressure makes the yield of a reaction higher if the number of gas molecules decreases.
- Alcohols (eg ethanol) are a homologous series of molecules containing the –OH functional group. They are used as fuels and solvents, and dissolve in water.
- Ethanol is oxidised to ethanoic acid. Ethanoic acid (found in vinegar) is a member of the carboxylic acid homologous series, containing the functional group –COOH.
- Carboxylic acids are weak acids and do not completely ionise to form H+ ions.
- Carboxylic acids have higher pH values than strong acids, and they react with carbonates to form carbon dioxide
- Carboxylic acids form esters when they react with alcohols in the presence of an acid catalyst.
- Esters (eg ethyl ethanoate) are pleasant-smelling compounds with the functional group –COO–. They are used in perfumes and flavourings.

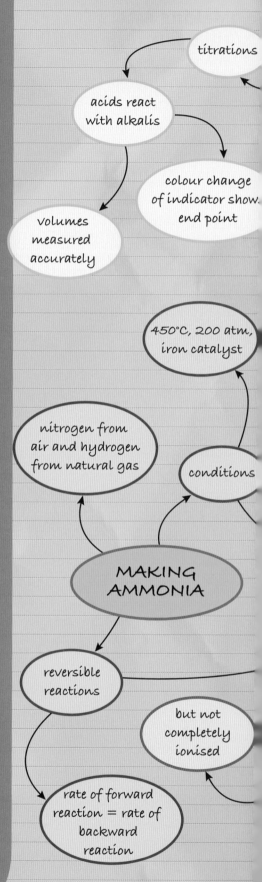

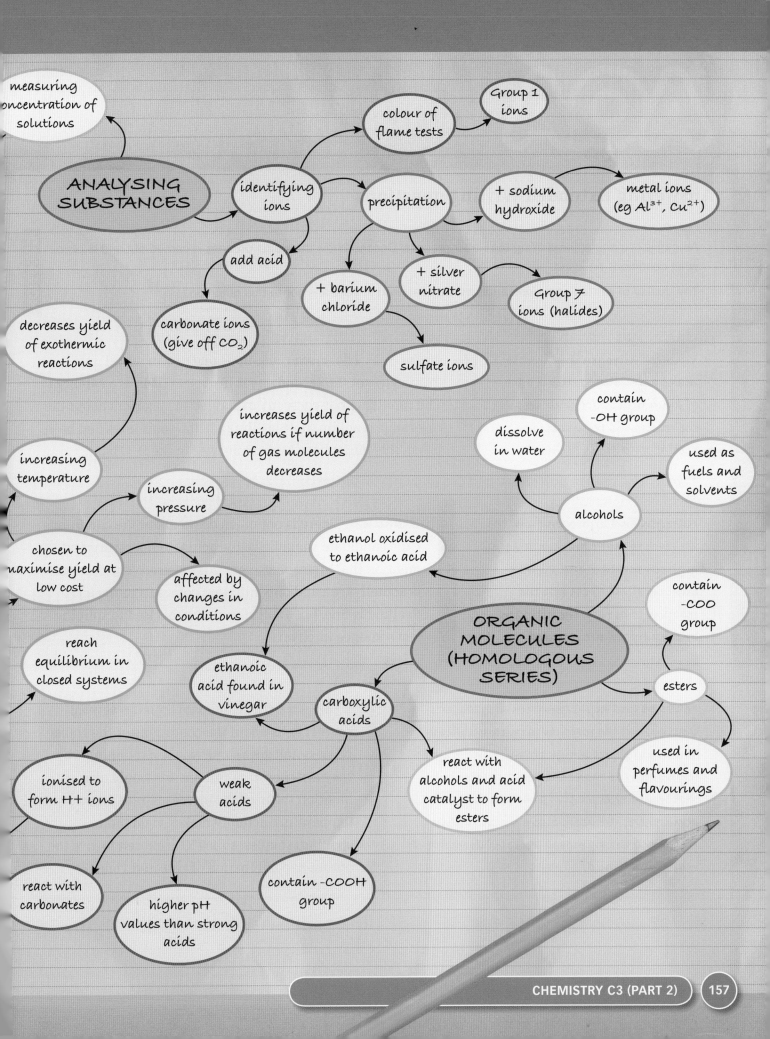

measuring concentration of solutions

ANALYSING SUBSTANCES

identifying ions

colour of flame tests

Group 1 ions

precipitation

+ sodium hydroxide

metal ions (eg Al^{3+}, Cu^{2+})

add acid

+ barium chloride

+ silver nitrate

Group 7 ions (halides)

carbonate ions (give off CO_2)

sulfate ions

decreases yield of exothermic reactions

increases yield of reactions if number of gas molecules decreases

contain -OH group

dissolve in water

used as fuels and solvents

increasing temperature

increasing pressure

alcohols

ethanol oxidised to ethanoic acid

chosen to maximise yield at low cost

affected by changes in conditions

ORGANIC MOLECULES (HOMOLOGOUS SERIES)

contain -COO group

reach equilibrium in closed systems

ethanoic acid found in vinegar

carboxylic acids

esters

react with alcohols and acid catalyst to form esters

used in perfumes and flavourings

ionised to form H+ ions

weak acids

react with carbonates

higher pH values than strong acids

contain -COOH group

AQA Upgrade

Answering Extended Writing questions

QUESTION

Ammonia is manufactured using the Haber process. Describe how the Haber process is carried out and explain what conditions are used.

The quality of written communication will be assessed in your answer to this question.

G–E

You need nitrogen and iron to make ammonia. Getting a lot of ammonia is difficult because the reaction is revursable so special conditions are used.

Examiner: The answer mentions one raw material (nitrogen) but the second one is hydrogen (iron is a catalyst). The candidate has correctly explained the problem about the reversible reaction (note spelling). If the conditions had been listed, this might have been an answer in the D–C band.

D–C

Nitrogen and hydrogen from the air react to make ammonia using high temperature and an iron oxide catalyst. These help the reaction to be fast, the nitrogen and hydrogen are recycled.

Examiner: There is not much detail about the conditions – the candidate should give the actual temperature and mention that atmospheric pressure is used. The catalyst is actually iron and only nitrogen comes from the air. Spelling is fine, but a full stop should be used to split the last sentence into two.

B–A*

Nitrogen and hydrogen from are reacted together, but the reaction is in equilibrium. You would expect a high pressure and high temperature to make the yeald greater but that would be expensive so 450 °C and 200 atmospheres are used, also an iron catalyst. At the end the ammonia is cooled down which makes it a liquid.

Examiner: The candidate includes several correct facts about the conditions of the Haber process and goes some way to explaining why they are chosen. A full answer would also mention the need for increased rate. High temperature actually makes yield (note spelling) smaller, so 450 °C is chosen to give the optimum combination of rate and yield.

Exam-style questions

1 Here are three organic molecules:

A ethanol

B ethyl ethanoate

C ethanoic acid

Complete the table with the correct letter, **A**, **B**, or **C**.

An alcohol	
Found in vinegar	
Used as a fuel	
Formed when **A** and **C** react together	
Has a pH of less than 7	

2 A chemical laboratory carries out tests on three substances.

Test	D	E	F
Flame test	Lilac	Not done	Red
Reaction with sodium hydroxide	No reaction	Blue precipitate	White precipitate
Reaction with silver nitrate and nitric acid	Cream precipitate	White precipitate	Yellow precipitate

Identify substances **D**, **E**, and **F**.

3 William has a bottle of sodium hydroxide of unknown concentration. He takes $25 \, cm^3$ ($0.025 \, dm^3$) of this solution and titrates it against hydrochloric acid with a concentration of $0.1 \, mol/dm^3$.

a $18.2 \, cm^3$ ($0.0182 \, dm^3$) of hydrochloric acid was the average volume needed to neutralise the sodium hydroxide. The hydrochloric acid and sodium hydroxide react in a one-to-one ratio.

i Calculate the average amount in moles of hydrochloric acid used in the titration.

ii What amount in moles of sodium hydroxide reacts with this amount of hydrochloric acid?

iii Use your result from **ii** and other information from the question to calculate the concentration of the sodium hydroxide in mol/dm^3.

b William thinks an unlabelled bottle of acid might be sulfuric acid, which contains sulfate ions. Describe how he could prove that it is sulfuric acid.

Extended Writing

4 Emily wants to do a titration to find out what volume of sulfuric acid is needed to neutralise a solution of sodium hydroxide. Write some instructions for a titration.

5 Hydrochloric acid (HCl) is a strong acid and ethanoic acid (CH_3COOH) is a weak acid. Explain the meaning of these terms and describe how the properties of the two acids differ.

6 The balanced equation for the Haber process (an exothermic reaction) is:

$$N_2 + 3H_2 \leftrightharpoons 2NH_3$$

A temperature of $450 \, °C$ and a pressure of $200 \, atm$ are used, along with an iron catalyst. Explain why.

A02

A03

A02

A02

A02

A01

A01

A01 Recall the science

A02 Apply your knowledge

A03 Evaluate and analyse the evidence

P3 Part 1

Physics in medicine

Why study this unit?

Physics is extremely important in a wide range of industries, including medicine. You've probably already had at least one X-ray, and maybe even an ultrasound. The technologies used by doctors in today's modern hospitals rely heavily on ideas found in physics. As part of this unit you will study how X-rays are used, learn about their benefits and dangers, and understand why sometimes it's better to use ultrasound.

You will learn more about light, how it is refracted by different materials, and how simple lenses can focus it into a point. In this unit you will also find out how the human eye works, learning how images are focussed, why some people need to wear glasses, and how these glasses help them see crystal clear images.

Finally, you will learn about how light can be sent down optical fibres, not only providing high-speed broadband, but also allowing doctors to look inside you without the need to cut you open and take a peek!

You should remember

1 The properties of electromagnetic waves.

2 The nature of sound waves and the meaning of ultrasound.

3 How waves are refracted when they travel from one medium to another.

4 The dangers of ionising radiation and some of the properties of gamma rays.

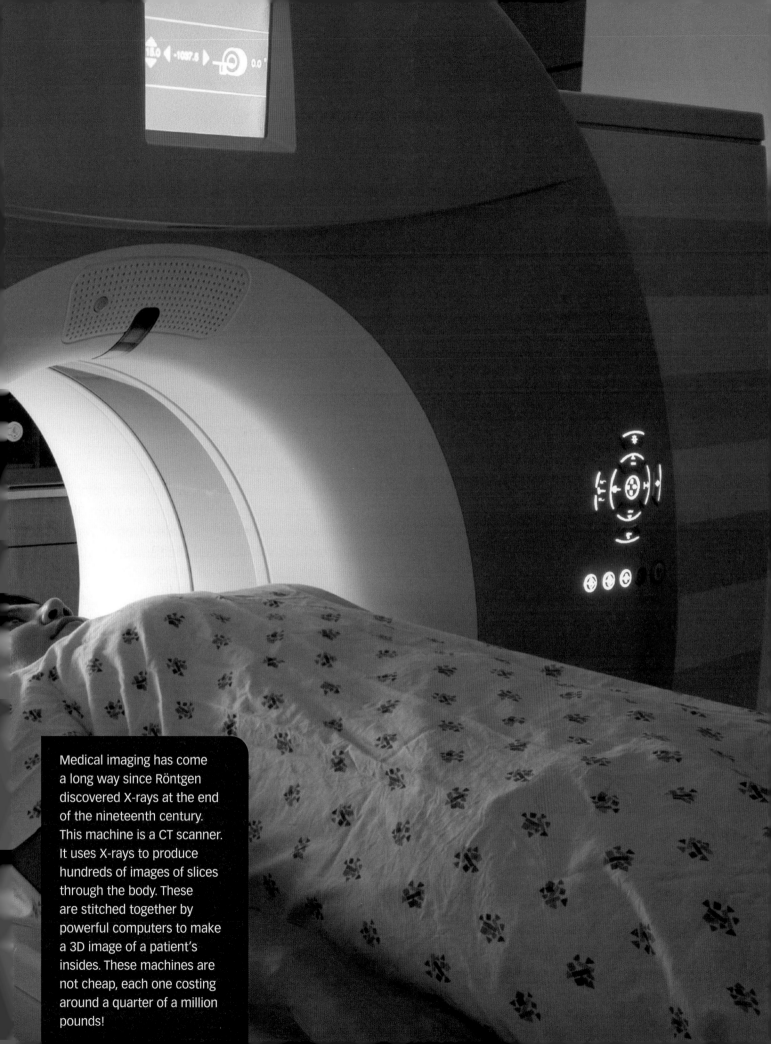

Medical imaging has come a long way since Röntgen discovered X-rays at the end of the nineteenth century. This machine is a CT scanner. It uses X-rays to produce hundreds of images of slices through the body. These are stitched together by powerful computers to make a 3D image of a patient's insides. These machines are not cheap, each one costing around a quarter of a million pounds!

1: X-rays

Key words

X-rays, electromagnetic waves, frequency, wavelength, transmitted, ionisation

Did you know...?

The Diamond synchrotron, located just outside Oxford, sends electrons around a high-speed particle accelerator ring. This makes the electrons emit very high energy X-rays. These are used to study different things, from the structures of chemical compounds and viruses to learning about the best conditions for manufacturing chocolate!

▲ The Diamond Light Source synchrotron can use intense high-energy X-rays to probe matter at a molecular level

What are X-rays?

If you've ever been unlucky enough to break a bone, you will have gone for an X-ray scan. Scans allow the doctor to treat your injury without needing to cut you open to take a look.

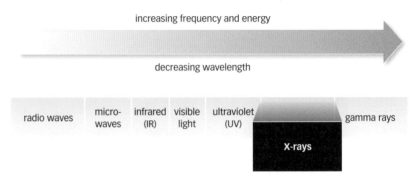

increasing frequency and energy

decreasing wavelength

| radio waves | micro-waves | infrared (IR) | visible light | ultraviolet (UV) | | gamma rays |

X-rays

▲ X-rays are part of the electromagnetic spectrum

An X-ray scan uses **X-rays** to produce an image of the inside of your body. X-rays are similar to the gamma rays in radioactive decay. They are both examples of **electromagnetic waves**. X-rays are produced by very fast-moving electrons, while gamma rays come from the nucleus of radioactive atoms. In hospitals, electron beams are accelerated by high voltages and then smashed into a metal plate, causing the emission of X-rays.

> **A** What kind of wave are X-rays an example of?

All electromagnetic waves travel very fast: they all travel at the speed of light in a vacuum. This includes X-rays. However, compared with visible light, X-rays have a much higher **frequency** and so a much shorter **wavelength** (only gamma rays have shorter wavelengths). Some X-rays are just 0.000 000 000 01 m long (0.01 nm). This means you could fit around one billion of them across your fingernail! The wavelength is about the same size as the diameter of the atom.

> **B** What part of the electromagnetic spectrum has an even shorter wavelength than X-rays?

As X-rays have such a tiny wavelength, they are easily **transmitted** through healthy body tissue. They are able to pass through the body with only some being absorbed by denser materials such as the bones. The denser the material, the more X-rays are absorbed. They are able to travel through most materials and are only fully absorbed by thick slabs of very dense material such as lead or steel.

X-rays and ionisation

Like gamma rays, high-energy X-rays can cause **ionisation**. When an X-ray strikes an atom it transfers all of its energy to the atom. This gives the electrons in the atom so much energy that they break free and fly away at high speed. This creates an ion and this ionisation can be dangerous. Ionisation from high-energy X-rays has exactly the same effect as alpha, beta, and gamma radiation. The ionisation can kill body cells, or potentially lead to cancer.

When photographic film is exposed to X-rays, the effect is similar to exposing it to light or to radiation from a nucleus. Where the film is ionised by the X-rays there is a chemical change, and a picture can be developed. Exposing an area of photographic film to X-rays darkens the film, leaving a cloudy patch. The longer the exposure, or the greater the intensity of the X-rays, the darker the area of the film becomes.

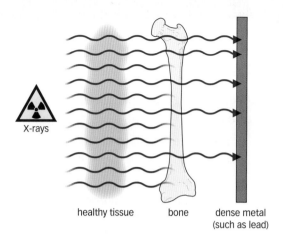

▲ X-rays are easily transmitted through healthy tissue; bone absorbs some X-rays, and lead absorbs most X-rays

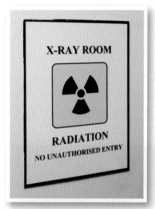

◀ Like other forms of ionising radiation, X-rays are potentially hazardous

Questions

1 Describe the similarities and differences between X-rays and visible light.

2 Describe and explain the effect X-rays have on photographic film.

3 Explain why exposure to X-rays is potentially dangerous to living tissue.

4 Describe what happens to X-rays when they are transmitted through the body.

5 Suggest a technique that could be used to reduce a hospital worker's exposure to X-rays.

▲ Photographic film turns cloudy when exposed to X-rays

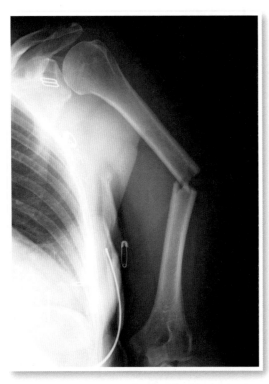

▲ X-ray scans are used to look inside the body without the need for surgery

X-rays in use

In spite of their dangers, X-rays have some very valuable uses. The most common is X-ray photography. This has an important role in security. Luggage is scanned by X-ray machines at airports, and customs officers can even use high-energy X-rays to scan entire vehicles when they enter the UK.

Most modern X-ray machines make use of **CCD**s (charge-coupled devices), rather than photographic film, to detect the X-rays. This is the same kind of sensor as that found in digital cameras. It produces an image that can be processed by a computer.

X-ray scans are widely used in hospitals to diagnose many different medical conditions. The X-rays are used to produce an image, usually of part of a patient's skeleton.

X-rays are fired into the patient. Most pass through the patient's body and they then strike a photographic film or a CCD. But the denser material inside the patient (such as their bones) absorbs some of the X-rays. This causes a variation in the intensity of the X-rays received by the detector, and so an image is produced.

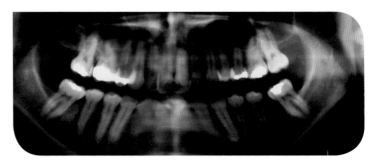

▲ Dentists can use dental X-ray images to check fillings (shown here in bright white) and look for any tooth decay

The same principle is used in dental scans. Denser materials, such as fillings, absorb more X-rays, whereas a decaying tooth inside the gum will absorb slightly less than a healthy tooth. This leads to differences in the intensity of the X-rays detected by the photographic film or CCD, allowing the dentist to make an accurate diagnosis.

> **A** Give two examples of uses of X-ray photography.

A computed tomography scan (**CT scan** for short) is an advanced technique that uses X-rays and CCDs. X-rays are fired through the patient and a series of images, like slices through the patient, are produced. These are processed by a computer to create a 3D image of the inside of the body.

X-ray treatment

X-rays are not only used for imaging inside the body. They can be used as part of **radiotherapy** treatment. They can be used to kill cancerous cells within a tumour.

Working with X-rays

An X-ray machine in a hospital is operated by a **radiographer**, who is responsible for ensuring that X-rays are used safely. X-rays can be dangerous, particularly if you are exposed to them on a regular basis.

> **B** What is the 'CT' in CT scan short for?
>
> **C** What is the name given to the person who takes X-ray images in a hospital?

To reduce their own exposure, the radiographer leaves the room or stands behind a large lead screen whenever the machine is used. X-rays are ionising and prolonged exposure can be very dangerous. People working with X-rays every day have to monitor their own exposure carefully.

> **Questions**
>
> 1 Give two examples of X-ray detectors.
>
> 2 Describe how X-rays may be used to produce an image of a broken bone.
>
> 3 Describe what happens during a CT scan.
>
> 4 Explain why a radiographer leaves the room whenever X-ray photographs are being taken.
>
> 5 Suggest some advantages of using X-rays as part of radiotherapy compared with using gamma rays.

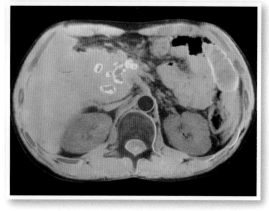

▲ A CT scan produces an image of a slice through the body, allowing the internal organs to be seen

Exam tip

✔ When describing a use of X-rays don't just say 'an X-ray'. Instead say 'producing an X-ray image of a broken bone'. Make sure you give a specific example.

Did you know...?

X-rays were discovered and given their name by the German physicist, Wilhelm Röntgen. He used his new discovery to produce an X-ray image of his wife's hand. She was so disturbed by what she saw that she proclaimed 'I have seen my death'. In fact, X-ray photography rapidly spread to hospitals and has been used to save hundreds of thousands of lives.

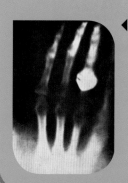

◀ X-ray technology has come a long way since Röntgen's first photograph of his wife's hand

> **A** What does 'frequency' mean?
>
> **B** State the range of human hearing.

▲ Electronic systems are often used to produce ultrasound

Can you hear that?

Your ears are amazing sensory organs. They can detect a wide variety of sound waves over a massive range of volumes, from the quietest of whispers to the loudest bass at a concert. You can hear sound waves with a range of wavelengths from just over 1 cm to over 16 m. However, some sounds are too low-pitched or too high-pitched for us to hear.

You should remember that a sound wave is a series of oscillations, or vibrations, that travel through air or another medium. The number of vibrations each second is called the frequency. A frequency of 50 Hz would mean 50 vibrations every second.

When these vibrations reach your ear they are channelled down the ear canal, causing your ear drum to vibrate. These vibrations pass through a series of tiny bones and eventually an electric signal is sent to the brain. The brain interprets the signal as a sound.

The human ear can detect a very wide range of frequencies. Human hearing ranges from just 20 Hz to up to 20 000 Hz. Sound waves above this frequency are called **ultrasound**. They are too high-pitched for the ear to detect.

Some animals, such as bats, dolphins. and orcas, produce ultrasound naturally. Humans use a variety of electronic methods to produce ultrasound. For example, one way is to use a small electronic speaker, called an ultrasonic transducer. Inside the speaker a small crystal is made to vibrate at a very high frequency, up to 20 million times per second. This produces ultrasound.

Reflections of ultrasound

Ultrasound has a very short wavelength, so it does not spread out (diffract) as much as sound as it travels through the air. This allows the ultrasound to be focussed into a narrow beam.

Ultrasound is able to pass through most materials. When a beam of ultrasound passes from one medium to another, the change in density causes some waves to be **reflected** back the way they came.

The greater the difference in density, the stronger the reflection. The change in density might be at the boundary between two layers of different materials, or it might even happen because there is a fine crack inside the object.

By timing how long it takes for the reflection to come back, we can calculate the distance to the boundary or crack.

$$\begin{matrix} \text{distance} \\ \text{travelled} \\ \text{(metres, m)} \end{matrix} = \begin{matrix} \text{speed of sound through} \\ \text{material} \\ \text{(metres per second, m/s)} \end{matrix} \times \begin{matrix} \text{time taken} \\ \\ \text{(seconds, s)} \end{matrix}$$

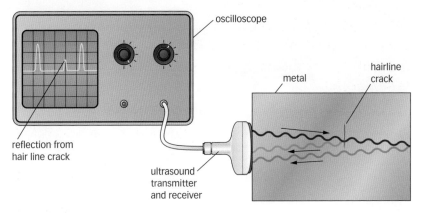

▲ Reflections from tiny cracks inside a piece of metal can been seen on an oscilloscope trace

An oscilloscope can be used to calculate the position of a crack inside a material, as shown in the diagram above. The ultrasound transmitter also acts as a receiver and detects any reflected ultrasound pulses. These are displayed on the screen. The large peak is a reflection from the end of the object; the smaller peak is a reflection from the crack. Using the time base of the oscilloscope, the time taken for the sound pulse to travel to and back from the crack can be calculated, and so the position of the crack can be determined.

If there are several different layers or cracks inside the object, the reflected waves return at different times, depending on the depth of the layers. A computer can process this information to build up a picture of the inside of the object that is being scanned.

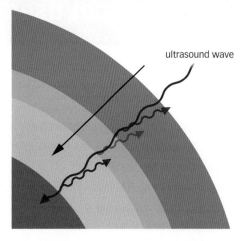

▲ Ultrasound is reflected whenever there is a change in density in the medium it is passing through

Questions

1 Describe what happens to ultrasound when it passes from one medium to another.

2 Define what is meant by ultrasound.

3 A beam of ultrasound is fired into a long metal bar that is known to have a crack inside. The sound travels at 3000 m/s through the metal. After 0.004 s a refection is received back at the transmitter. How far along the bar is the crack?

4 Describe how the traces on an oscilloscope can be used to determine the distance to a crack. Include a diagram of a sample trace in your answer.

E

C

A*

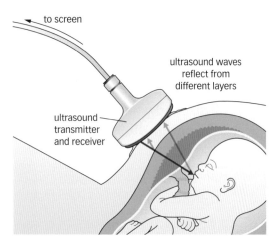

▲ Ultrasound reflects from different layers in the mother and baby

Ultrasound and medicine

You've probably already had an **ultrasound scan**, but you would have been too small to remember. In fact, you were not even born.

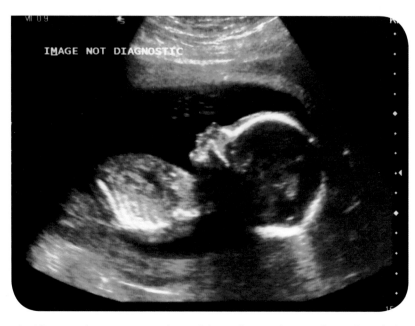

IMAGE NOT DIAGNOSTIC

▲ Ultrasound waves are used to safely produce an image of an unborn baby

As you may remember, ultrasound waves have a high frequency and a short wavelength. This means they are able to travel inside the body and produce images useful for doctors. Ultrasound scans are commonly used to check that babies are developing without any problems, whilst still inside their mother.

An ultrasound beam passes into the mother and then reflects off different layers inside her. There is a strong reflection back from the unborn baby's skeleton. The reflections are then processed by a computer to produce an image.

Ultrasound scans are not only used for scans of unborn babies; they are also used to check on a patient's heart, kidneys or liver.

> **A** Give three examples of things that might be scanned as part of an ultrasound body scan.

Ultrasound has other important medical uses. It can even be used to monitor the blood flow inside a patient's veins.

Another common medical use of ultrasound is to break up **kidney stones**. These sometimes form in a patient's kidney. They can block important ducts and can be very painful.

Ultrasound is used to break up the kidney stones inside the body, preventing the need for surgery. Ultrasound is directed at the kidney stone. This makes the stone vibrate at a very high frequency, causing it to break up into small enough pieces to pass out of the body in the patient's urine.

Comparing ultrasound and X-ray scans

Both ultrasound and X-rays are used to obtain images of the inside of the human body. Ultrasound body scans have advantages over X-ray scans. An ultrasound scan does not damage living cells as some higher energy X-rays can. The ultrasound waves are non-ionising, unlike X-rays. This makes them suitable for scanning unborn babies. A pregnant woman should never have an X-ray as the baby's cells are particularly vulnerable to the effects of ionising radiation.

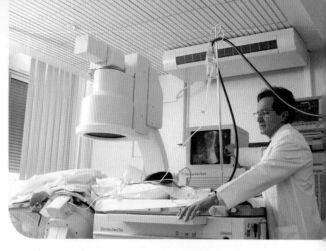

▲ Ultrasound is used to break up painful kidney stones

B What is a kidney stone and why is it a problem?

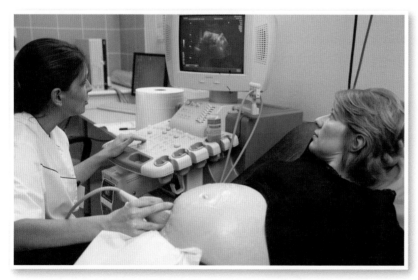

▲ Unlike X-rays, ultrasound waves are non-ionising, and so they can be used to scan women who are pregnant

In spite of their dangers, X-rays have one significant advantage over ultrasound. X-rays have much shorter wavelengths. The images produced are therefore often much clearer, giving more detail than an ultrasound scan. This allows tiny, hairline cracks or small anomalies to be spotted by doctors.

Questions

1 Give two examples of medical uses of ultrasound.

2 Describe how ultrasound is used to break up kidney stones.

3 Describe how ultrasound is used to produce an image of an unborn baby.

4 Compare the advantages and disadvantages of an ultrasound body scan as opposed to an X-ray scan.

5 Suggest a reason why a thick layer of gel is applied to the mother's skin before an ultrasound pregnancy scan (think about the reflections).

◀ The reflection of light leads to some strange optical effects

Bending rays of light

The **refraction** of light leads to some unusual optical effects. Mirages in deserts are caused by refraction, swimming pools look shallower than they actually are, and fish that are seen from above the surface of the water are not where they appear to be.

> **A** Give an example of an unusual optical effect caused by refraction.

As you will remember, refraction is the bending of light (or any wave) when it travels from one medium to another. When light moves from one medium to another its speed changes, depending on the density of the material. This speed change causes a change in the direction of the light (unless the light wave hits the new medium head-on, in which case the direction of the ray is along the normal).

The direction that the light bends in depends on the relative density of the two media. If the light enters a denser material, such as when travelling from air to glass, the light slows down. This makes the light bend towards the normal.

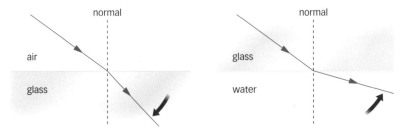

▲ Light either refracts towards or away from the normal depending on the relative density of the two media

If the light goes from a denser medium to one that is less dense, such as when travelling from glass to water, the light speeds up. This makes the light bend away from the normal.

> **B** What happens to the direction of light when it passes from a medium into one that has a lower density?

Refractive index

The **refractive index** of a material is a measure of the speed of light through the material compared with the speed of light in a vacuum. The more slowly the light travels through the material, the higher its refractive index. The denser the material, the higher its refractive index. Water has a refractive index of 1.3, and the refractive index of glass is 1.4.

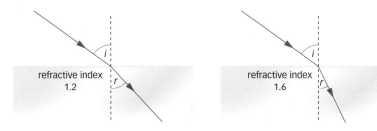

▲ The greater the refractive index, the more the light ray bends when it enters the material

Materials with a higher refractive index cause the light to slow down more and bend more towards the normal.

The refractive index of a material can be calculated using this equation:

$$\text{refractive index} = \frac{\text{sine of the angle of incidence}}{\text{sine of the angle of reflection}} = \frac{\sin i}{\sin r}$$

Worked example

A ray of light passes into a specially made glass block. The angle of incidence is measured as 30°, and the angle of refraction is found to be 18°. Find the refractive index of the glass.

$$\text{refractive index} = \frac{\text{sine of the angle of incidence}}{\text{sine of the angle of reflection}} = \frac{\sin i}{\sin r}$$

angle of incidence = 30° and angle of refraction = 18°

$$\text{refractive index} = \frac{\sin 30°}{\sin 18°}$$

$$= \frac{0.5}{0.3}$$

$$= 1.7$$

Plotting a graph of sin i against sin r gives a straight line through the origin. Sin i is directly proportional to sin r. The refractive index can be found by measuring the gradient of the graph. Materials with a higher refractive index show a steeper line.

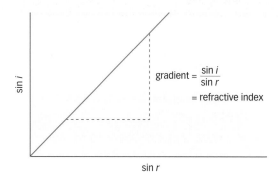

$$\text{gradient} = \frac{\sin i}{\sin r}$$
$$= \text{refractive index}$$

▲ A graph of sin i (the sine of the angle of incidence) against sin r (the sine of the angle of reflection) shows a straight line through the origin. This is a directly proportional relationship.

Questions

1 Describe what happens to the direction of light when it passes from a low density medium into one with a higher density.

2 Explain what causes a ray of light to change direction when it passes from one material to another.

3 Explain what is meant by refractive index and describe how it might be calculated.

4 A ray of light passes into a glass block. The angle of incidence is 49°, and the angle of refraction is found to be 30°. Find the refractive index of the glass.

5 Describe an experiment you could do, including the measurements you would take, to determine the refractive index of a transparent block.

6: Introduction to lenses

Learning objectives

After studying this topic, you should be able to:

✔ understand that a lens forms an image by refracting light

✔ describe the difference between a converging and a diverging lens

Key words

converging, convex, principal axis, principal focus, focus, focal length, concave, diverging, virtual focus

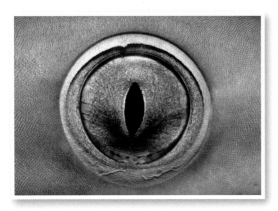

▲ Like most eyes, the eyes of a shark contain a lens to focus the light

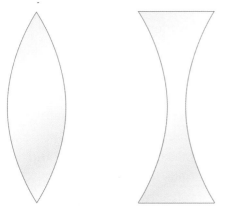

▲ A simple convex, converging lens

▲ A simple concave, diverging lens

Life through a lens

Lenses are found in cameras, telescopes, glasses, and in the eyes of most animals. There are lots of different types of lens, but they all work in exactly the same way.

A lens is used to refract the light that passes through it. The light then forms an image. The lens is usually denser than the medium around it, so when light enters the lens it bends towards the normal. When it leaves the lens it bends away from the normal.

> **A** Give two examples of uses of lenses.

Although the light refracts both when it enters and when it leaves the lens, we often simplify our drawings by showing the light refracting at the centre of the lens.

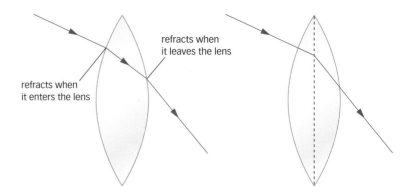

refracts when it leaves the lens

refracts when it enters the lens

▲ A lens refracts light when it enters and when it leaves the lens. To simplify this we just draw the light refracting in the middle of the lens.

The most commonly used type of lens is a **converging** one. A **convex** lens is an example of a converging lens. When rays of light parallel to the **principal axis** pass through a convex lens, they are focussed to a single point called the **principal focus** (or just the **focus**). The distance from the centre of the lens to the principal focus is called the **focal length**. The lens has two principal foci, one on each side of the lens.

> **B** What type of lens can be used to focus light at a principal focus?

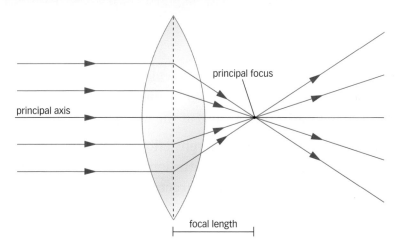

Parallel rays of light through a convex lens are focussed at the principal focus

The converging lens used in a magnifying glass focuses the sunlight. This can create a hot spot.

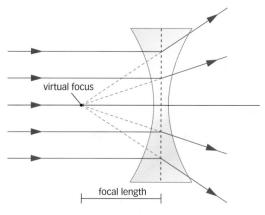

A diverging lens spreads out the rays of light. The light then appears to come from a virtual focus.

Other types of lens

A **concave** lens is an example of a **diverging** lens. Here the parallel rays of light spread out when they pass through the lens.

On a diagram such as that shown on the right you can extrapolate the rays back to a **virtual focus**. There is no actual focus here; it is just where the rays of light appear to come from, hence the use of the term 'virtual'.

Diverging lenses also have a focal length. This is the distance from the centre of the lens to the virtual focus.

Questions

1   What are the most common types of lens?

2   Draw a diagram to show how a converging lens can focus rays of light.

3   Draw a diagram to show how a diverging lens spreads out rays of light, and how the virtual focus can be found.

4   Two convex lenses are 10 cm apart along the same principal axis. They both have a focal length of 5 cm. Draw a diagram to show the path followed by parallel rays of light that enter the lens on the left, before passing through the lens on the right.

Did you know...?

The oldest known artificial lens is the Nimrud lens. This is a 3000-year-old piece of rock crystal discovered in modern Iraq. Scientists are not sure what this lens was used for. Some think it may have been used as a magnifying glass, others believe it was used to start fires by focussing sunlight.

Exam tip

✓ Don't mix up convex and concave lenses. A concave lens curves inwards – like a cave.

Key words

diminished, magnified, upright, inverted, real, virtual

▲ A projector contains a converging lens to focus an image on a screen

Forming an image

We use lenses to form images of a wide variety of objects. From distant planets right down to microscopic cells, lenses are used to help us make sense of the world around us.

All lenses are designed to use refraction to bend the light in a specific way, depending on the lens. Inside most optical instruments, a lens is used to refract the light to form an image.

> A What is the name of the bending of light that happens when lenses form an image?

Lenses are used to make very different types of image. A digital camera uses a lens to produce a tiny image on film or a light-sensitive CCD. A digital projector produces an image on a screen much larger than the tiny screen inside the projector.

The images formed depend on the lens used and the distance of the object from the lens.

> B What two factors affect the nature of the image formed by a lens?

Image characteristics

The image formed by a lens is described according to four features (characteristics).

Feature	Description
Position	Is the image closer to or further from the lens than the object?
Size	Is the image smaller (**diminished**) or larger (**magnified**) than the object?
Orientation	Is the image the same way up (**upright**) as the object or has it been flipped upside down (**inverted**)?
Type of image	Is the image a **real** image or a **virtual** image?

A real image is one that can be formed on a screen or surface. Rays of light from the same part of an object take different paths through the lens to cross at a focus on the other side of the lens. If you place a screen at that focus, where the rays intersect, it will show an image of the object. A virtual image is when the rays of light appear to the observer to have come from a focus. But the rays have not intersected: there is nowhere you could place a screen to form an image.

▲ You can use a convex lens to produce a real image on a screen

A convex lens can be used to produce an image of an object far away from the lens. In this case the image is closer to the lens than the object, diminished, inverted, and (as it can be formed on a screen) it must also be real.

Here is another example of using a simple converging lens to form an image. This time the object is much closer to the lens and so the characteristics of the image are different.

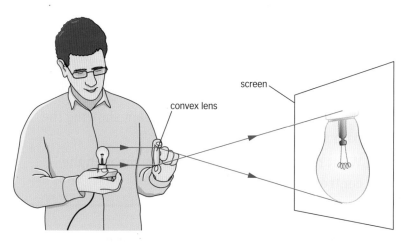

▲ Projecting an image using a convex lens

Questions

1 Give two examples of optical instruments that use lenses to form images. ↓ E

2 State the four characteristics that must be used when describing the image formed by a lens.

3 Describe the difference between a real image and a virtual image. ↓ C

4 Describe the characteristics of the image formed by a convex lens when the object is close to the lens (as seen in the diagram on the left).

5 Using the four characteristics in the table, describe the image formed inside a digital camera. ↓ A*

8: Converging lenses

Learning objectives

After studying this topic, you should be able to:

✔ construct ray diagrams to show how images are formed by a converging lens

✔ describe the images formed by a converging lens

Key words

ray diagram

▲ This symbol represents a converging (convex) lens. It is often used when drawing ray diagrams as an alternative to drawing a full lens.

▲ Some telescopes use a pair of lenses to produce an enlarged image of objects in the night sky. In the seventeenth century, Galileo used one to provide evidence that the Earth was not at the centre of the Universe.

Constructing ray diagrams

We often draw (or construct) **ray diagrams** showing the path of light through a lens to help us determine the nature of the image formed.

In these examples an arrow is used to represent the object. Light is reflected off all parts of the object, but we just consider the light that is being reflected from the tip.

Light is being reflected from the tip in many directions, but we can find out where the image will be by considering light that follows one of three paths.

1. *Light passing through the centre of the lens.* The light that passes through the centre of a lens continues through in a straight line.
2. *Light travelling parallel to the principal axis.* The light that is travelling parallel to the principal axis is refracted by the lens so that it passes through the principal focus on the other side.
3. *Light passing through the focus.* The light that passes through the principal focus is refracted by the lens so that it comes out travelling parallel to the principal axis.

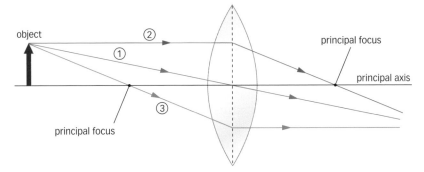

▲ The three rules for rays of light passing through a converging (convex) lens

A What is the name given to a diagram showing the path followed by a ray of light?

B What happens to light that passes through the centre of a converging lens?

Forming different images

Using these three paths, we can construct ray diagrams to show how images are formed.

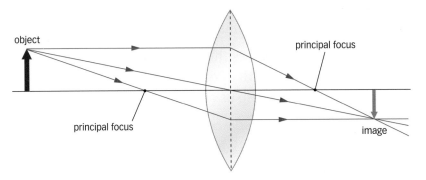

▲ Using a converging lens to form an image of an object that is far away from the lens

The image forms where the rays cross. If an object is far away, the image formed is closer to the lens, smaller, inverted and real (the rays do cross over).

If the object is much closer to the lens, then the image is very different.

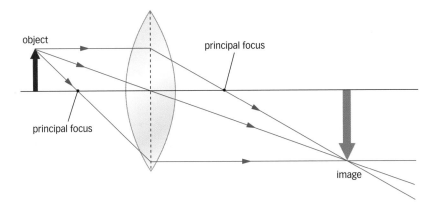

▲ If the object is much closer to the lens, the image formed is very different

Questions

1 What happens to light that enters a converging lens parallel to the principal axis?

2 Carefully draw a diagram showing the three rules for the path followed by rays of light through a converging lens.

3 Using the four image characteristics in the table on spread P3.7, describe the image formed in the second ray diagram on this page.

4 Use graph paper to carefully produce your own ray diagrams for the two examples on this page.

9: Diverging lenses

Learning objectives

After studying this topic, you should be able to:

- ✔ construct ray diagrams to show how images are formed by a diverging lens
- ✔ describe the images formed by a diverging lens

▲ This symbol represents a diverging (concave) lens. It is often used when drawing ray diagrams as an alternative to drawing a full lens.

▲ Some types of glasses contain diverging lenses. They can help the wearer focus on objects that are far away.

Ray diagrams for diverging lenses

A concave lens is an example of a diverging lens. In a similar way to how we used a converging lens, we can use a diverging lens to form an image of an object.

When the rays of light pass through the lens they are refracted and, just as with a converging lens, we look at the paths of three rays to help us construct a ray diagram.

1. *Light passing through the centre of the lens.* Just like a converging lens, when light passes through the centre of a diverging lens it continues through in a straight line.
2. *Light travelling parallel to the principal axis.* When light travelling parallel to the principal axis passes through the lens, it is refracted away from the principal axis. When we trace back along the path of the refracted ray we find that it passes through the virtual focus.
3. *Light heading for the virtual focus.* When light that is heading for the virtual focus on the other side of the lens passes through the lens, it is refracted so that it comes out travelling parallel to the principal axis.

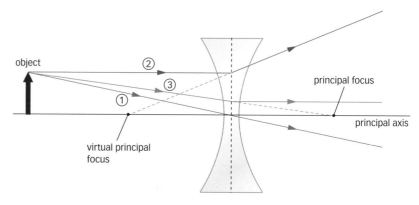

▲ The three rules for rays of light passing through a diverging (concave) lens

> **A** What happens to the path of a ray of light that passes through the centre of a diverging lens?

Describing the images formed by a diverging lens

Unlike a converging lens, the image from a diverging lens always forms on the same side of the lens as the object. In order to see the image, you must look through the lens.

The image from a diverging lens is always closer to the lens than the object, smaller than the object (diminished), upright and virtual.

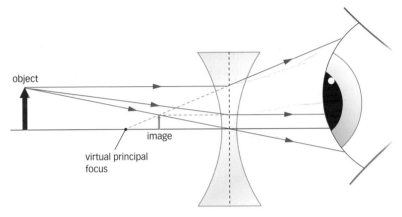

▲ Forming a virtual image with a diverging lens

The image formed by a diverging lens is always a virtual image. It cannot be formed onto a screen or camera film.

> **B** Why is it not possible to form an image from a diverging lens on a screen?

When the object moves further away from a diverging lens, the virtual image gets smaller and smaller. This allows you to see a wider field of view through the lens. This makes this kind of lens useful as a security peep hole in front doors. If there was no lens in the hole you would not be able to see much at all.

▲ A diverging lens is used in a peephole to provide a wider field of view

Questions

1 What happens to light that enters a diverging lens parallel to the principal axis? **↓ E**

2 Carefully draw a diagram showing the three rules for the path followed by a ray of light through a diverging lens. **↓ C**

3 Use graph paper to carefully produce your own ray diagram showing the image formed by a diverging lens.

4 Describe what happens to the image formed by a diverging lens as the object moves further from the lens. Construct two ray diagrams to help illustrate your answer. **↓ A***

Learning objectives

After studying this topic, you should be able to:

- ✔ calculate the magnification of an object
- ✔ describe how a converging lens is used in a magnifying glass

Key words

magnification

Calculating magnification

Lenses are often used to magnify tiny objects. As the light passes through the lens, it is refracted in such a way as to produce a larger image. This allows the observer to see minute details usually invisible to the naked eye.

The **magnification** of an object can be calculated using the equation:

$$\text{magnification} = \frac{\text{image height}}{\text{object height}}$$

If the magnification is 1, the image is the same height as the object. If the magnification is less than 1, the image is smaller than the object. For example, a magnification of 0.5 would mean the image is half the size of the object. A 40 cm object would produce a 20 cm image.

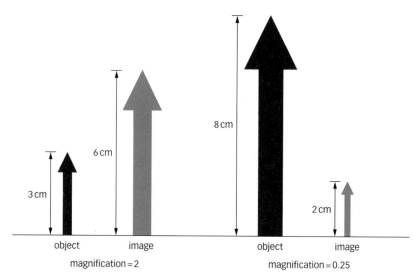

Examples of different magnifications

Any magnification greater than 1 means the image is larger than the object. A magnification of 5 would mean the image is five times larger than the object: a 2 cm object would produce a 10 cm image.

Worked example

Light from a 4 cm high object passes through a lens onto a screen. The image is 36 cm high. Calculate the magnification.

$$\text{magnification} = \frac{\text{image height}}{\text{object height}}$$

image height = 36 cm and object height
= 4 cm

so, magnification $= \dfrac{36 \text{ cm}}{4 \text{ cm}}$

= 9

A What is meant by a magnification of 3?

B An image, 2 cm high, is focussed by a lens onto a photographic film. The object being photographed is 10 cm high. Calculate the magnification.

The magnifying glass

Telescopes and microscopes use combinations of lenses to magnify an object. A magnifying glass uses a single converging (convex) lens.

For the lens to act as a magnifying glass, the object being magnified must be close to the lens. It needs to be nearer to the lens than the principal focus (its distance from the lens must be less than the focal length). The magnifying glass produces an image on the same side of the lens as the object, so the user must look through the lens in order to see the magnified image.

Using a convex lens as a magnifying glass produces a magnified, upright, virtual image, which is further away from the lens.

▲ A magnifying glass is a single convex lens

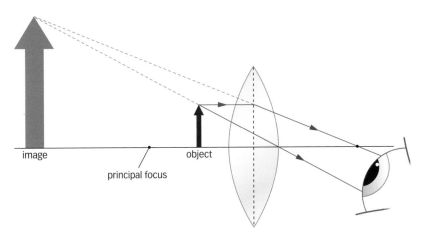

▲ Using a convex lens as a magnifying glass produces a magnified, virtual image

Exam tip AQA

- ✔ When constructing a ray diagram for a magnifying glass, only two rays can be drawn.
- ✔ A converging lens can produce both real and virtual images. A virtual image is only produced when the distance from the object to the lens is less than the focal length.

Questions

1 What type of lens is used in a magnifying glass?

2 Light from a 2 cm high object is projected through a lens onto a screen, producing an image 56 cm high. Calculate the magnification.

3 An image, 4.8 cm, high is focussed on a CCD by a lens. The object being photographed is 19.2 cm tall. Calculate the magnification.

4 Use graph paper to carefully construct a ray diagram for a magnifying glass and calculate the magnification.

5 Compare the similarities and differences between images formed by a magnifying glass and a diverging lens.

E

C

A*

Learning objectives

After studying this topic, you should be able to:

✔ describe the structure of the human eye, including the functions of the key parts

✔ state the range of vision of the human eye

Key words

suspensory ligaments, retina, cornea, iris, pupil, ciliary muscles, range of vision

▲ The human eye is an amazing optical instrument

Did you know...?

It is not just light which causes the pupil to open wider. When you see someone you fancy, your pupil dilates. You can't stop it: it is a biological reaction aimed at making you look more attractive to a potential mate!

Eye, eye

Imagine what the world be like if the human eye had not evolved. The eye is an amazing object. It allows us to see the world around us, to make sense of the beauty and complexity of the natural world.

The human eye, like the eyes of most animals, contains a convex lens. This is held in place by a series of **suspensory ligaments**. Unlike the glass lenses we have been discussing, the lens in your eye is made of a jelly-like substance which allows it to change its shape. Light passes through the lens, is refracted, and is focussed onto the back of the eye (called the **retina**).

The retina contains special cells that detect light intensity and colour. They send a signal, via the optic nerve, to your brain.

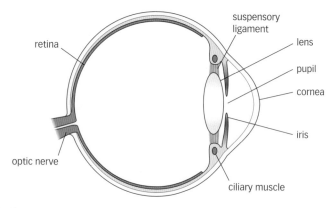

▲ The human eye

> **A** What is the name of the part of your eye that has light-sensing cells?

Other important parts of the eye help to produce clear images. The **cornea** is the transparent front part of the eye that covers the **iris** and **pupil**. Like the lens, the cornea also refracts light passing through it, helping to form a focussed image. Refraction at the cornea plays a very important role in forming an image, but unlike the lens it is a fixed shape and cannot change its focus.

The iris is the coloured part of the eye. It can expand or contract, allowing differing amounts of light to pass through the gap in the centre (the pupil). The larger the pupil, the more light can enter the eye. At night your iris slowly relaxes, so that the pupil becomes larger. This dilated pupil helps you to see more clearly in low light conditions. It takes around 20 minutes to reach full 'night vision'. A quick glance at a bright light causes the pupil to shrink back, losing the night vision

Changing focus

The shape of the lens inside the eye can be changed by the **ciliary muscles**. When these contract, they pull on the suspensory ligaments and change the shape of the lens. This allows the eye to focus on nearby objects, and then rapidly change the focus to look at objects far away.

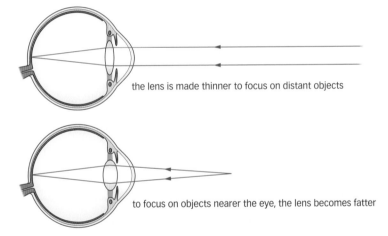

the lens is made thinner to focus on distant objects

to focus on objects nearer the eye, the lens becomes fatter

▲ The shape of the lens changes so that light from objects that are far away as well from those that are closer to the eye can be focussed on the retina

The lens is stretched and made thinner for looking at distant objects. It springs back to a much fatter shape to focus the light from nearby objects.

The **range of vision** describes the distance from the nearest point to the furthest point that the eye can focus on. If you move your fingers too close to your eye, it can't focus and you see a blurry image. This near point is around 25 cm; objects much closer than this cannot be focussed by the eye alone.

The far point is much further away. The eye can focus on objects at infinity; these objects are so far away that the light entering the eye from all parts of these objects is effectively parallel to the principal axis.

> **B** What is the name given to the coloured part of the eye?

▲ The eye can focus on objects that are very far away, as well as on objects that are much closer, for instance when reading

Questions

1 Describe what happens to light when it enters the eye.

2 Produce a table summarising the function of the following structures in the eye: iris and pupil; retina; lens; cornea; ciliary muscle; suspensory ligaments.

3 What is the range of human vision?

4 Describe how the lens changes shape to focus on objects at different distances.

5 Suggest a reason why it becomes more difficult to focus on nearby objects as you age.

Key words

short-sightedness, long-sightedness, corrective lenses

▲ Sometimes people have difficulty focusing on some objects, and see a blurry image

---

B Which problem with vision becomes more common as people age?

Seeing near and far

The eye is such a complex organ that it is not surprising that we experience problems with our vision. This becomes more frequent as you age, but often people are born with slight vision defects. The lens, the cornea, or even the shape of the eye itself can lead to problems when focussing on objects. This produces a blurry image, with some loss of detail.

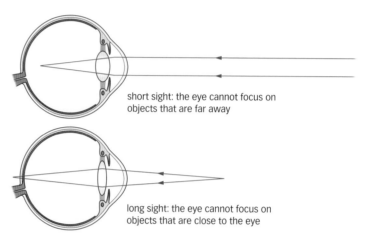

short sight: the eye cannot focus on objects that are far away

long sight: the eye cannot focus on objects that are close to the eye

▲ If the eye cannot focus the light onto the retina, a blurry image is seen

Two common problems with vision are **short-sightedness** and **long-sightedness**, often just called short sight and long sight.

A What are the two most common problems with vision?

People with short sight cannot focus on objects that are far away. This can happen because the eye is slightly too long, or cannot make the lens thin enough to focus the light on the retina.

People with long sight cannot focus on objects that are close to the eye. This may be because the eye is slightly too short, or cannot make the lens fat enough to focus the light. This often happens as people get older. The lens loses some of its elasticity and so does not spring back into a fat enough shape to focus the light.

Using glasses

To help form a clear image, **corrective lenses** are used. These are used in glasses and refract the light passing through them in such a way as to produce a sharp image on the retina.

To correct short-sightedness a diverging (concave) lens is used. This allows the light from distant objects to be focussed on the retina instead of in front of it, producing a clear image.

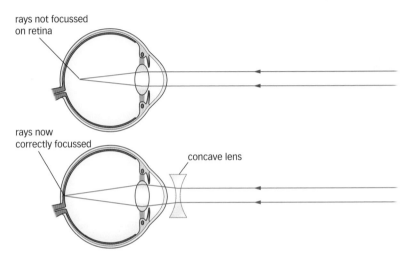

▲ A concave lens is used to correct short-sightedness

To correct long-sightedness a converging (convex) lens is used. The lens helps the eye produce a clear image by converging the light from nearby objects on to the retina.

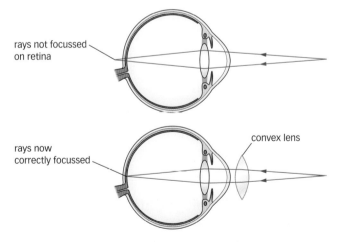

▲ A convex lens is used to correct long-sightedness

▲ Wearing glasses allows an image to be clearly focussed on the retina

Did you know...?

Lenses were first used to help with eyesight in ancient Egypt. Hieroglyphs from the fifth century BC show the use of simple lenses. It is not clear exactly when modern glasses (that you wear on your face all the time) were invented, or who invented them. It is likely that glasses were invented between 1280 and 1300, in Italy.

Questions

1 What is a corrective lens?

2 Explain what is meant by short sight and long sight, and suggest a reason for each.

3 Draw diagrams to show how in long sight and short sight a clear image cannot be focussed on the retina.

4 Draw ray diagrams showing how glasses can be used to correct for long sight and short sight.

Learning objectives

After studying this topic, you should be able to:

✔ describe how a camera forms an image

✔ compare the structure of the eye with a camera

Key words

camera

Cameras are everywhere! There is probably a camera on your mobile phone, and there are thousands of CCTV cameras in towns and cities.

Despite recent advances with digital images, the mechanical parts of cameras, such as the lens, haven't really changed much in principle since the earliest cameras.

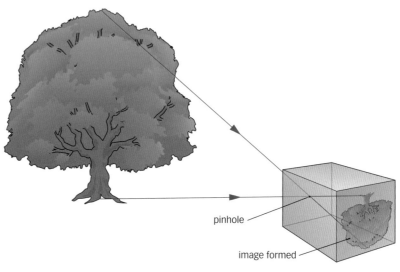

pinhole

image formed

▲ An image can be produced using a simple pinhole camera

A pinhole camera is the simplest form of camera. It does not even have a lens. Light passes through a tiny hole into a light-proof box. This produces an inverted image on the back of the box.

It was not until around 1600 that a simple converging (convex) lens was added to the pinhole camera. However, the camera was still not able to take a photo – it could only project an image, not record it.

> **A** What was the first type of lens to be used in a pinhole camera?

Over 200 years later, the first photographic image was taken. Light was focussed onto a plate that contained chemicals that reacted differently depending on the brightness of the light shone onto them. Over the years scientists developed better chemical compounds. These were more sensitive to light and produced clearer images.

▲ A camera shares some features of the human eye. Both have a lens to focus the light. However, to get clear images of objects at different distances, lenses in cameras are often moved forwards or backwards while the lens in the human eye changes its shape. The shutter in a camera performs a similar role to the iris and pupil. It allows more or less light in, depending on the conditions.

A modern camera uses a lens to focus the light onto either a very fine-grain chemical film or onto a light-sensitive component called a CCD (charge-coupled device).

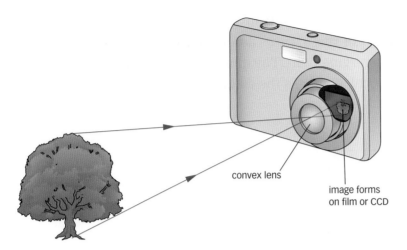

convex lens

image forms on film or CCD

▲ A camera focuses an image onto film or a CCD

Detecting the light

The light-sensitive parts of a camera are very similar to the retina in the human eye. Camera film and CCD chips react when light shines on them. In camera film there is a permanent chemical change. Each photograph needs a fresh piece of film.

A CCD has millions of tiny light-sensitive pixels that each produce an electric current when light strikes them. This signal is then processed and stored as a digital picture. This only takes a fraction of a second. The camera is then ready to take another picture.

Questions

1 What part of a digital camera is equivalent to the retina in the human eye?

2 Describe how a modern camera focuses an image onto a CCD or a piece of film.

3 Describe the differences between the use of camera film and the use of CCDs found in digital cameras.

4 Give some advantages and disadvantages of using a CCD to take photos.

Did you know...?

Nearly all commercial cameras now use CCDs, which contain millions of megapixels. A 7 MP camera takes pictures made up of 7 million pixels. Each pixel forms a tiny part of the image. However the number of megapixels is not always the best indicator of quality. Other factors such as the size and type of lens are very important.

The cells within your retina are much more sensitive than most CCDs. Your eye produces a much clearer image than most digital cameras.

B Give two examples of a light-sensitive part of a camera.

▲ The CCD used in digital cameras behaves in a similar way to the retina in the eye

Learning objectives

After studying this topic, you should be able to:

✔ describe the factors affecting the power of converging and diverging lenses

✔ calculate the power of a lens

✔ explain the relation of lens shape and refractive index for a given focal length

Key words

lens power, dioptres

Worked example 1

A convex lens used in a pair of glasses has a focal length of 50 cm. Find its optical power in dioptres.

$$\text{optical power} = \frac{1}{\text{focal length}} \quad \text{or} \quad P = \frac{1}{f}$$

focal length, $f = 50$ cm $= 0.50$ m

$$\text{optical power} = \frac{1}{0.5\,\text{m}} = +2\,\text{D}$$

Worked example 2

The focal length of a diverging lens is negative (because the principal focus is virtual). A diverging concave lens has a focal length of −0.4 m. Find its optical power in dioptres.

$$P = \frac{1}{f}$$

focal length, $f = -0.4$ m

$$\text{optical power} = \frac{1}{-0.4\,\text{m}} = -2.5\,\text{D}$$

The power of a lens

The lenses we use are of many different shapes and are made of a range of transparent materials. The **lens power** of any of these lenses describes how good it is at converging or diverging light. The more powerful the lens, the shorter its focal length. In the diagram, the lenses on the left are much 'stronger'.

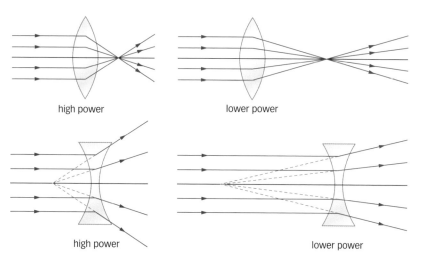

high power   lower power

high power   lower power

▲ The higher power lenses have shorter focal lengths

A   What is meant by the power of a lens?

Lens power is measured in **dioptres**. A typical lens found in a pair of glasses may have a power of +3 D. The more powerful a lens, the higher this number.

The power of a converging lens is always a positive number. The power of a diverging lens is always a negative number.

B   A lens has a power of −2 dioptres. Is it a converging or diverging lens?

The power of a lens is given by:

$$\text{optical power (dioptres, D)} = \frac{1}{\text{focal length (metres, m)}}$$

If P is power in dioptres, and f is focal length in metres, then:

$$P = \frac{1}{f}$$

What affects the focal length of a lens?

Two things determine the power of a lens and therefore the focal length.

- Refractive index of the material of the lens. The higher the refractive index, the more the lens will bend the rays of light. The lens has a higher power and a shorter focal length.
- Curvature of the two surfaces of the lens. The greater the curvature (the fatter the lens is), the more the lens bends the rays of light. The lens power is higher and the focal length is shorter.

these lenses are made of the same material

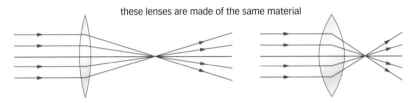

▲ The refractive index of the material is the same for these two lenses. The fatter lens is more powerful and has a shorter focal length.

The lenses in modern glasses can be very thin, yet they still have a high power. This is done by making the lenses from a special glass that has a much higher refractive index (it bends the light more) than normal glass. The lens is still just as powerful, with the same focal length as the older type made with normal glass, but does not need to be so curved. Because the lens can be flatter (lower curvature), it can also be manufactured thinner.

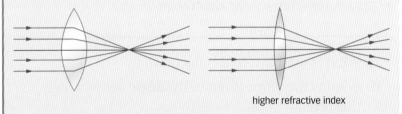

higher refractive index

▲ A lens with a higher refractive index can have a lower curvature and still have the same focal length as a fatter lens

◄ Lenses manufactured for modern glasses can be made thinner. The higher refractive index means that a less curved lens can provide the same power and focal length. Flatter lenses can be made thinner.

Questions

1 What two factors affect the focal length of a typical lens? E

2 Two convex lenses are used in a telescope. The first has a focal length of 20 cm, the second a focal length of 60 cm. Find the optical power of each lens in dioptres. C

3 A diverging lens is used in a peep hole. It has a focal length of –10 cm. Find its optical power in dioptres.

4 Describe the effect on its power of changing the curvature of a lens. Use diagrams to help illustrate your answer.

5 Explain why a lens made from a material with a higher refractive index will have a higher power than a similarly shaped lens made from glass with a lower refractive index. A*

Learning objectives

After studying this topic, you should be able to:

✔ describe the conditions needed for total internal reflection

✔ calculate the critical angle

Key words

total internal reflection (TIR), critical angle

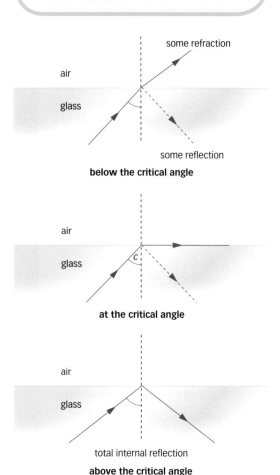

Total internal reflection

Total internal reflection

When light travels from one medium to another it refracts (bends), but there is also a small amount of internal reflection. For example, if light travels from glass to air it bends away as it leaves the glass, but a small amount is reflected back into the glass.

If the light hits the boundary between the glass and air at a large enough angle from the normal, all of the light is reflected back inside the glass. This is called **total internal reflection** (sometimes TIR).

This happens if the angle at which the light hits the boundary is above the **critical angle** for the glass.

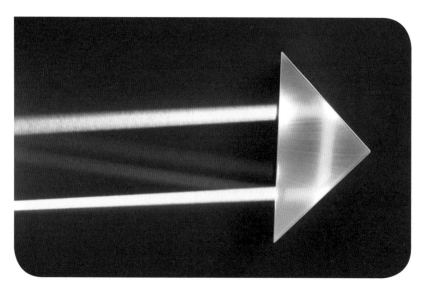

▲ Total internal reflection inside a glass prism

> **A** What is total internal reflection?
>
> **B** What is the name given to the angle above which this occurs?

The effect can be seen whenever light travels from an optically dense material to an optically less dense one (for example, from water to air, glass to air or Perspex to air). Total internal reflection only happens when:

- the angle of the light is above the critical angle, *and*
- the light is travelling in the more optically dense of the two materials.

Refractive index and the critical angle

The critical angle of a material depends on its refractive index. The higher the refractive index, the lower the critical angle.

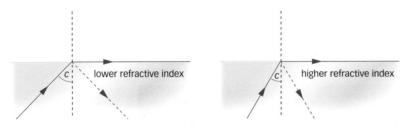

▲ Materials with a higher refractive index have a smaller critical angle

The refractive index of a material and its critical angle are related in the equation below:

$$\text{refractive index} = \frac{1}{\sin c}$$

c is the critical angle of the material.

Questions

1 State the two requirements for total internal reflection.

2 Draw a diagram to show what happens to the ray of light inside a glass block when it hits the edge of the block:
   (a) below the critical angle
   (b) at the critical angle
   (c) above the critical angle.

3 A block has a critical angle of 30°. Find the refractive index of the block.

4 A different block has a refractive index of 1.7. Calculate the critical angle of the block.

5 Describe an experiment that could be carried out to determine the critical angle of a glass block.

Worked example 1

The critical angle of a specially made glass block is found to be 42°. Find the refractive index of the block.

$$\text{refractive index} = \frac{1}{\sin c}$$

critical angle, $c = 42°$

$$\text{refractive index} = \frac{1}{\sin 42°}$$

Worked example 2

A Perspex block has a refractive index of 1.2. Calculate the critical angle of the block.

$$\text{refractive index} = \frac{1}{\sin c}$$

$$1.2 = \frac{1}{\sin c}$$

$$\sin c = \frac{1}{1.2}$$

$$= 0.83$$

critical angle, c = the angle whose sine is 0.83 (or $\sin^{-1} 0.83$)

critical angle, $c = 56°$

Learning objectives

After studying this topic, you should be able to:

- ✔ describe how light is sent along optical fibres by total internal reflection (TIR)
- ✔ give examples of uses of total internal reflection
- ✔ describe how lasers are used as an energy source

A What material are most optical fibres made from?

▲ An endoscope uses fibre optics to produce images from inside the body

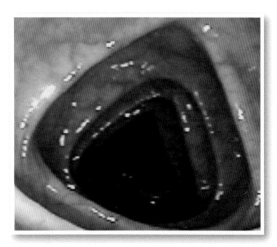

▲ Light travels along an endoscope, allowing the doctor to see inside the patient's body

Optical fibres

If you have cable TV or broadband then you already have an **optical fibre** running into your house. Optical fibres are very fine glass cables that can be used to transmit large amounts of information very quickly. Fibre optic broadband is generally much faster than using normal phone lines.

◀ Information is transmitted very quickly along fibre optic cables

Pulses of visible light or infrared are sent down optical fibres. They travel along the fibre by total internal reflection, reflecting off the inside of the glass fibre until they reach the other end.

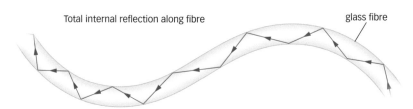

Total internal reflection along fibre   glass fibre

▲ Light is totally internally reflected along an optical fibre

Optical fibres are not only used for communication. A laparoscope is a medical instrument that is inserted through a tiny keyhole incision to get an image of the inside of the body without having to cut the patient open. An **endoscope** also uses optical fibres, but in this case there is no incision; for example the long tube is often passed through the patient's mouth down to the stomach to obtain images.

Inside the endoscope there are several bundles of optic fibres. The endoscope is inserted into the body and visible light is sent down one of the bundles of cables. The light illuminates the inside of the body and is then reflected back down a separate bundle of fibres. The doctor either looks along the fibre, or the image is sent to a TV screen providing a clear picture of the patient's insides.

Laser light

Lasers produce a narrow beam of light that does not spread out very much as it travels through the air. You may have seen the effects at a laser light show or from a laser pointer. The beams remain very narrow, even over long distances.

▲ Lasers have many uses

As the light from a laser is very intense, it is often used as an energy source. The light from powerful lasers is used to cut metal sheets, burn through or etch materials, and cauterise objects.

Specially designed lasers are even used for corrective eye surgery. A laser is used to reshape the cornea so that it will focus a clear image on the retina.

Questions

1 Give two examples of uses for fibre optic cables.

2 Draw a diagram to show how light is totally internally reflected along an optical fibre.

3 Explain why light must first be sent down an endoscope before an image of the inside of the body can be seen.

4 Describe the differences between laser light and the light from a light bulb.

5 Suggest how the cornea of a long-sighted patient might be reshaped.

E
↓ C
↓ A*

Key words

optical fibre, endoscope, laser

Did you know...?

Blu-ray disc players use blue lasers (hence the 'Blu' part of their name). Most CD and DVD players use red light. Blue laser light has a smaller wavelength, which means you can put more information on the disc. This is how it is possible to store a high-definition movie on a Blu-ray disc whereas it would need about six or seven normal DVDs.

B Give two uses for a laser.

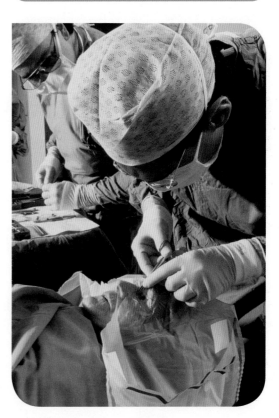

▲ Special lasers can be used to reshape the cornea, eliminating the need for glasses

Course catch-up

Revision checklist ✔

- ⚪ X-rays are electromagnetic waves with a short wavelength. They are ionising, so potentially dangerous.
- ⚪ Ultrasound waves are sound waves with a frequency above 20 000 Hz. Ultrasound reflects off boundaries between materials.
- ⚪ Refraction is the bending of light when it moves from one medium to another. Lenses use refraction to form an image.
- ⚪ Refractive index is a measure of the speed of light through a material compared with the speed of light in a vacuum.
- ⚪ The nature of an image is determined by its distance from the lens, its size, its orientation, and whether it is real or virtual.
- ⚪ The image produced by converging lenses is real and inverted, or virtual, upright, and magnified.
- ⚪ The image produced by diverging lenses is virtual, upright, and diminished.
- ⚪ Magnification = image height/object height.
- ⚪ The human eye has a range of vision from 25 cm to infinity. Features of the eye: retina; cornea; iris; pupil; ciliary muscles; suspensory ligaments.
- ⚪ Short sight is inability to focus on far away objects, corrected by diverging lenses.
- ⚪ Long sight is inability to focus on near objects, corrected by converging lenses.
- ⚪ In a camera a converging lens focuses light onto photographic film or a CCD (charge-coupled device) to produce a real image.
- ⚪ More powerful lenses have shorter focal lengths. Lens power is measured in dioptres. Power = 1/focal length.
- ⚪ If the angle of light travelling from a denser medium towards a less dense medium exceeds the critical angle, total internal reflection (TIR) occurs.
- ⚪ Optical fibres channel light through total internal reflection, and are used for communication and in endoscopes.
- ⚪ Laser beams remain very narrow even over long distances. Their intensity means they can be used to cut, etch, or cauterise objects (including in laser eye surgery).

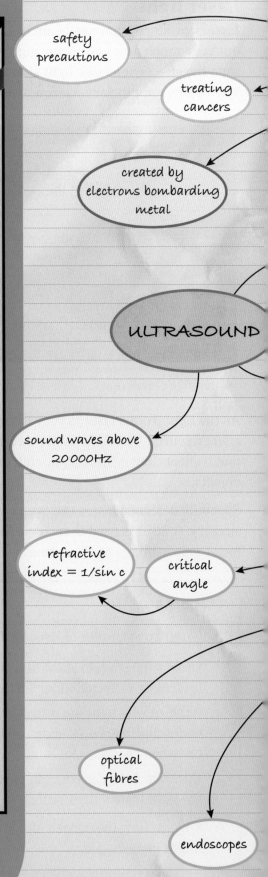

...nising

X-RAYS

electromagnetic waves

security scanning

detected by CCD or photographic film

soft tissue transmits, dense material absorbs

CT scans

crack detection

reflects off boundaries between materials

uses

medical imaging

monitor blood flow

break up kidney stones

refractive index

refraction: light is slower in denser media

power (dioptres) = 1/focal length

lasers

camera, telescope

focal length (metres)

light

...al internal ...flection

bends at boundary

LENSES

ray diagrams

image

real

projector

parts of eye

eye

spectacles

virtual

magnification

...ange 25 cm ...o infinity

magnifying glass

long or short sight

AQA Upgrade

Answering Extended Writing questions

Explain the processes involved when you take a photo using a digital camera.

The quality of written communication will be assessed in your answer to this question.

G–E

The lense makes an image on the pixls at the back, you can zoom in or out to change the size of the image you get It's like your eye the picture is upside down but your brane turns it back again the CCD makes it into a digtal number for the card to store it there are milions of pixls to make the pictur

Examiner: This answer is jumbled with ideas. A few are relevant, but most are not. The answer is not structured well. The starting and ending statements are roughly accurate, though not well linked. The digression into zooming and the eye comparison are unhelpful. Spelling and grammar are poor, and there is a lack of punctuation.

D–C

Light comes into the camera and the lens focuses it onto the back of the camera – it's a real image cos the light is achully there. The CCD takes the light and turns it into electricity. There are millions of CCDs called pixls,, each one sends electricity to the memory which stores it digitally till you want to look at it or send it to your computer.

Examiner: Most of the described physics is correct. The sequence is logical, but the candidate tends to include irrelevant information (such as justifying the realness of the image, or describing the stored information). There is confusion between pixels and CCDs, and vague use of the term 'electricity'. There are occasional errors in spelling, grammar, and punctuation.

B–A*

Light reflected from the field of view enters the lens of the camera. The lens creates a focussed upside-down real image of the field of view on the light sensor at the back of the camera. The sensing CCD (charge-coupled device) has millions of pixels on it – each pixel is one little spot on the image. The CCD converts the light into electrical signals which go to the camera's processor. There the signals are turned into binary numbers (strings of 1s and 0s).

Examiner: This answer is well ordered and accurate. Use of technical terms is detailed and almost perfect (though maybe 'scattered' would be better than 'reflected'). The process inside the camera is well explained, for example the distinction between pixel and CCD, and CCD is spelt out. The term 'digital' is explained. Spelling, punctuation, and grammar are all good.

Exam-style questions

1 Match these parts of a human eye with their function:

A01

Part	Function
lens	Hole that controls the amount of light entering.
cornea	Surface consisting of light-sensitive cells.
pupil	Front surface where first refraction occurs.
retina	Adjusts focal length to achieve focussed image.

2
A01 **a** Explain how a converging lens affects light.

A01 **b** Explain the meaning of focal length for a converging lens.

A01 **c** Explain the meaning of real image.

A02 **d** Using a particular projector, a transparency of width 15 cm produces an image 1.8 m wide on a screen. Calculate the magnification achieved.

A01 **e** What is a virtual image?

3
A02 **a** An object 4 cm tall is 8 cm from a converging lens with focal length 5 cm. Draw a ray diagram at actual size on a sheet of A4 graph paper to find the size and nature of the image. Show all three possible construction rays. (Hint: use the paper in landscape orientation, and put the lens about 10 cm from the left edge of the paper.)

A02 **b** Describe how the image changes if the object is brought gradually closer to the lens.

A02 **c** Calculate the power of this lens.

4
A02 **a** A ray of light enters a glass block at an angle of incidence of 40°. Calculate the angle of refraction of the ray within the block. The refractive index for glass is 1.5.

A02 **b** A ray travelling in the glass strikes the glass/air surface at an angle of 35° to the normal. Calculate the angle at which the ray emerges from the glass.

A02 **c** A ray travelling in the glass strikes the glass/air surface at an angle of 55° to the normal. Explain what happens to this ray.

Extended Writing

5 What is ultrasound? Describe some of the uses of ultrasound in medicine.
A01

6 Explain how total internal reflection (TIR) occurs. Why is TIR not possible if light is travelling in air towards a glass surface?
A01

7 What are X-rays? Describe how they are created, some of their medical uses, and why radiographers have to take care when using them.
A01

A01 Recall the science
A02 Apply your knowledge
A03 Evaluate and analyse the evidence

PHYSICS P3 (PART 1)   197

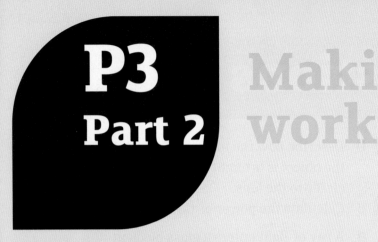

P3 Part 2

Making things work

Why study this unit?

You can use physics to explain why many simple machines around you work. Many things, such as toys and fairground rides, are based on principles such as the lever. Simple machines are also used in many other things that we see and use in everyday life, from scissors to the cranes on building sites. Engineers need to be able to understand the principles behind how and why these simple machines work, so that they can apply them in designing new ones.

In this unit you will learn about the centre of mass of an object, and why some objects are more stable than others. You will look at the forces acting on levers. You will also be introduced to the principles of hydraulics systems, and how objects move in circles. You will learn how the electric motors that power some of these systems work, and how the electrical energy they need is transferred to them. You will also learn about the different kinds of transformers, and how they are used in many electronic devices.

You should remember

1 How forces can act on objects.

2 The effect of gravity on objects.

3 How electricity is generated and transmitted to users.

4 The effects of a magnetic field on charged particles.

5 That the power used by an electrical device depends on the potential difference across it and the current flowing through it.

The largest trucks in the world are used at mines in the USA, Australia, Chile, and South Africa. This truck is over 7 metres tall and has a mass, when empty, of 203 tonnes. It can carry a load of over 350 tonnes.

Even though this truck is unusually large, it is still designed with the basic principles of physics used to make much smaller vehicles work. It has a hydraulic system to push the dumper part up to empty it. The hydraulic system exerts a force on the dumper, causing it to rotate about the pivot at the back of the vehicle. The system works in the same way as in a much smaller dumper truck – it is just much more powerful!

Learning objectives

After studying this topic, you should be able to:

- ✔ explain what the centre of mass of an object is
- ✔ explain how to find the centre of mass of a thin object by suspending it
- ✔ describe where the centre of mass is in a symmetrical object

Key words

centre of mass

▲ This child's centre of mass is directly below the hand that he is hanging from

Centre of mass

Can you balance a book on the end of your finger? A ruler? A pencil? When the object is balanced, all its mass seems to be acting through a point that is above your fingertip. This point is called the **centre of mass**.

Every object has a mass, and the mass is spread out throughout the object. Every object has a point where all of the mass appears to be concentrated.

> **A** What is the centre of mass of an object?

When you hang an object from something, it may swing for a little while from side to side, but then it will come to rest. The centre of mass will be directly below the point it is hanging from. You can use this to find the centre of mass of an object. The diagram shows how you can find the centre of mass of a thin sheet of material that has an irregular shape.

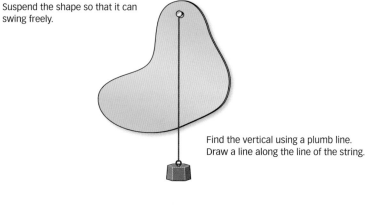

Suspend the shape so that it can swing freely.

Find the vertical using a plumb line. Draw a line along the line of the string.

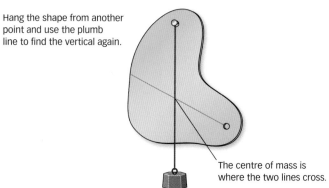

Hang the shape from another point and use the plumb line to find the vertical again.

The centre of mass is where the two lines cross.

▲ How to find the centre of mass of a thin sheet

Symmetry and centre of mass

When the mass of an object is evenly distributed throughout the object, you can use symmetry to find the centre of mass. For example, a pool ball is a sphere that is symmetrical. Its centre of mass lies where the lines of symmetry intersect.

There are equal amounts of mass all around the centre of mass. In a shape with an axis of symmetry, there are equal amounts of mass on either side of the axis.

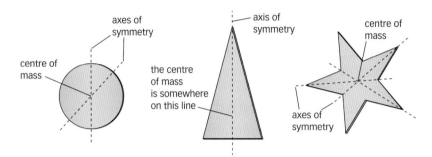

▲ Centres of mass for various regular shapes. We need two lines of symmetry to pinpoint the centre of mass.

> **B** Where would you find the centre of mass of a rectangle?

The centre of mass does not have to be inside the object itself. For example, the centre of mass of a ring is not in the solid part of the ring.

Questions

1 Where is the centre of mass of a football?

2 Explain how you could find the centre of mass of an irregular shape cut out of thin card.

3 Josh hangs a mobile over his baby's cot. Where will the centre of mass of the mobile lie?

4 Why will the centre of mass of the triangle in the diagram above be nearer to the base of the triangle?

5 Explain where the centre of mass of a doughnut is. You could draw a diagram to help your explanation.

▲ Where might the centre of mass of this boomerang be?

Did you know...?

This toy balances because its centre of mass is below the point that the toy rests on.

▲ This toy balances on the point that the bottom of the horse is resting on

> **C** How could you find the centre of mass of a regular hexagon?

Exam tip — AQA

✓ Remember that an object always has a centre of mass, but it might not be inside the solid part of the object.

Learning objectives

After studying this topic, you should be able to:

✔ describe the motion of a pendulum.

✔ explain how the time period of a pendulum is related to its length

Key words

pendulum, time period, frequency

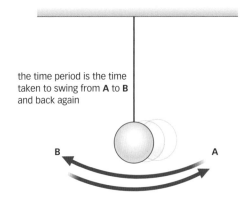

the time period is the time taken to swing from **A** to **B** and back again

B   A

🔺 A pendulum

🔺 The pendulum in this clock has a period of 1 second

What is a pendulum?

A simple **pendulum** consists of an object attached to one end of a long thin piece of material (this can be a bar or a string). The object can swing freely under gravity. The mass of the object is much larger than the mass of the bar or string. The other end of the bar or string is attached securely to something.

When you pull the pendulum slightly to one side and let go, it will swing from side to side with a regular movement. Pendulums have been used in clocks for hundreds of years.

Time period of a pendulum

The **time period** of a pendulum is the time it takes to move from one side of its swing to the other and all the way back again. This is another way of saying that the period is the time taken for one complete cycle of the pendulum's movement.

The number of cycles that the pendulum completes in one second is called the **frequency**, so:

$$\frac{\text{time period}}{\text{(seconds, s)}} = \frac{1}{\text{frequency (hertz, Hz)}}$$

If T is the time period in seconds, and f is the frequency in hertz (cycles per second), then:

$$T = \frac{1}{f}$$

Worked example

The frequency of a pendulum is 0.5 Hz. What is its time period?

$$\text{time period} = \frac{1}{\text{frequency}} \quad \text{or} \quad T = \frac{1}{f}$$

$f = 0.5$ Hz

$$T = \frac{1}{0.5} = 2 \text{ seconds}$$

A A pendulum has a frequency of 1 Hz. What is its time period?

The time period of a pendulum depends on its length. A short pendulum has a short time period. A long pendulum has a long time period. The longer the pendulum is, the longer its time period.

Pendulums around us

You can find simple pendulums around you. For example, a swing is a simple pendulum. Some fairground rides are also just large pendulums.

A Foucault pendulum is a simple pendulum with a long wire – usually several tens of metres long. It is free to swing in any direction. As the pendulum swings, the direction of the motion changes slowly during the day. There are many examples of Foucault pendulums around the world.

▲ A swing is a pendulum

▲ The Foucault pendulum in the Science Museum in London

▲ This fairground ride is a large pendulum

Questions

1 What is a pendulum?

2 Explain how the time period of a simple pendulum is varied.

3 A pendulum has a frequency of 0.1 Hz. What is its time period?

4 A pendulum has a time period of 0.25 seconds. What is its frequency?

5 Sam says that a fairground ride like the one in the photo above will swing faster when there are more people on it. Explain why he is wrong.

E

C

A*

B What features of the swinging boat in the photo make it a pendulum?

Did you know...?

The Taipei 101 skyscraper in Taiwan contains a large pendulum that stretches over 10 floors. It is used to help keep the building stable in high winds. It absorbs energy when the building sways in the wind.

Key words

pivot, moment, perpendicular distance

A What is a moment?

B Where is the pivot for a door?

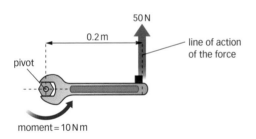

moment = 10 N m

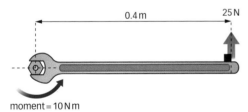

moment = 10 N m

▲ The moment about each nut shown here is the same, but the forces and perpendicular distances from the pivot are different

---

C Sam exerts a force of 25 N at the end of a 40 cm long spanner when tightening a nut. What is the moment on the nut?

Turning effect of a force: the moment

When you apply a force to the revolving door in the photo, it turns about a fixed point or **pivot**. The turning effect of the force is called a **moment**.

◀ People use a turning effect (moment) to move this revolving door

Every time you use a force to turn something about a pivot, there is a moment. When you open a door in your house, the force you use to turn the door knob has a moment, and then the force you use to push open the door also has a turning effect about the hinges.

The size of the force you need depends on where you push the door. You need to use a larger force if you push the door nearer the hinge.

The size of a moment is given by the equation:

$$
\begin{array}{ccc}
\text{moment of the force} & = & \text{force} & \times & \text{perpendicular} \\
\text{(newton-metres, Nm)} & & \text{(newtons, N)} & & \text{distance from the line of action of the force to the pivot (metres, m)}
\end{array}
$$

If M is the moment in newton-metres, F is the force in newtons, and d is the perpendicular distance in metres from the line of action of the force to the pivot, then:

$$M = F \times d$$

Worked example

A force of 10 N acts at a perpendicular distance of 50 cm from the pivot. What is the turning effect (moment) of the force?

$$M = F \times d$$

$F = 10$ N

$d = 50$ cm $= 0.5$ m

$M = 10$ N $\times 0.5$ m

$= 5$ N m

When you measure the distance from the force to the pivot, it must be measured correctly. The perpendicular distance is measured along a line that is at right angles to the direction of the force.

In the revolving door shown in the diagram below, the force is not acting at right angles to the door. This means that the perpendicular distance is less than the actual distance from the point where the force is acting to the pivot.

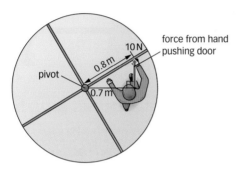

The distance from the line of action of the force to the pivot is measured perpendicularly from the line. Here the perpendicular distance from the line of action of the pushing force to the pivot is 0.7 m.

Questions

1 What is a pivot?

2 Give three examples of applying a moment.

3 Ben pulls on a door handle with a force of 5 N. The handle is 60 cm from the hinges. What is the moment about the hinges?

4 What is the moment about the pivot of the revolving door in the diagram above?

5 The diagram shows a person lifting the handles of a wheelbarrow. What turning effect about the wheel axis is the person applying?

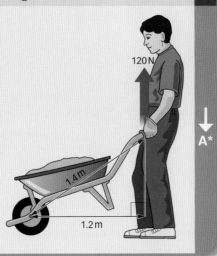

D What is the perpendicular distance?

Did you know...?

Mechanics sometimes use a torque wrench to apply a specific moment to a nut or a bolt. ('Torque' is another word for 'moment'.) A torque wrench is used to prevent nuts and bolts being overtightened. The moment to be applied is set in the wrench and the nut or bolt is tightened. When the moment needed to turn the spanner reaches the value set, the spanner does not move any more.

This torque wrench has been set to limit the moment to 6 Nm

Exam tip AQA

✓ Remember that a moment is a turning effect – many students lose a mark because they do not realise this.

✓ Make sure you use the correct units for moments in answers to calculations. The units are newton-metres (Nm).

Balanced moments

In the seesaw shown in the diagram below, there are two forces that produce moments (turning effects) about the pivot.

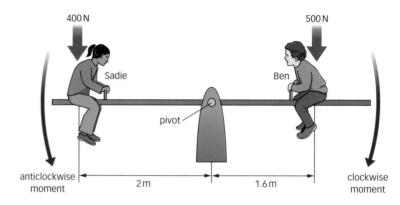

▲ The seesaw is balanced – the clockwise and anticlockwise moments are equal

The weight of the girl has an anticlockwise turning effect on the seesaw, and the weight of the boy has a clockwise turning effect.

$$\text{anticlockwise moment} = F \times d = 400 \text{ N} \times 2 \text{ m} = 800 \text{ N m}$$
$$\text{clockwise moment} = F \times d = 500 \text{ N} \times 1.6 \text{ m} = 800 \text{ N m}$$

The moments are equal, but acting in opposite directions – they are balanced and the seesaw is not moving.

When an object is balanced, the total clockwise moment about the pivot is equal to the total anticlockwise moment.

▲ This crane uses a counterweight to produce a balanced moment to allow it to lift heavy objects

A If an object is balanced, what can you say about the moments acting on it?

B Are moments balanced when an object is turning? Explain your answer.

▲ The clockwise and anticlockwise moments on this seesaw are balanced

Calculations with balanced moments

The clockwise and anticlockwise moments do not have to be on different sides of the pivot.

In the wheelbarrow shown in the diagram, the person holding the wheelbarrow handles is exerting a clockwise moment about the pivot. The 400 N weight of the wheelbarrow is exerting an anticlockwise moment about the pivot.

> ### Worked example
>
> Looking at the diagram, what force does the person need to exert to hold the wheelbarrow steadily with its legs off the ground?
>
> When the person is holding the wheelbarrow steady as shown, the clockwise and anticlockwise moments are balanced.
>
> clockwise moment = anticlockwise moment
>
> clockwise moment = $F \times 1.2$ m
>
> anticlockwise moment = 400 N $\times$ 0.3 m = 120 N m
>
> $$F \times 1.2 \text{ m} = 120 \text{ N m}$$
>
> $$F = \frac{120 \text{ N}}{1.2 \text{ N}}$$
>
> $$= 100 \text{ N}$$
>
> The force exerted by the person is 100 N.

C Where is the pivot on the wheelbarrow?

▲ Moments on a wheelbarrow that is being held steady

Questions

1 What is the turning effect of a force called?

2 Why might an object not turn when moments are acting on it?

3 Show that the moments on the seesaw shown here are balanced

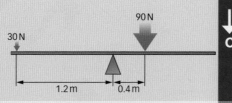

4 In the seesaw diagram at the top of the previous page, Sadie moves so that she is 1.5 m from the pivot. How far does Ben need to be from the pivot for the seesaw to be balanced?

E

↓ C

↓ A*

Key words

lever, force multiplier

A What is a lever?

B Where is the pivot on the crowbar?

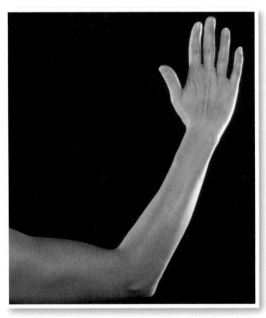

▲ The human body contains a number of simple levers that help us to lift a wide range of objects.

C What do you notice about the pivot of the bottle opener?

Examples of levers

When you use a crowbar to remove a nail from a piece of wood, you are using a simple machine that increases the force you apply. The crowbar is acting as a **lever**.

▲ This crowbar is being used as a lever

A lever uses a force to turn something around a **pivot**. As you know, the turning effect of a force is called a moment. In the scissors shown in the diagram below, the force that is applied to the handles has a moment about the pivot.

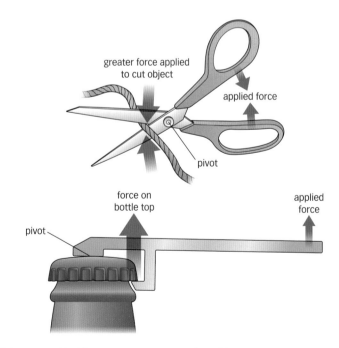

▲ Scissors and bottle openers are examples of levers

208

Increasing the force

The moment about the pivot is given by the force multiplied by the perpendicular distance from the line of action of the force to the pivot.

When you use scissors as shown in the diagram on the previous page, the moment of the force that you apply to the handles is equal to the moment of the force acting on the object.

But the distance of the handles from the pivot is greater than the distance of the material from the pivot. As the moments are the same, this means that the force applied to the object is greater. The scissors are acting as a **force multiplier**.

Levers are used to change smaller forces into larger ones in many everyday devices.

▲ You can't crack a nut easily with your hands. This nutcracker acts as a force multiplier. The force you apply at a distance from the pivot is applied as a greater force on the nut nearer the pivot. The nut cracks open.

> **D** What is a force multiplier?

▲ The screwdriver is being used as a lever

Did you know...?

Archimedes wrote about the principles of levers over 2200 years ago. It is assumed that levers would have been used by the ancient Egyptians to move large lumps of rock with masses of up to 100 tonnes.

Questions

1 Give two examples of levers.

2 Why is a lever usually a force multiplier?

3 Look at the picture of a screwdriver being used to open a can of paint. Where is the pivot?

4 How can you increase the size of the force applied to the load in a lever?

5 When can a seesaw act as a force multiplier?

Exam tip **AQA**

✓ When answering an exam question, make sure you have read the question properly and that you are actually answering the question.

Learning objectives

After studying this topic, you should be able to:

- ✔ know the factors that affect the stability of an object
- ✔ explain when an object will or will not topple

Key words

line of action, **stability**

▲ Traffic cones are very stable

▲ This pencil is very unstable. A small push would move the line of action of the weight outside the base, toppling the pencil.

Increasing stability

Stability is a measure of how hard it is to make an object topple over.

Some objects are much more stable than others – they do not topple over easily.

You can design objects to be more stable by:
- making the centre of mass lower
- making the base of the object wider.

For example, traffic cones have a wide, heavy base. Making the base heavier lowers the centre of mass. This makes it much more difficult for them to be toppled over.

> **A** What features make a traffic cone very stable?

Why objects fall over

The diagram below shows a box on a flat surface, The weight of the box always acts in the same direction. The **line of action** of the weight is through the centre of mass and is always downwards.

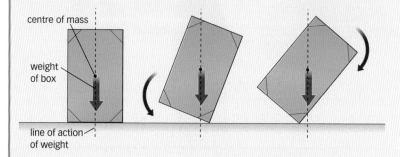

On the left, the line of action of the weight is inside the base of the box. The box is stable – it does not move.

> **B** Where is the line of action of the weight of the boxes?

In the middle diagram, the box has been tilted. The line of action of the weight is still inside the base of the box, so the box will fall back to its original position. We could say that there is a resultant anticlockwise moment about the bottom right-hand edge of the box.

On the right, the box has been tilted further, so that the line of action of the weight is now outside the base of the box. The box will topple over to the right. There is a resultant clockwise moment about the bottom right-hand edge of the box.

> **C** Where is the pivot of the box in the middle diagram?
>
> **D** How would the stability of the box on the right be affected if it were lying on its side?

Questions

1 Where is the line of action of the weight in a stable object?

2 Why do drinking glasses sometimes have thick heavy bases?

3 Look at the photos of bar stools. Which has the most stable design? Explain your answer.

▲ Two designs for bar stools

4 Look at the diagram of the box on the flat surface on the previous page. Explain in terms of moments what happens when you tilt the box and let it go:

　(a) when the line of action of the weight is inside the base

　(b) when the line of action of the weight is outside the base.

Exam tip　**AQA**

✔ The base of an object does not have to be solid. For example, a chair has four legs – it is the area between the bases of the legs of the chair that affects how stable the chair is.

E

↓ C

↓ A*

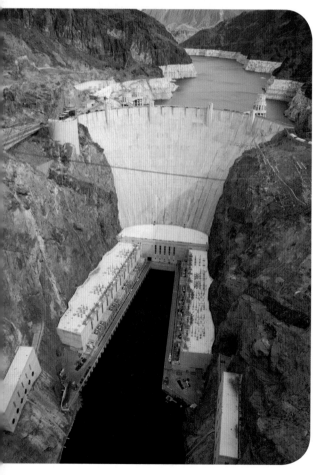

The pressure in a fluid increases with depth. Large dams like the Hoover Dam have to be thicker at the base to cope with the extra pressure.

Incompressible liquids

As you know, the particles in a liquid are very close together, touching one another, although they are moving about all the time. This means that liquids are almost **incompressible**.

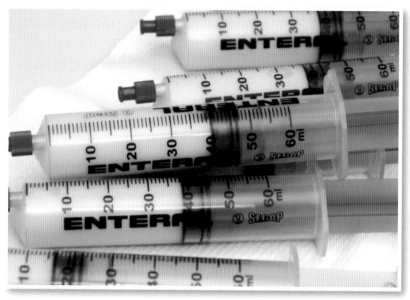

▲ If you put your finger over the open end of a filled syringe and try to push the plunger, it will not move

A Why are liquids almost incompressible?

The pressure at each point in a liquid acts equally in all directions. This means that if you apply a force to a liquid at one point, the pressure from the force will be transmitted equally throughout the liquid.

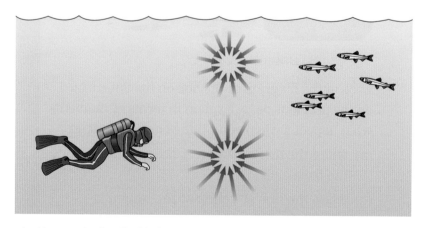

▲ At any point in a liquid, the pressure acts equally in all directions

Hydraulic systems

Hydraulic systems use liquids in pipes to take advantage of the fact that pressure in a liquid will be transmitted equally in all directions. They are used to move devices remotely, controlling the size of the forces applied.

> **B** What is a hydraulic system?

For example, in cars a hydraulic system is used to transfer the action of the driver pushing the brake pedal to the application of the brakes.

The pushing force on the brake pedal applies pressure to the liquid in the braking system. This pressure is transmitted throughout the liquid, and a much larger force is applied to the brake pads at the wheels.

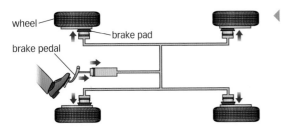

◀ When a car brakes, pressure from the driver's foot is transmitted through the hydraulic system to apply the brakes at the wheels

> **C** What happens when the brake pedal is pushed?

Hydraulic systems are also used in many other machines such as hydraulic car jacks, inspection platforms and excavating machines. They are also used to control the wing flaps and landing gear on aeroplanes.

Did you know...?

In aeroplanes, the rudder (which changes the aeroplane's direction) and elevator (which allows the aeroplane to ascend and descend) used to be connected to the joystick by a hydraulic system. In modern aeroplanes, a fly-by-wire system is used. The joystick sends an electrical signal to a pump that pumps liquid in the hydraulic system.

▲ Hydraulic systems are used to extend the wing flaps on this aircraft and then take them back in again

Questions

1 What does it mean when a liquid is said to be incompressible?

2 Why can you not compress a liquid?

3 Explain how a braking system works.

4 Why would a braking system not work if you replaced the liquid with a gas?

5 A hydraulic system has a leak in it. Alex says that the pressure by the leak will be lower than somewhere a long way from the leak. Is he correct? Explain your answer.

E

↓
C

↓
A*

Learning objectives

After studying this topic, you should be able to:

✔ use the equation linking pressure, force, and area

✔ explain how using different cross-sectional areas multiplies the force in a hydraulic system

Key words

pascal

Using a hydraulic system to magnify a force

The picture below shows two pistons connected by a pipe filled with liquid. If you push on piston A, the pressure is transmitted through the liquid and pushes on piston B. You may recall that pressure is force per unit area. The pressure is the same for A and B. The effect of a small force at A, which has a small area, is to produce the same pressure at B. B has a larger area, so the total force is greater.

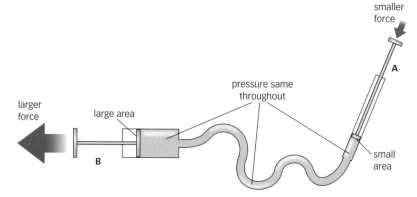

▲ Pressure is transmitted equally throughout an hydraulic system

As pressure is the total force divided by the area over which it acts, it is measured in newtons per square metre (N/m²) or **pascals** (Pa).

The pressure in the different parts of the hydraulic system is given by:

$$\text{pressure (pascals, Pa)} = \frac{\text{force (newtons, N)}}{\substack{\text{cross-sectional area}\\\text{(metres squared, m}^2\text{)}}}$$

If P is the pressure in pascals, F is the force in newtons, and A is the cross-sectional area in square metres, then:

$$P = \frac{F}{A}$$

> A A force of 250 N is exerted on an area of 0.02 m².
> What is the pressure?
>
> B What is a pascal?

Worked example

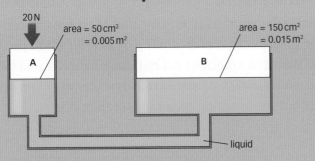

Piston A is pushed with a force of 20 N.

i What is the pressure in the liquid?

$$\text{pressure} = \frac{\text{force}}{\text{cross-sectional area}} \quad \text{or} \quad P = \frac{F}{A}$$

For piston A:

force $F = 20$ N

cross-sectional area $A = 50$ cm² $= 0.005$ m²

$$P = \frac{20\text{ N}}{0.005\text{ m}^2} = 4000\text{ Pa}$$

ii What is the force exerted by piston B?

For piston B:

pressure $P = 4000$ Pa

cross-sectional area $A = 150$ cm² $= 0.015$ m²

$$P = \frac{F}{A}$$

$$4000\text{ Pa} = \frac{F}{0.015\text{ m}^2}$$

$$F = 4000\text{ Pa} \times 0.015\text{ m}^2$$

$$= 60\text{ N}$$

The force exerted by piston B is 60 N, which is three times greater than the force applied at piston A.

This principle is used in many systems. Hydraulic systems are often used as force multipliers, that is to increase the effect of the force applied. For example, in a car braking system a relatively small force (effort) is applied to the brake pedal. The hydraulic system multiplies the force so that a much larger force (load) is applied to the brake pads.

◀ Using a hydraulic car jack allows a car to be lifted easily by one person

▲ This excavator uses a hydraulic system to move the excavating bucket

Questions

1 What are the units of pressure?

2 The piston of a hydraulic system has a surface area of 0.03 m². A force of 45 N is applied. What is the pressure?

3 A mechanic uses a force of 50 N to operate a car jack. The surface area of the piston being pumped is 0.001 m². What area of piston is needed to lift a car with weight 12 500 N?

4 Which should have the largest surface area: the cylinder where the effort is applied or the cylinder where the load is?

5 In the worked example, the small piston moves three times as far as the large piston. How could you use the equation for work done to show that energy is conserved in the hydraulic system?

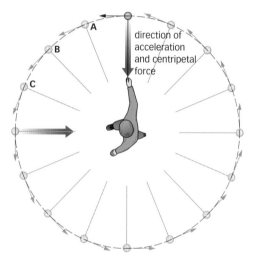

▲ The cork is being whirled around at a constant speed, but its direction, and so its velocity, is changing all the time. It is accelerating.

Moving in a circle

You may remember that a force is needed to change either the speed or the direction of a moving object. So when the direction of travel of an object is changing, a force must be acting on it, even though its speed may be constant. You also know that if a force is acting on an object then it is accelerating.

> **A** What is needed to change either the speed or the direction of something that is moving?

The diagram on the left shows a cork being whirled around at a steady speed on the end of a string. We know that the tension force in the string changes the direction of travel of the cork, because if the string were to break, the cork would fly off in a straight line.

The force on the cork towards the centre, from the **tension** in the string, is called a **centripetal force**. ('Centripetal' means 'searching for the centre'.)

As there is a continuous force on the cork towards the centre, the cork must be continuously accelerating towards the centre.

This makes sense – we can see from the diagram that the velocity of the cork is always changing direction. Looking at the velocity of the cork at A, B, and C we can see that the change in the velocity is always towards the centre.

Any object that is moving in a circle at a steady speed is continuously accelerating towards the centre. This acceleration is a change of direction but not speed.

▲ This racing car is going round a bend. Its direction is changing, so it is accelerating.

> **B** Why must the racing car in the photo be accelerating?
>
> **C** In which direction does the centripetal force on the racing car act?

Where is the centripetal force coming from?

The centripetal force is provided by, to take some examples, gravity, friction between two surfaces, or tension in a rope or string. It does not exist on its own.

The centripetal force for the racing car in the photo on the previous page is provided by the force of friction between the tyres and the road surface. The force of friction stops the car from carrying on moving in a straight line. The centripetal force is acting towards the centre of the circle. (While it is going round a bend the racing car is travelling in part of a circle.)

A centripetal force could also be provided by your hanging on to something, for example if you hang on to a roundabout with your hands. The centripetal force is then the tension in your arms.

▲ The tension in the child's arms is the centripetal force here

> D What provides the centripetal force on the fairground ride in the photo on the right?

Questions

1 What is a centripetal force?

2 An object is moving in a circle at a steady speed. Describe how its velocity is changing.

3 For each of the following, state what is providing the centripetal force:

   (a) A rollercoaster where the cars hang from a rail and the cars go round a loop.

   (b) A train going round a bend.

4 Explain why the direction of the acceleration of an object moving in a circle and the direction of the centripetal force are the same.

5 Most machines have a maximum speed at which they can operate. What do you think might happen if they rotated much faster than the maximum speed?

▲ The seats on this fairground ride are attached to the central part of the carousel by a chain

Exam tip AQA

✔ Remember that acceleration does not just involve a change in speed. When an object is changing direction it is accelerating, even if its speed is constant.

Learning objectives

After studying this topic, you should be able to:

✔ explain how increasing the mass of an object increases the centripetal force needed for the object to move in a circle

✔ explain how increasing the speed of an object increases the centripetal force required for circular motion

✔ explain how decreasing the radius of the circle increases the centripetal force needed for circular motion

You may recall that the greater the mass of an object, the greater the force needed to provide a particular acceleration.

This can help you to understand the changes in the centripetal force needed to keep an object moving in a circle, if the mass, speed, or radius of the circle change.

Increasing mass

A mass M is moving in a circle, as shown in the diagram on the left. If the mass is increased, the centripetal force needed to keep the same acceleration will increase. Doubling the mass will double the centripetal force required.

> **A** What does increasing the mass do to the size of the centripetal force needed for circular motion?

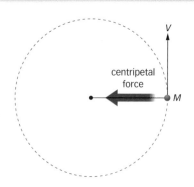

▲ The object M is in circular motion. If the mass is increased, a greater centripetal force will be needed for the same motion.

Increasing speed

The diagram below shows two objects with the same mass moving in circles with the same radius. The speed of one object is twice the speed of the other object. The diagram also shows how far each object travels in a given time.

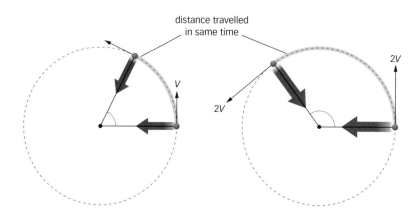

▲ Changing speed in circular motion

> **B** Two cars with the same mass go round the same bend. One is going faster than the other. Which one needs the higher centripetal force?

The faster object has moved through a much bigger angle than the slower one. This means that the rate at which its direction has changed is higher, so its acceleration is also higher. So the centripetal force needed to keep it moving in a circle will also be higher. As the speed of an object increases, the centripetal force needed to keep it in circular motion also increases.

Decreasing radius

Two objects with the same mass are moving at the same speed in circles with different radii. The object moving around the smaller circle moves through a bigger angle in a given time than the object moving in the larger circle. The change of direction has been greater, so the acceleration is higher. Again, the centripetal force needed for the higher acceleration is also higher.

The centripetal force needed to keep an object in circular motion increases as the radius decreases.

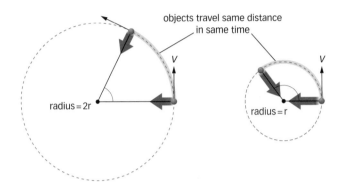

▲ Changing the radius of circular motion

▲ There is a centripetal force on these rollercoaster cars

C Two runners with the same mass are racing at the same speed round a bend in a running track. One is on the inside track. Which runner needs the greater centripetal force?

Questions

1 What affects the size of the centripetal force needed to make an object move in a circle?

E

2 Look at the photo of the rollercoaster above. How would the centripetal force needed change if:

   (a) all the riders were adults rather than children

   (b) the cars went faster

   (c) the cars went round a smaller loop?

C

3 A car and a bus travel round the same bend at the same speed. Which one needs the higher centripetal force? Explain your answer.

4 How would you decrease the centripetal force needed for the fairground ride shown on spread P3.25?

A*

Exam tip **AQA**

✔ Remember that the centripetal force needed for an object to perform circular motion increases as:

• the mass of the object increases
• the spread of the object increases
• the radius of the circle decreases.

Electromagnets are used to lift and move large objects in scrapyards

Currents create magnetic fields

When an electric current flows in a wire, it creates a **magnetic field** around the wire. This magnetic field is only there when there is a current. If the current stops, the magnetic field collapses. It is a bit like the wake from a moving boat. When the boat is moving, it creates a wake behind it. When the boat is not moving, there is no wake.

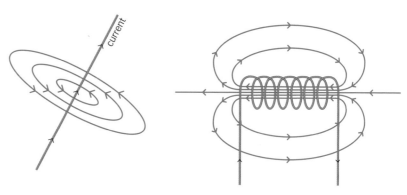

▲ An electric current in a wire has a magnetic field around it. The shape of the field depends on how the wire is arranged.

The shape of the magnetic field around a single wire is concentric circles.

If the wire is looped into a coil (making a solenoid), the magnetic fields for all the turns of the wire combine. The shape of the magnetic field looks like the magnetic field of a bar magnet.

Electromagnets make use of this effect. They are designed to produce a strong magnetic field when there is a current in their wires. When the current is switched off, the electromagnet loses its magnetism.

> A Describe the shape of the magnetic field around a coil of wire.
>
> B Give one use of an electromagnet.

The motor effect

If a current-carrying wire is placed inside another magnetic field (for example in between the poles of two other magnets), the two magnetic fields interact. The magnetic field from the current and the magnetic field from the magnets push on each other, creating a force on the wire. This is called the **motor effect**.

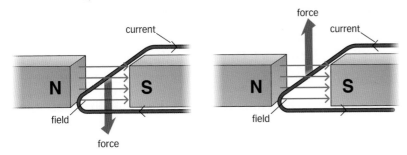

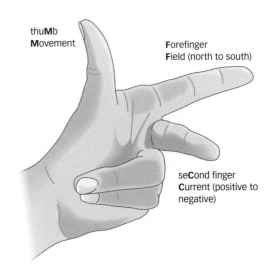

▲ Fleming's left-hand rule. The thumb shows the direction that the wire moves in (and therefore the direction of the force.)

▲ The motor effect. The magnetic field from the current in the wire interacts with the field from the magnets, making a force that pushes the wire, making it move. Reversing the direction of the current flips the direction of the force.

The direction of the force acting on the wire can be found using **Fleming's left-hand rule**.

It is important to note that if the wire is parallel to the magnetic field then there is no force acting on the wire.

> **C** What is the direction of the forces in the motor effect diagram?
>
> **D** A wire is placed in a magnetic field so that it is parallel to the field. A current is passed through the wire. What happens?

Changing the size or direction of the force

The size of the force on the wire can be increased by:

- increasing the strength of the magnetic field (for example, by using a stronger magnet)
- increasing the size of the current in the wire.

The direction of the force on the wire can be reversed by:

- reversing the direction of the magnetic field (for example, by swapping the poles of the magnets round)
- reversing the direction of the current in the wire.

Questions

1 What must pass through a wire in order to create a magnetic field around it? E

2 Describe how the motor effect happens.

3 State Fleming's left-hand rule and draw a diagram showing how it might be used. C

4 Explain what would happen to the direction of the force acting on a current-carrying wire placed inside a magnetic field if (a) the current was reversed (b) the poles of the magnets were swapped. A*

5 In terms of magnetic fields, suggest why reversing the direction of the current reverses the direction of the force on the wire.

Key words

electric motor, split-ring commutator

A Give one example of a use of an electric motor.

Electric motors

Electric motors have a wide range of uses, from providing the tiny vibrations in game controllers and some mobile phones to powering hybrid cars and even some high-speed trains.

All electric motors make use of the motor effect. A simple electric motor has a loop of wire inside a magnetic field between two magnets. When there is a current in the wire, the magnetic fields interact. One side of the loop is pushed down and the other side is pushed up. This makes the motor spin.

For the motor to continue to spin in the same direction, the current needs to be reversed every half-turn of the loop. This is done using a device called a **split-ring commutator**. Each time the loop is vertical, the current inside it reverses. The side of the loop that was pushed up is now pushed down. This allows the motor to continue to spin.

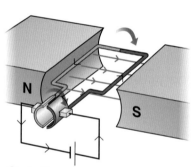

① The blue part of this coil is pushed upwards and the red half downwards. (Check with Fleming's left-hand rule.)

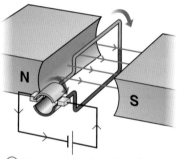

② No current, but the coil continues to turn because of its own momentum.

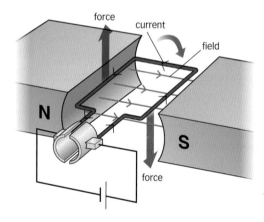

▲ A simple motor spins due to the motor effect

▲ Electric motors are not just found in small devices. They can be used in large machines, including trains and cars.

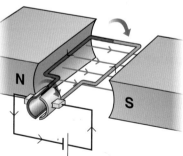

③ The direction of the current in the coil and commutator is reversed. Now the blue part is pushed downwards and the red half upwards.

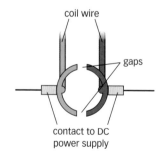

▲ Reversing the current in the wire loop. Look at the direction of the current in the part of the commutator and coil that is shaded blue. The direction of the current changes with each half-turn of the commutator. The same applies to the part shaded red.

Other uses of the motor effect

A traditional analogue ammeter makes use of the motor effect. It has a coil attached to a small spring in between a pair of small magnets. This spring is in turn attached to a needle that points to a value on a dial showing the size of the current.

When there is a current in the coil it rotates; compressing the spring. The greater the current, the stronger the force and the more the spring is compressed. This has the effect of moving the needle further. The greater the current the further the needle moves, giving a higher reading on the ammeter.

▲ The motor effect can be used in an analogue ammeter to determine the current

> **B** Explain why a higher current causes the needle in an analogue ammeter to move further.

Loudspeakers also use the motor effect. Inside each speaker there is a small paper or plastic cone (you can sometimes see this cone moving in and out). On the back of this cone there is a coil of wire loosely wrapped around a magnet.

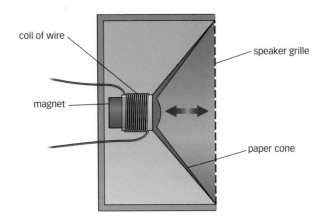

coil of wire
speaker grille
magnet
paper cone

▲ A loudspeaker cone moves in and out due to the motor effect

When there is a current in the coil, the magnetic field it creates interacts with the field from the magnet. This creates a force and the coil is pushed out. This in turn pushes the cone out. If the current then reverses, the cone is pulled back in.

When the loudspeaker is being used, the electrical signal that it receives, which creates the current in the coil, is changing very rapidly in size and direction. So the cone vibrates in and out several thousand times each second, creating the sound waves that we hear.

Did you know...?

Your headphones contain tiny magnets and coils of wires. They work exactly the same way as a loudspeaker. It is amazing that the sound you hear from them is produced by moving a tiny paper cone forwards and backwards!

Questions

1 Other than the electric motor, give one use of the motor effect. E

2 Describe the purpose of the split-ring commutator found in most simple motors.

3 Describe how the motor effect is used inside a simple analogue ammeter. C

4 Use Fleming's left-hand rule to explain how, inside a simple motor, one side of the loop of wire is pushed down while the other side is pushed up.

5 Suggest how the current in the coil in a speaker changes to make sounds with different pitches and different volumes. A*

Learning objectives

After studying this topic, you should be able to:

✔ describe how a potential difference is induced when a conductor moves in a magnetic field or when a magnet moves in a coil of wire

✔ describe the structure of a transformer

✔ explain how a transformer works

Key words

induced, electromagnetic induction, iron core, primary coil, secondary coil

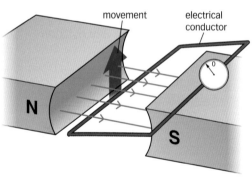

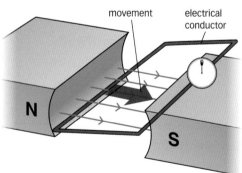

When a conductor is moved so that it cuts across a magnetic field, an induced current will flow if there is a complete circuit. If the conductor is moved parallel to the field, there is no induced current.

Electromagnetic induction

You have already learnt that when an electric current flows through a wire, a magnetic field is produced around it. So, might the reverse effect happen? Might it be possible to get electricity from magnetism?

The answer is yes. When a wire is moved so that it cuts across a magnetic field, a potential difference is **induced** across the ends of the conducting wire. If the circuit is complete, a current flows. This is called **electromagnetic induction**.

> A What is electromagnetic induction?

The wire must be moved so that it cuts across the magnetic field. If it is moved in the same direction as the magnetic field (parallel to the magnetic field), no potential difference is induced.

We can get the same effects if we keep the wire in the same place but move the magnet instead. The wire is still cutting across a magnetic field.

So when a magnet is moved into a coil of wire, a potential difference is induced across the ends of the coil.

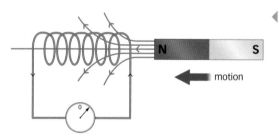

◀ Moving a magnet into or out of a coil induces a potential difference

Transformers

Transformers use both the idea that an electric current can produce a magnetic field and the idea that a magnetic field can be used to create a potential difference.

You already know that a current flowing in a coil of wire will create a magnetic field shaped like the field of a bar magnet. If the coil is wrapped round an **iron core**, the iron becomes magnetised and the strength of the field seems to become much greater.

The coil in the diagram has been wrapped round an iron core shaped like a ring, and the magnetic field caused by the current runs all the way round the core.

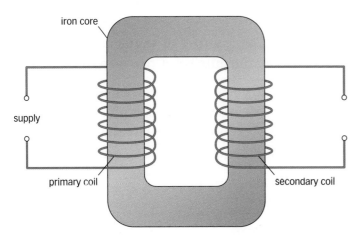

iron core

supply

primary coil   secondary coil

▲ The main parts of a transformer

A transformer has an iron core with two coils of wire wound around it. The **primary coil** is connected to a power supply. The current flowing through the primary coil sets up a magnetic field – it works like an electromagnet.

If the current through the primary coil is steady, the magnetic field in the core does not change. There is no effect on the **secondary coil**.

If the primary coil is connected to an alternating (a.c.) supply, the current changes continuously, so the magnetic field also changes continuously. This has the same effect as moving a magnet in and out of the secondary coil. An alternating potential difference is set up between the ends of the secondary coil, and when the secondary coil is connected to a circuit, a current flows.

The two coils of wire are separate – they are not connected so current cannot flow from the primary coil to the secondary coil. They are only connected by the magnetic field.

> **B** What happens when there is an alternating current in the primary coil?
> **C** Why does an electric current not flow from the primary coil to the secondary coil?

A transformer only works with an alternating current – it does not work with direct current.

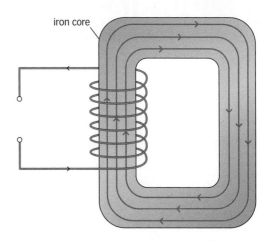

iron core

▲ The current in the coil creates a magnetic field. The iron core makes the effect of the field much stronger.

Exam tip **AQA**

✔ Remember all the parts of a transformer.

✔ No current flows between the primary and secondary coils – they are not connected electrically.

✔ Transformers do not change alternating current to direct current.

Questions

1 What happens when a wire is moved so that it cuts across a magnetic field?

2 What are the main parts of a transformer?

3 Explain how a transformer works.

4 Why will a transformer not work with direct current?

5 Explain why no potential difference is induced across the ends of a wire when the wire is moved in a direction parallel to the magnetic field.

↓ E

↓ C

↓ A*

30: Step-up and step-down transformers

Key words

number of turns

A In a step-up transformer, which coil has the greater potential difference?

B In a step-down transformer, which coil has the greater number of turns?

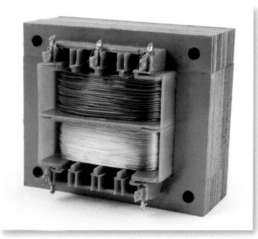

▲ The inside of a transformer

Types of transformer

In a step-up transformer, the potential difference across the secondary coil is greater than the potential difference across the primary coil. The **number of turns** on the secondary coil is greater than the number of turns on the primary coil.

In a step-down transformer, the potential difference across the secondary coil is less than the potential difference across the primary coil. The number of turns on the secondary coil is less than the number of turns on the primary coil.

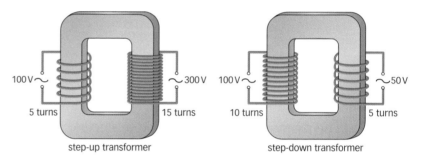

| 100 V | 300 V | 100 V | 50 V |
| 5 turns | 15 turns | 10 turns | 5 turns |

step-up transformer · step-down transformer

▲ A step-up transformer and a step-down transformer

Transformer equation

The potential difference across the primary and secondary coils of a transformer are related by the equation:

$$\frac{\text{potential difference across primary coil}}{\text{potential difference across secondary coil}} = \frac{\text{number of turns on primary coil}}{\text{number of turns on secondary coil}}$$

If:

- V_p is the potential difference across the primary coil in volts, V
- V_s is the potential difference across the secondary coil in volts, V
- n_p is the number of turns on the primary coil
- n_s is the number of turns on the secondary coil

then:

$$\frac{V_p}{V_s} = \frac{n_p}{n_s}$$

Worked example

A computer runs off the mains supply, but only needs a potential difference of 11.5 V. There are 1000 turns on the secondary coil. How many turns are there on the primary coil?

$$\frac{V_p}{V_s} = \frac{n_p}{n_s}$$

V_p = 230 V (mains voltage)

V_s = 11.5 V

n_s = 1000

Substituting the values into the equation, we get:

$$\frac{230\text{ V}}{11.5\text{ V}} = \frac{n_p}{1000}$$

$$n_p = 1000 \times \frac{230\text{ V}}{11.5\text{ V}}$$

$$= 1000 \times 20$$

$$= 20\,000\text{ turns.}$$

There are 20 000 turns on the primary coil.

▲ A transformer in an electronic circuit

C The potential difference across the secondary coil of a transformer is 6.1 V, and the number of turns is 10. The number of turns on the primary coil is 380. What is the potential difference across the primary coil?

Questions

1 What are the two types of transformer?

2 A transformer has 200 turns on the primary coil and 2400 turns on the secondary coil. The potential difference across the primary coil is 11 kV. What is the potential difference across the secondary coil?

3 A transformer has 1000 turns on the primary coil and 20 turns on the secondary coil. The potential difference across the primary coil is 230 V. What is the potential difference across the secondary coil?

4 The primary coil of a transformer has 100 turns, and the mains supply is 230 V. What is a suitable number of turns on the secondary coil for:

(a) a laptop needing a supply of 19 V

(b) a mobile phone charger needing 6.5 V

(c) a battery charger needing 4.2 V.

Exam tip   AQA

✓ Remember that the correct term is the number of turns on a coil.

Learning objectives

After studying this topic, you should be able to:

✔ use the transformer power equation

✔ compare the types of transformer used for different applications

◀ An industrial transformer that steps the potential difference down from 11 kV to 433 V

Transformers and power

You have learnt earlier that power, potential difference (or voltage), and current are related by the equation:

power = potential difference × current
(watts, W)   (volts, V)   (amperes, A)

If power is P, potential difference is V and current is I, then:

$$P = VI$$

This equation can also be used for transformers.

Transformers are very efficient. If a transformer is assumed to have an efficiency of 100%, the electrical power input applied to the primary coil is equal to the power output from the secondary coil:

power in primary coil, P_p = power in secondary coil, P_s

or $P_p = P_s$

- V_p is the potential difference across the primary coil in volts, V
- I_p is the current in the primary coil in amperes, A
- V_s is the potential difference across the secondary coil in volts, V
- I_s is the current in the secondary coil in amperes, A
- n_p is the number of turns on the primary coil
- n_s is the number of turns on the secondary coil.

From the equations linking power, potential difference and current:

$$V_p \times I_p = V_s \times I_s$$

Worked example

The potential difference across the primary coil of a transformer is 230 V and the current through the primary coil is 2 A. The potential difference across the secondary coil is 12 V. What is the current through the secondary coil?

$$V_p \times I_p = V_s \times I_s$$

$V_p = 230\text{ V}, I_p = 2\text{ A}, V_s = 110\text{ V}$

Substituting the values into the equation, we get:

$$230\text{ V} \times 2\text{ A} = 110\text{ V} \times I_s$$

$$I_s = \frac{230\text{ V}}{110\text{ V}} \times 2\text{ A}$$

$$= 4.2\text{ A}$$

The current in the secondary coil is 4.2 A.

A The potential difference across the secondary coil of a transformer is half of the potential difference across the primary coil. If the transformer is 100% efficient, what can we say about the currents in the secondary coil and primary coil?

Applications of transformers

Some electrical devices use the 230 V mains electricity supply directly. These include cookers, washing machines, microwave ovens, and electric heaters. Other devices need a much lower potential difference. Most electronic devices use a much lower potential difference. Step-down transformers are used in their power units to reduce the potential difference to what is needed.

▲ The power supplies for all of these devices include a transformer. The laptop needs 19 V, the phone charger 6.5 V, and the battery charger 4.2 V.

> **B** Why do some devices need transformers?

Questions

1   What assumption is made about transformers in the power equation? ↓ E

2   Calculate the potential difference across the primary coil of a transformer when the current through the primary coil is 0.25 A, the potential difference across the secondary coil is 230 V, and the current through the secondary coil is 13 A.

3   Calculate the current in the secondary coil of a transformer when the potential difference across the secondary coil is 132 kV, the potential difference across the primary coil is 11 kV, and the current in the primary coil is 100 A. ↓ C

4   Why is the assumption made when using the transformer power equation likely to be incorrect? ↓ A*

Exam tip AQA

✔ Always show your working in any calculations. Even if you get the answer wrong, you will get a mark if you have shown that you have used the correct method.

Learning objectives

After studying this topic, you should be able to:

- ✔ explain that switch mode transformers operate at high frequencies
- ✔ describe the advantages of switch mode transformers over traditional transformers

Key words

switch mode transformer, load

Transformers for electronic devices

Electronic devices such as mobile phones, digital cameras, TVs and computers need a supply that is much lower than the 230 V of the mains electricity supply, often a potential difference of somewhere between 3 V and 20 V.

They also use direct current rather than alternating current. The power units they use to operate, or to recharge their batteries must reduce the potential difference of the a.c. mains supply and convert it to direct current. They may use a conventional transformer or a **switch mode transformer**.

These devices also transform potential differences, but use very complex circuits to do this. A standard transformer operates at the frequency of the alternating mains supply, which is 50 Hz. Switch mode transformers usually operate at frequencies between 50 kHz and 1000 kHz. They are used extensively within electronic devices.

A What is a switch mode transformer?

▲ This power unit for a PC uses a switch mode transformer

Advantages of switch mode transformers

Switch mode transformers are usually much smaller and lighter than a conventional transformer.

▲ This power supply for a mobile phone contains a switch mode transformer and is the same size as a normal plug

The efficiency in a typical a.c. to d.c. power supply for an electronic device that uses a conventional transformer is between 30% and 40%. The efficiency of a switch mode transformer is between 60% and 70%. A well-designed switch mode transformer can have an efficiency of 95%.

> **B** What is the efficiency of a switch mode transformer?

Switch mode transformers use very little power when they are switched on but no **load** is being applied. For example, a switch mode transformer for a battery charger will use very little power when it is switched on but no batteries are actually being charged.

The potential difference and frequency of the mains supply varies around the world. In the UK it is 230 V, 50 Hz. In North America it is 110 V, 60 Hz. Switch mode transformers can be used with all the different mains supplies around the world and produce the same output. So manufacturers do not have to make different models for each mains electricity supply.

However, switch mode transformers have much more complex circuits than conventional transformers.

Did you know...?

When a transformer is working, you can sometimes hear 'mains hum'. The transformer may vibrate at the frequency of the mains supply. If you stand outside an electricity substation, you can sometimes hear the transformers.

Questions

1 What frequency range do switch mode transformers use? E

2 What are the advantages of a switch mode transformer?

3 What are the differences between a conventional transformer and a switch mode transformer? C

4 What happens to the energy that is wasted in a transformer?

5 The upper limit of hearing is less than 20 kHz for most humans.
What are the advantages of using a frequency between 50 kHz and 200 kHz for mains electricity supplies? A*

Course catch-up

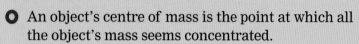

Revision checklist

- An object's centre of mass is the point at which all the object's mass seems concentrated.
- The time period of a pendulum is the time taken to complete a full swing.
- Moment is the turning effect of a force.
- When an object is balanced, the total clockwise moment about the pivot is equal to the total anticlockwise moment. This is the principle of moments. Levers multiply forces using moments.
- An object will topple if the line of action of its weight falls outside the base of the object. Stability is increased by making the base wider and the centre of mass lower.
- Liquids are almost incompressible. Pressure in liquids is transmitted equally in all directions.
- Hydraulic systems multiply force.
- An object moving in a circle is constantly changing direction, so is constantly accelerating towards the centre of the circle.
- The force between an object in circular motion and the centre of the circle is a centripetal force.
- Flow of electric current through a wire produces a magnetic field around the wire.
- If a current-carrying wire is placed within another magnetic field, the magnetic fields interact, creating the motor effect.
- When a wire cuts across a magnetic field, a potential difference is induced across the ends of the wire.
- A transformer has an iron core with two coils of wire around it. If the primary coil is connected to an a.c. supply an alternating potential difference is induced in the secondary coil.
- In a step-up transformer, potential difference is higher across the secondary coil than the primary coil.
- In a step-down transformer, potential difference is lower across the secondary coil than the primary coil.
- Potential differences across the primary and secondary coils and the number of turns in the coils are related.
- In a transformer with 100% efficiency, the power input to the primary coil is equal to the output from the secondary coil.
- Most electronic devices use a lower potential difference than the 230 V mains supply. Step-down transformers are used.

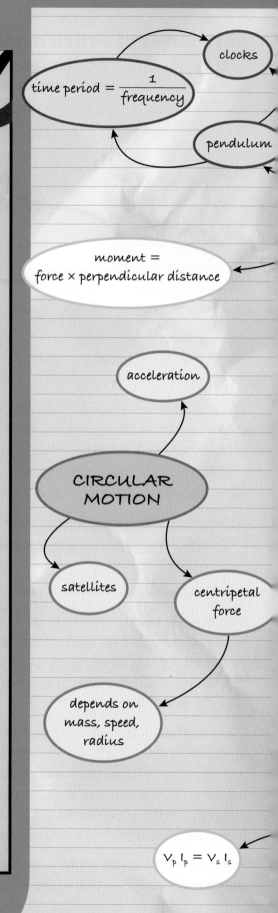

clocks

$$\text{time period} = \frac{1}{\text{frequency}}$$

pendulum

$$\text{moment} = \text{force} \times \text{perpendicular distance}$$

acceleration

CIRCULAR MOTION

satellites

centripetal force

depends on mass, speed, radius

$$V_p I_p = V_s I_s$$

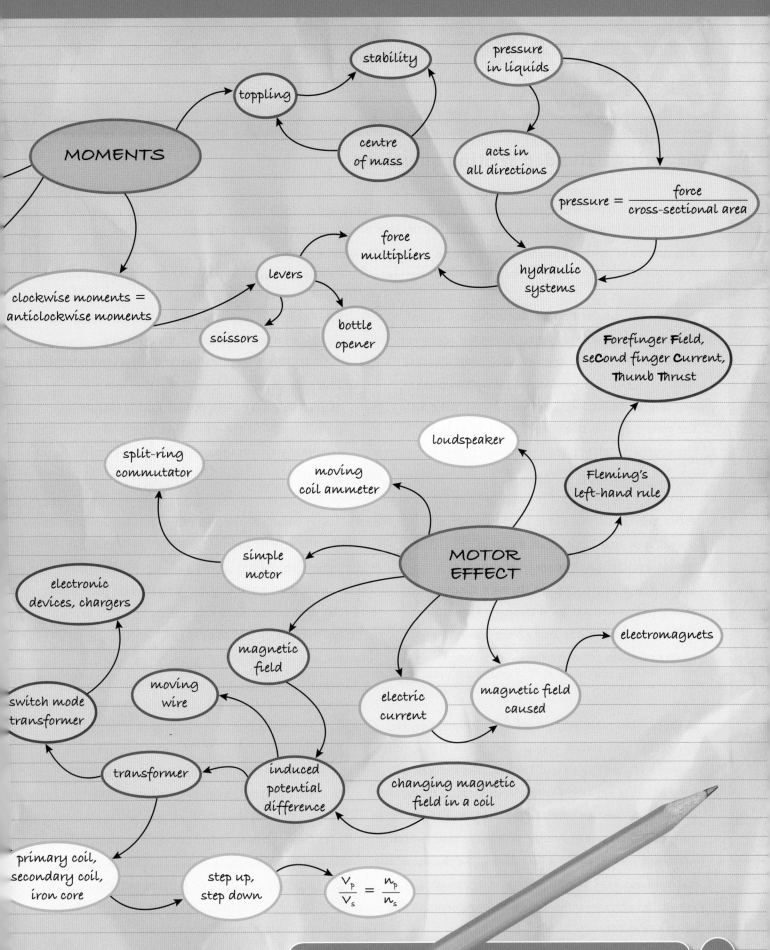

MOMENTS

stability

toppling

centre of mass

pressure in liquids

acts in all directions

$$\text{pressure} = \frac{\text{force}}{\text{cross-sectional area}}$$

clockwise moments = anticlockwise moments

levers

force multipliers

scissors

bottle opener

hydraulic systems

Forefinger Field, seCond finger Current, Thumb Thrust

loudspeaker

split-ring commutator

moving coil ammeter

Fleming's left-hand rule

simple motor

MOTOR EFFECT

electronic devices, chargers

magnetic field

electromagnets

moving wire

electric current

magnetic field caused

switch mode transformer

transformer

induced potential difference

changing magnetic field in a coil

primary coil, secondary coil, iron core

step up, step down

$$\frac{V_P}{V_S} = \frac{n_P}{n_S}$$

AQA Upgrade

Answering Extended Writing questions

You are given a piece of Perspex cut into the shape of the islands of Great Britain. Explain how you could find the centre of mass of the piece, and explain the physics on which your method is based.

The quality of written communication will be assessed in your answer to this question.

G–E

Stick a pin in the Perspex somewhere it dusnt mater where and let it hang down the centre of mass is underneeth so draw it on that's becose gravity pulls it down then do it again from another place an another if you have time an the centre of mass is wher thay cros maybe they wont exacly so its somewhere there

Examiner: The candidate clearly remembers the experiment. However, the written description is unplanned and ungrammatical. The practical details and the physics explanation are both vague and lack the correct technical terms. Spelling and grammar are poor, and punctuation is non-existent.

D–C

Put a pin through a place on the corner of the perspex and hang it in a clamp, gravity pulls it so the centr of mass is strait down under the pin. Draw a line down (use a waight on a string). Hang it from another place and do the same, the centre of mass is where the lines cross.

Examiner: Most of the described physics is correct. However, the use of technical terms is vague: no reference to 'moments', 'vertical', or 'plumb-line', and use of 'place' rather than 'point'. The physics of the method is glossed over and other details are left out. There are occasional errors in spelling, punctuation, and grammar.

B–A*

Suspend the piece from a point somewhere on the edge, so it can swivel freely, with a pin through it. Hang a plumb-line from the pin. The Perspex will rotate till its centre of mass is vertically below the pin – this happens because the weight of the Perspex causes a moment about the pivot (the pin) which makes it rotate. Draw a line along the thread of the plumb-line. Use another suspension point and repeat the process. Where the two lines cross is the centre of mass.

Examiner: This answer is well ordered and accurate. The physics explanation and the use of technical terms is good throughout. This is a difficult question to answer briefly, and all the key ideas are there – though the candidate might also suggest safety glasses to protect against sharp pins, and/or a third suspension to check the others. Spelling, punctuation, and grammar are all good.

Exam-style questions

1 Match the words on the left with the correct description on the right:

G–E

Term	Description
centripetal force	Point where all an object's mass appears to act
centre of mass	Force multiplier that uses the principle of moments
pressure	Turning effect of a force about a pivot
moment	System to exert a larger force, starting with a smaller one
force multiplier	Force needed to keep an object in a circular path
lever	Exerts force on a surface within a liquid

2 The diagram illustrates a hydraulic system using two pistons.

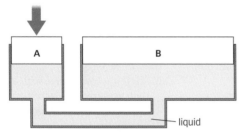

liquid

Piston A cross-section = 20 cm².
Piston B cross-section = 80 cm².
Piston A is pushed with a force of 300 N.

a Calculate the pressure in the liquid behind piston A:
   i in N/cm²   **ii** in Pa.

b What is the pressure in the liquid behind piston B in N/cm²? Explain this answer.

c Calculate the force on piston B.

d Piston A moves a distance of 60 cm. How far does piston B move back?

e Explain how this system can be called a force multiplier.

D–C

3 The diagram below shows the main parts of a simple electric motor.

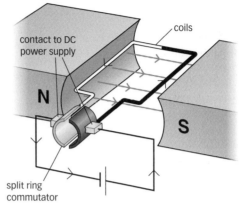

coils

contact to DC power supply

N

S

split ring commutator

B–A*

a Explain why there is a force on the white part of the coil.

b Use Fleming's left-hand rule to work out the direction of the force.

c What is the direction of the force on the black part of the coil?

d What is the combined effect of the forces on the two parts of the coil?

e Explain how the split ring commutator allows the motor to work as required.

Extended Writing

4 What is meant by the principle of moments? Describe two examples where the principle applies.

5 A GPS satellite is in a circular orbit around the Earth. Explain why it keeps moving in its circular path.

6 Many household appliances include a simple step-down transformer. Explain how a step-down transformer works, and why one might be used.

G–E   D–C   B–A*

A01 Recall the science
A02 Apply your knowledge
A03 Evaluate and analyse the evidence

Glossary

activated carbon Carbon that contains very many pores in its structure so has a very large surface area. This means that it can adsorb substances that would give water a bad taste or smell.

activation energy Minimum amount of energy that particles need in order to react when they collide.

active transport Process that can move substances across cell membranes from low concentrations to high concentrations (against the concentration gradient). Active transport uses energy and is carried out by protein carriers in the cell membrane.

adsorption Process in which molecules of a substance stick to the surface of a solid such as activated carbon.

alcohol Organic compound that contains the functional group –OH.

alkali metal An element in Group 1 of the periodic table (lithium, sodium, potassium, rubidium, caesium, francium).

alveolus Structure in the lung that provides a large surface area with an extensive network of capillaries to carry out gaseous exchange.

ammonia The simplest compound of hydrogen and nitrogen. The molecular formula is NH_3.

antigen Special protein in the body that can destroy a particular pathogen.

atomic number The number of protons in the nucleus of an atom.

atria Upper chambers of the heart that receive blood from veins.

battery farming Rearing large numbers of animals in small spaces, to maximise efficiency of production.

biofuel Fuel such as wood or ethanol, derived from biological materials that absorb carbon dioxide while they are growing, so their use is less harmful to the environment than burning fossil fuels.

blood Tissue specialised for transport of substances including oxygen, carbon dioxide, food molecules, and wastes in larger animals. Blood is made up of plasma, red and white blood cells, and platelets.

bond energy The amount of energy required to break a bond in a molecule.

burette Piece of apparatus used to measure accurately the volume of liquid delivered into a container.

camera Device for capturing images.

capillaries Small blood vessel with a very thin wall and narrow diameter. Capillaries allow exchange of substances between cells and blood.

carbon neutral Describes a fuel that absorbs as much carbon dioxide when it is made as it gives out when it burns.

carboxylic acid Organic compound that contains the functional group –COOH.

CCD Electronic sensor of visible light that can be used to record an image.

centre of mass Point at which all of the mass of an object appears to be acting.

centripetal force Force that keeps an object moving in a circle.

ciliary muscles Muscles that pull and relax to change the shape of the lens in an eye.

closed system System in which no material can enter or leave.

concave Describes a lens whose thickness increases with increasing distance from its centre.

concentration Mass of solute in a given volume of solution, usually measured in g/cm^3 or mol/cm^3.

concentration gradient Difference in concentration of a substance from one region to another.

converging Describes a lens that changes the direction of parallel rays of light so that they meet at a focus once they have passed through the lens.

convex Describes a lens whose thickness decreases with increasing distance from its centre.

cornea Transparent curved surface where light enters the eye.

corrective lenses Lenses placed in front of the eyes to improve their performance.

critical angle Light will only totally internally reflect if its angle of incidence is greater than the critical angle.

CT scan Uses a series of X-ray scans to produce cross-sectional images of the inside of the body.

deforestation Large-scale felling of trees to allow use of the land for building or agriculture.

dehydrated Not containing enough water to function properly.

desalination Process of removing dissolved salts from seawater, making the water fit to drink.

diabetes Condition in which blood glucose levels rise because the pancreas does not produce enough insulin.

dialysis Mechanical means of filtering the blood and removing harmful substances, used when the kidneys do not work properly.

diminished Made smaller.

dioptres Unit of lens power.

displacement reaction Reaction in which a less reactive metal is displaced from its compounds by a more reactive metal.

distillation Process of obtaining a product from a mixture by boiling the mixture so that the product evaporates and can be collected.

diverging Describes a lens that changes the direction of parallel rays of light so that they appear to come from a focus once they have passed through the lens.

donor Someone who donates (gives) something, such as an organ in an organ transplant.

dynamic equilibrium The state of a reversible reaction when the forward and backward reactions are taking place at the same rate.

elastic Stretchy.

electric motor Device with a rotating shaft powered by electric current interacting with a magnet.

electromagnetic induction Creation of a potential difference across the ends of a wire when it moves through a magnetic field, or when the magnetic field is changing.

electromagnetic wave Wave that has oscillating electric and magnetic fields at right angles to its direction of motion.

end point The point in a titration when the chemical being added has exactly reacted with the chemical in the flask or beaker.

endoscope Instrument for imaging inside the body using optical fibres.

endothermic Describes a reaction in which heat is absorbed from the surroundings.

energy level diagram Diagram showing the relative amounts of energy stored in the reactants and products of a reaction.

ester Compound formed by the reaction of an alcohol with an acid. Their molecules contain the functional group –COO–.

esterification Reversible reaction between an acid and an alcohol to form an ester.

ethanoic acid Carboxylic acid with the molecular formula CH_3COOH.

ethanol Alcohol whose molecular formula is CH_3CH_2OH.

evaporation Liquid turning to gas. Evaporation transfers heat energy away so it cools the surface from which the liquid evaporates.

exchange system Organ system that exchanges materials, such as oxygen, carbon dioxide, and other wastes, between the organism and its surroundings.

excretion Removal of waste materials produced by the reactions of the body.

exothermic Describes a reaction in which heat is transferred to the surroundings.

fermenter Large container used for growing large numbers of microorganisms.

filtration Removing particles from a liquid by passing it through a medium with small holes that do not allow the particles to pass through. In the kidney, filtration allows water and dissolved substances to pass into the kidney tubule, while blood cells and proteins remain in the capillaries.

fish stocks The numbers of fish in waters that are fished. Overfishing reduces fish stocks.

flame test Test that helps to identify metals in compounds by observing the colour a compound produces in the flame of a Bunsen burner.

Fleming's left-hand rule Uses thumb and first two fingers of left hand to show directions of force, current, and magnetic field in a motor.

fluoridated water Water that has had a fluorine compound (usually sodium fluoride) added to it. This helps to reduce tooth decay.

focal length Distance from the centre of a lens to the principal focus.

focus Point in space where rays originating from a point on an object come together after passing through a lens.

force multiplier Something that increases the size of a force.

frequency (pendulum) The number of cycles that a pendulum completes in one second.

frequency (waves) The number of oscillations per second for a vibration.

fuel cell Device that converts chemical energy directly to electrical energy without using combustion.

functional group Reactive group of atoms in an organic molecule that gives the molecule particular chemical properties.

global warming Change in climate caused by the emission of more greenhouse gases.

glucagon Hormone that causes the liver to break down glycogen to glucose, and release more glucose into the blood.

glucose Type of sugar.

greenhouse gas Gas that produces a greenhouse effect in the atmosphere, preventing heat energy being radiated away from the Earth.

Haber process Industrial process by which ammonia is made from hydrogen and nitrogen gases.

haemoglobin Soluble protein that also contains an iron atom. Found in red blood cells. It carries oxygen from lungs to respiring tissues.

halide ion Negative ion formed from a halogen atom by the loss of one electron (F^-, Cl^-, Br^-, I^-, At^-).

halogen An element in Group 7 of the periodic table (fluorine, chlorine, bromine, iodine, astatine).

hard water Water that does not easily form a lather with soap.

heat exchanger Device for transferring energy from a hot output stream to a cold input stream so that the energy is not wasted.

homologous series Series of organic compounds that contain different numbers of carbon atoms but the same functional group. They have a common general formula.

hydraulic system System that uses a liquid to transfer forces.

immunosuppressant Describes drugs that suppress the immune system, given to recipients of a transplanted organ to reduce the risk of rejection.

incompressible Describes something that cannot be squashed.

induced One thing having caused something else to happen in a system.

insulin Hormone produced by the pancreas that causes body cells to take up glucose from the blood.

internal combustion engine Engine in which the energy produced by burning fuel in a cylinder is used to drive a piston or turbine.

inverted Describes an image that is upside down compared with the object.

ion exchange column Column containing an ion exchange resin. The resin holds sodium ions and as hard water passes over it the calcium or magnesium ions in the water are exchanged for sodium ions.

ionise Process in which a molecule splits into oppositely charged ions when it dissolves in water.

ionising Describes radiation that removes electrons from atoms to create ions.

iris Coloured disc in front of lens that controls amount of light reaching the retina by altering the size of the hole at its centre.

iron core Central part of a transformer around which the primary and secondary coils are wrapped.

isotonic Having equal concentrations of dissolved substances.

joule Unit of energy.

kidney stone Lump of material that forms in the kidney, blocking ducts and causing pain.

kilojoule An amount of energy equal to 1000 joules.

laser Device that emits light of a single wavelength as a narrow intense beam.

law of octaves Observation by the English chemist John Newlands (1837–1898) that when the elements are arranged in order of their atomic weight, each successive eighth element shows similar properties.

lens power Equal to 1 divided by its focal length in metres.

lever Simple machine with a pivoted rod that can increase the size of a force.

line of action Line passing through an object in the direction of the force on that object.

load Device attached to a power source that draws electrical energy from it.

long-sightedness Inability to see close objects clearly.

lumen Space in a blood vessel through which blood flows.

lung Organ of many land animals, specialised to exchange oxygen and carbon dioxide.

magnetic field Region of space around a magnet where magnetic forces act on objects.

magnification Height of an image of an object divided by the height of the object itself.

magnified Made larger.

methanoic acid Carboxylic acid with the molecular formula HCOOH.

methanol Alcohol with the molecular formula CH_3OH.

microstrainer A rotating drum covered in a fine mesh, used to remove particles such as algae from water.

moment Turning force, calculated as force x distance of its line of action from the pivot.

motor effect The push on an electric current placed in a magnetic field.

muscle Tissue made up of muscle fibres, specialised to contract and bring about movement in the organism.

mycoprotein High-protein food produced from a fungus.

nerve impulses Electrical signals that carry information along nerves.

number of turns Number of times a wire is wrapped round in a transformer to create a coil.

optical fibre Long thin cylinder made from very transparent glass down which light can be sent over long distances.

organic compound Compound of carbon.

osmosis Diffusion of water through a partially permeable membrane, from a dilute solution to a more concentrated solution.

oxyhaemoglobin Haemoglobin with oxygen atoms attached.

partially permeable membrane Membrane that has small pores through which small molecules such as water can pass, but not larger molecules such as proteins.

particulate Small particles, mostly of carbon (soot), formed by the incomplete combustion of fossil fuels.

pascal Unit of pressure, newtons per square metre.

peat Type of soil formed from rotting vegetation that is rich in carbon, and is burned as a fuel.

pendulum Heavy object attached to one end of a long, thin piece of material.

periodic table Table in which the elements are arranged in rows (periods) and columns (groups) in order of their atomic number.

permanent hard water Water from which the hardness cannot be removed by boiling the water.

perpendicular distance Distance that is at right angles to the line of action of the force to a pivot.

phloem Plant tissue made up of living cells that has the function of transporting food substances through the plant.

pipette Piece of apparatus designed to deliver accurately a particular volume of liquid.

pivot Point around which an object can rotate.

plasma Fluid in blood in which the cells are suspended. Plasma transports carbon dioxide, digested food molecules, and urea.

pollutant Substance put into the environment by human activity, which is not normally there.

pollution Contamination of the environment by harmful substances.

population The number of organisms of a species in a given area.

pore Small opening. Pores on the surface of a leaf allow water and gases to move in and out of the leaf.

potometer Apparatus used to measure the rate of transpiration by measuring the uptake of water by a plant.

primary coil Coil in a transformer where the input is applied.

principal axis Line through the centre of a lens, at right angles to its plane.

principal focus Point to which parallel rays of light are focussed by a converging lens.

propanoic acid Carboxylic acid with the molecular formula CH_3CH_2COOH.

propanol Alcohol with the molecular formula $CH_3CH_2CH_2OH$.

protein carrier Protein that carries something; for example, some protein carriers transport sodium ions out of nerve cells by active transport.

pupil Hole in the iris that lets light into the eye.

quotas Limits to the numbers of fish that can be caught in a particular area, set to prevent damage to fish stocks.

radiation Transfer of heat energy by infrared radiation.

radiographer Technician who uses X-rays or gamma rays for medical procedures.

radiotherapy Use of radioactive materials to cure people with cancer.

range of vision Difference between the furthest and nearest distance over which a person can see clearly.

rate of transpiration How quickly a plant is losing water by transpiration (evaporation from its leaves). The rate is affected by factors including humidity, air movement, and temperature.

ray diagram Diagram showing the passage of rays of light through a lens.

reabsorption Process of reabsorbing (taking back) useful substances including glucose, ions, and water into the blood from the kidney tubule so they are not excreted. Takes place in the kidney.

real Type of image that can be displayed on a screen.

reflection The change of direction of a wave when it bounces off a surface.

refraction The change of speed and direction of a wave when it goes from one medium to another.

refractive index Sine of the angle of incidence of light divided by the sine of the angle of refraction; a measure of the speed of light in a transparent material.

rejection Attack on a transplanted organ by the immune system within a recipient's body.

renal Relating to the kidney.

retina Light-sensitive surface at the back of the eyeball.

reversible reaction Reaction in which the products of a reaction can react to produce the original reactants.

rough titration Titration carried out to give an approximate value for the end point.

sand filter A deep bed of sand that removes bacteria and fine particles of solid from water as the water passes through it.

secondary coil Coil in a transformer from where the output is taken.

shivering Automatic response to cold, where muscles under the skin contract repeatedly to release more heat by respiration.

short-sightedness Inability to see distant objects clearly.

soft water Water that easily forms a lather with soap.

solute Substance dissolved in a solvent to make a solution.

specific heat capacity The amount of energy required to raise the temperature of 1 g of a substance by 1 °C.

split-ring commutator Rotary switch in an electric motor that reverses current in the coil every half revolution.

stability The greater an object's stability, the more likely it is that an object will return to its original position when displaced.

stent Narrow mesh tube that is inserted into a blocked artery.

sterilise Process of killing bacteria in water using the gases chlorine or ozone.

stomata Pores on the surface of a leaf that allow water, carbon dioxide, and oxygen to move in and out of the leaf.

strong acid Describes an acid that has all of its molecules ionised when dissolved in water.

suspensory ligaments Tissue holding the lens in place within the eye.

sustainable Describes the use of resources for/by humans without harming the environment.

switch mode transformer Transformer that operates at a high frequency.

temporary hard water Water from which the hardness can be removed by boiling the water.

tension Force that is trying to pull something apart.

thermoregulation Regulating body temperature.

time period Time taken for a pendulum to swing from one extreme to the other and back again.

tissue Group of cells of similar structure and function working together, such as muscle tissue in an animal and xylem in a plant.

tissue-typing Matching the tissues of donor and recipient in a transplant operation, so that their antigens are similar and there is less chance of rejection.

titration Reaction carried out using a solution whose concentration is known to find out the concentration of a chemical in a second solution.

total internal reflection (TIR) Where light inside a transparent medium reflects off its surface without any refraction out of the medium.

transition element Describes a metallic element in the central block of the periodic table. Transition elements are hard and have high melting points. They can form ions with different positive charges and are often good catalysts.

translocation Transport of sugars made in photosynthesis in the leaf to areas of the plant that store them or use them.

transmitted Passed through.

transpiration Movement of water through the xylem of a plant, from the roots up to the leaves.

transpiration stream Continuous flow of water through the xylem of a plant, from the roots up to the leaves where it evaporates.

trauma Serious injury, for example resulting from an accident.

ultrasound Sound wave that has too high a frequency (above 20 kHz) for it to be heard by humans.

ultrasound scan Detection of ultrasound echoes at the skin's surface to construct an image of the inside of the body.

upright Describes an image that is the same way up as the object.

urea Substance produced in the liver from the breakdown of amino acids, and removed in the urine by the kidneys.

valves Structures that allow one-way movement of a fluid and prevent backflow.

vasoconstriction Narrowing of blood vessels, so that less blood can flow through.

vasodilation Widening of blood vessels, so that bood can flow through more easily.

ventilation Movement of air into and out of the lungs, brought about by inhaling and exhaling.

ventricles Lower chambers of the heart that contract and force blood out of the heart into the arteries.

villus Structure in the small intestine that provides a large surface area with an extensive network of capillaries to absorb the products of digestion by diffusion and active transport.

virtual Type of image that cannot be displayed on a screen.

virtual focus Point from which parallel rays of light appear to come after they have passed through a diverging lens.

volatile Describes a liquid that evaporates quickly.

washing soda The compound sodium carbonate, which removes hardness when it is dissolved in hard water.

wavelength Distance from one peak of a wave to the next peak.

weak acid Describes an acid that has only some of its molecules ionised when dissolved in water.

X-rays Electromagnetic waves of frequency between that of gamma rays and ultraviolet.

xylem Plant tissue made up of dead cells that has the function of transporting water and dissolved substances through the plant.

yield Amount of the required product made in a reaction.

Index

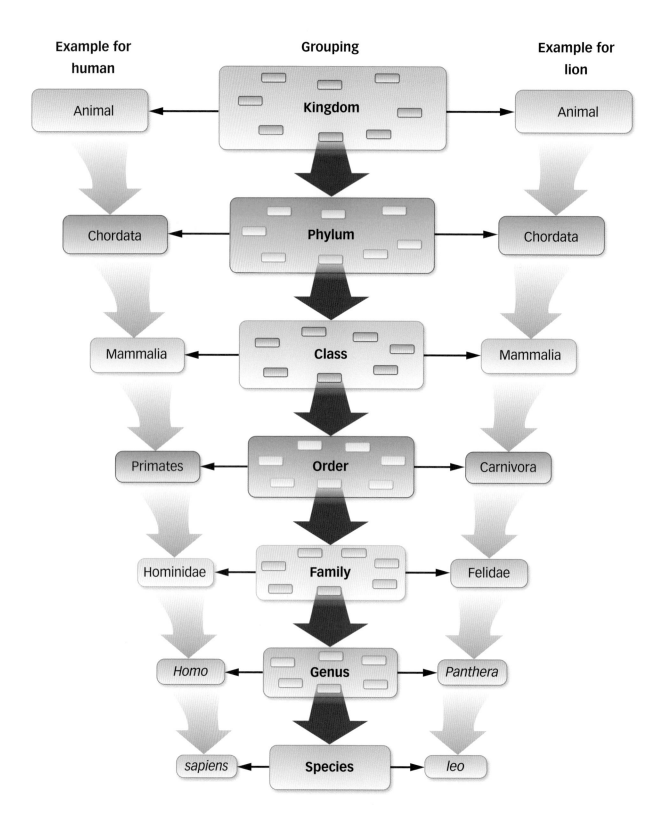

Example for human	Grouping	Example for lion
Animal	Kingdom	Animal
Chordata	Phylum	Chordata
Mammalia	Class	Mammalia
Primates	Order	Carnivora
Hominidae	Family	Felidae
Homo	Genus	*Panthera*
sapiens	Species	*leo*

Periodic table

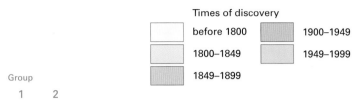

Times of discovery

before 1800	1900–1949
1800–1849	1949–1999
1849–1899	

Group

| 1 | 2 | | | | | | | | | | | 3 | 4 | 5 | 6 | 7 | 8 |

Key:
relative atomic mass
atomic number
name
atomic (proton) number

1.0
H
hydrogen
1

Period	1	2											3	4	5	6	7	8
②	7 **Li** lithium 3	9 **Be** beryllium 4											11 **B** boron 5	12 **C** carbon 6	14 **N** nitrogen 7	16 **O** oxygen 8	19 **F** fluorine 9	20 **Ne** neon 10
③	23 **Na** sodium 11	24 **Mg** magnesium 12											27 **Al** aluminium 13	28 **Si** silicon 14	31 **P** phosphorus 15	32 **S** sulfur 16	35.5 **Cl** chlorine 17	40 **Ar** argon 18
④	39 **K** potassium 19	40 **Ca** calcium 20	45 **Sc** scandium 21	48 **Ti** titanium 22	51 **V** vanadium 23	52 **Cr** chromium 24	55 **Mn** manganese 25	56 **Fe** iron 26	59 **Co** cobalt 27	59 **Ni** nickel 28	63.5 **Cu** copper 29	65 **Zn** zinc 30	70 **Ga** gallium 31	73 **Ge** germanium 32	75 **As** arsenic 33	79 **Se** selenium 34	80 **Br** bromine 35	84 **Kr** krypton 36
⑤	85.5 **Rb** rubidium 37	88 **Sr** strontium 38	89 **Y** yttrium 39	91 **Zr** zirconium 40	93 **Nb** niobium 41	96 **Mo** molybdenum 42	(98) **Tc** technetium 43	101 **Ru** ruthenium 44	103 **Rh** rhodium 45	106 **Pd** palladium 46	108 **Ag** silver 47	112 **Cd** cadmium 48	115 **In** indium 49	119 **Sn** tin 50	122 **Sb** antimony 51	128 **Te** tellurium 52	127 **I** iodine 53	131 **Xe** xenon 54
⑥	133 **Cs** caesium 55	137 **Ba** barium 56	139 **La** lanthanum 57 *	178.5 **Hf** hafnium 72	181 **Ta** tantalum 73	184 **W** tungsten 74	186 **Re** rhenium 75	190 **Os** osmium 76	192 **Ir** iridium 77	195 **Pt** platinum 78	197 **Au** gold 79	201 **Hg** mercury 80	204 **Tl** thallium 81	207 **Pb** lead 82	209 **Bi** bismuth 83	210 **Po** polonium 84	(210) **At** astatine 85	222 **Rn** radon 86
⑦	(223) **Fr** francium 87	(226) **Ra** radium 88	(227) **Ac** actinium 89 #	(261) **Rf** rutherfordium 104	(262) **Db** dubnium 105	(266) **Sg** seaborgium 106	(264) **Bh** bohrium 107	(277) **Hs** hassium 108	(268) **Mt** meitnerium 109	(271) **Ds** darmstadtium 110	(272) **Rg** roentgenium 111							

Elements with atomic numbers 112–116 have been reported but not fully authenticated

4 **He** helium 2

*58–71 Lanthanides

140 **Ce** cerium 58	141 **Pr** praseodymium 59	144 **Nd** neodymium 60	(145) **Pm** promethium 61	150 **Sm** samarium 62	152 **Eu** europium 63	157 **Gd** gadolinium 64	159 **Tb** terbium 65	162.5 **Dy** dysprosium 66	165 **Ho** holmium 67	167 **Er** erbium 68	169 **Tm** thulium 69	173 **Yb** ytterbium 70	175 **Lu** lutetium 71

#90–103 Actinides

232 **Th** thorium 90	231 **Pa** protactinium 91	238 **U** uranium 92	237 **Np** neptunium 93	239 **Pu** plutonium 94	243 **Am** americium 95	247 **Cm** curium 96	247 **Bk** berkelium 97	252 **Cf** californium 98	(252) **Es** einsteinium 99	(257) **Fm** fermium 100	(258) **Md** mendelevium 101	(259) **No** nobelium 102	(260) **Lr** lawrencium 103

Reactivity series of metals

Potassium	most reactive ↑
Sodium	
Calcium	
Magnesium	
Aluminium	
Carbon	
Zinc	
Iron	
Tin	
Lead	
Hydrogen	
Copper	
Silver	
Gold	
Platinum	least reactive ↓

(elements in italics, though non-metals, have been included for comparison)

Formulae of some common ions

Name	Formula	Name	Formula
Hydrogen	H^+	Chloride	Cl^-
Sodium	Na^+	Bromide	Br^-
Silver	Ag^+	Fluoride	F^-
Potassium	K^+	Iodide	I^-
Lithium	Li^+	Hydroxide	OH^-
Ammonium	NH_4^+	Nitrate	NO_3^-
Barium	Ba^{2+}	Oxide	O^{2-}
Calcium	Ca^{2+}	Sulfide	S^{2-}
Copper(II)	Cu^{2+}	Sulfate	SO_4^{2-}
Magnesium	Mg^{2+}	Carbonate	CO_3^{2-}
Zinc	Zn^{2+}		
Lead	Pb^{2+}		
Iron(II)	Fe^{2+}		
Iron(III)	Fe^{3+}		
Aluminium	Al^{3+}		

Equations	
$E = m \times c \times \theta$	E is energy transferred in joules, J m is mass in kilograms, kg θ is temperature change in degrees Celsius, °C c is specific heat capacity in J/kg°C
efficiency = $\dfrac{\text{useful energy out}}{\text{total energy in}}$ (× 100%)	
efficiency = $\dfrac{\text{useful power out}}{\text{total power in}}$ (× 100%)	
$E = P \times t$	E is energy transferred in kilowatt-hours, kWh P is power in kilowatts, kW t is time in hours, h This equation may also be used when: E is energy transferred in joules, J P is power in watts, W t is time in seconds, s
$v = f \times \lambda$	v is speed in metres per second, m/s t is frequency in hertz, Hz λ is wavelength in metres, m

Fundamental physical quantities	
Physical quantity	**Unit(s)**
length	metre (m) kilometre (km) centimetre (cm) millimetre (mm)
mass	kilogram (kg) gram (g) milligram (mg)
time	second (s) millisecond (ms)
temperature	degree Celsius (°C) kelvin (K)
current	ampere (A) milliampere (mA)
voltage	volt (V) millivolt (mV)

Derived quantities and units	
Physical quantity	**Unit(s)**
area	cm^2; m^2
volume	cm^3; dm^3; m^3; litre (l); millilitre (ml)
density	kg/m^3; g/cm^3
force	newton (N)
speed	m/s; km/h
energy	joule (J); kilojoule (kJ); megajoule (MJ)
power	watt (W); kilowatt (kW); megawatt (MW)
frequency	hertz (Hz); kilohertz (kHz)
gravitational field strength	N/kg
radioactivity	becquerel (Bq)
acceleration	m/s^2; km/h^2
specific heat capacity	J/kg°C
specific latent heat	J/kg

	Equations
$a = \dfrac{F}{m}$ or $F = m \times a$	F is the resultant force in newtons, N m is the mass in kilograms, kg a is the acceleration in metres per second squared, m/s²
$a = \dfrac{v - u}{t}$	a is the acceleration in metres per second squared, m/s² v is the final velocity in metres per second, m/s u is the initial velocity in metres per second, m/s t is the time taken in seconds, s
$W = m \times g$	W is the weight in newtons, N m is the mass in kilograms, kg g is the gravitational field strength in newtons per kilogram, N/kg
$F = k \times e$	F is the force in newtons, N k is the spring constant in newtons per metre, N/m e is the extension in metres, m
$W = F \times d$	W is the work done in joules, J F is the force applied in newtons, N d is the distance moved in the direction of the force in metres, m
$P = \dfrac{E}{t}$	P is the power in watts, W E is the energy transferred in joules, J t is the time taken in seconds, s
$E_p = m \times g \times h$	E_p is the change in gravitational potential energy in joules, J m is the mass in kilograms, kg g is the gravitational field strength in newtons per kilogram, N/kg h is the change in height in metres, m
$E_K = \dfrac{1}{2} \times m \times v^2$	E_K is the kinetic energy in joules, J m is the mass in kilograms, kg v is the speed in metres per second, m/s
$p = m \times v$	p is the momentum in kilograms metres per second, kg m/s m is the mass in kilograms, kg v is the velocity in metres per second, m/s
$I = \dfrac{Q}{t}$	I is the current in amperes (amps), A Q is the charge in coulombs, C t is the time in seconds, s
$V = \dfrac{W}{Q}$	V is the potential difference in volts, V W is the work done in joules, J Q is the charge in coulombs, C
$V = I \times R$	V is the potential difference in volts, V I is the current in amperes (amps), A R is the resistance in ohms, Ω
$P = \dfrac{E}{t}$	P is power in watts, W E is the energy in joules, J t is the time in seconds, s
$P = I \times V$	P is power in watts, W I is the current in amperes (amps), A V is the potential difference in volts, V
$E = V \times Q$	E is the energy in joules, J V is the potential difference in volts, V Q is the charge in coulombs, C

Electrical symbols

junction of conductors	ammeter **A**	diode	capacitor
switch	voltmeter **V**	electrolytic capacitor	relay ○NO ○COM ○NC
primary or secondary cell	indicator or light source	LDR	LED
battery of cells	or	thermistor	NOT gate
power supply	motor **M**	AND gate	OR gate
fuse	generator **G**	NOR gate	NAND gate
fixed resistor	variable resistor		

Acknowledgements

The publisher and authors would like to thank the following for their permission to reproduce photographs and other copyright material:

p13 AJ Photo/SPL; **p14** Biophoto Associates/SPL; **p15BR** Michael Abbey/SPL; **p15TR** Michael Abbey/SPL; **p15L** Steve Gschmeissner/SPL; **p16** Mike Manzano/Istockphoto; **p17** Francesco Ridolfi/Istockphoto; **p20** Claude Nuridsany & Marie Perennou/SPL; **p21** Eye Of Science/SPL; **p25TR** Dr Jeremy Burgess/SPL; **p25BR** Dr Jeremy Burgess/SPL; **p26L** Martyn F. Chillmaid/SPL; **p26R** Cindy Hughes/Shutterstock; **p28** Eye Of Science/SPL; **p29** Jim Varney/SPL; **p31R** Hank Morgan/SPL; **p31L** Steve Allen/SPL; **p32** Dr. Gladden Willis, Visuals Unlimited/SPL; **p34L** Pasieka/SPL; **p34R** Eye Of Science/SPL; **p37T** Dr Gopal Murti/SPL; **p37B** Prof. P. Motta/Dept. Of Anatomy/University "La Sapienza", Rome/SPL; **p38** Power and Syred/SPL; **p39TR** Dr Arnold Brody/SPL; **p39L** Michael Ross/SPL; **p39BR** National Cancer Institute/SPL; **p40** Power and Syred/SPL; **p47** Alex Bartel/SPL; **p48** Martin Oeggerli/SPL; **p49L** Ian Hooton/SPL; **p49R** Sheila Terry/SPL; **p51** BSIP VEM/SPL; **p53** Life In View/SPL; **p54** Life In View/SPL; **p58** Tony McConnell/SPL; **p59** Annie Griffiths Belt/National Geographic/Getty Images; **p60** AJ Photo/SPL; **p62** Dr P. Marazzi/SPL; **p63** Saturn Stills/SPL; **p65B** Bjorn Svensson/SPL; **p65T** Paul Bradbury/OJO Images/Getty Images; **p67L** Jeremy Walker/SPL; **p67R** Brian Bell/SPL; **p68L** Gary Cook, Visuals Unlimited/SPL; **p68TR** Brasil2/Istockphoto; **p68BR** Jacques Jangoux/SPL; **p69T** Guenter Guni/Istockphoto; **p69MT** Chris Hellier/SPL; **p69M** Prill Med(iendesign & Fotografie/Istockphoto; **p69MB** Adrian Brockwell/Istockphoto; **p69B** Chris Sattlberger/SPL; **p71T** Michael Szoenyi/SPL; **p71TR** Simon Fraser/SPL; **p71BR** S.R. Maglione/SPL; **p71BL** John Shaw/SPL; **p71TL** Jerry Schad/SPL; **p72L** Hubert Raguet/Look At Sciences/SPL; **p72R** Simon Fraser/SPL; **p73** Victor de Schwanberg/SPL; **p74TR** Geoff Kidd/SPL; **p74TM** Geoff Kidd/SPL; **p74BM** Subjug/Istockphoto; **p74BR** Cordelia Molloy/SPL; **p74L** Dennis Inc/Photolibrary; **p77** Perets/Istockphoto; **p78T** Dirk Wiersma/SPL; **p78B** HelleM/Istockphoto; **p85** Eye Of Science/SPL; **p86T** Duncan Walker/Istockphoto; **p86B** SPL; **p87** Ria Novosti/SPL; **p88** US Library Of Congress/SPL; **p89** Dave Lo/Mindspark; **p90** Zack Seckler/Getty Images News/Getty Images; **p91** Martyn F. Chillmaid/SPL; **p92L** Andrew Brookes, National Physical Laboratory/SPL; **p92R** Jerry Mason/SPL; **p93TL** Charles D. Winters/SPL; **p93TR** Charles D. Winters/SPL; **p93B** Philip Evans; **p94L** Rex Features; **p94M** Steve Meddle/Rex Features; **p94R** Emmeline Watkins/SPL; **p95TL** Matt Meadows, Peter Arnold Inc./SPL; **p95M** Matt Meadows, Peter Arnold Inc./SPL; **p95TR** Andrew Lambert Photography/SPL; **p95BR** Martyn F. Chillmaid/SPL; **p95BL** Andrew Lambert Photography/SPL; **p96** Andrew Lambert Photography/SPL; **p98L** DCA Productions/Taxi/Getty Images; **p98R** Alexey Samoylenko/Istockphoto; **p102** StockLite/Shutterstock; **p103TL** Environment Agency, Thames Region and South West Water; **p103TR** Rachel Dewis/Istockphoto; **p103BL** Nickos/Istockphoto; **p103BR** Mauro Fermariello/SPL; **p105R** Dennis Kunkel Microscopy, Inc./Visuals Unlimited/Corbis; **p105L** Michael Blann/Photodisc/Getty Images; **p106** Nikada/Istockphoto; **p107L** Jochen Tack/Photolibrary; **p107R** James Steidl/Istockphoto; **p108R** Floortje/Istockphoto; **p108L** Fuat Kose/Istockphoto; **p110** Byronsdad/Istockphoto; **p112** Jeannot Olivet/Istockphoto; **p115** Bruce Mackie/SPL; **p116L** David McNew/Getty Images News/Getty Images; **p116R** David McNew/Getty Images News/Getty Images; **p123** Du Cane Medical Imaging Ltd/SPL; **p124T** Kenneth Sponsler/Istockphoto; **p124B** Andrew Lambert Photography/SPL; **p125** Andrew Lambert Photography/SPL; **p126** Marcus Jones/Istockphoto; **p127** Andrew Lambert Photography/SPL; **p128R** Tek Image/SPL; **p128L** Keith/Custom Medical Stock Photo/SPL; **p129R** Charles D. Winters/SPL; **p129L** Charles D. Winters/SPL;

p130 Richard McGowan/Istockphoto; **p132** AJ Photo/SPL; **p133** Steve Horrell/SPL; **p134** Martyn F. Chillmaid/SPL; **p136TR** Peter Hendrie/Photographer's Choice/Getty Images; **p136TL** Tomas Bercic/Istockphoto; **p136B** Brian McEntire/Istockphoto; **p138** Ozturk Kemal Kayikci/Istockphoto; **p139** Ken Lucas, Visuals Unlimited/SPL; **p140** Andrew Lambert Photography/SPL; **p141** Dirk Wiersma/SPL; **p142R** Charles D. Winters/SPL; **p142L** Charles D. Winters/SPL; **p144TL** Tjanze/Istockphoto; **p144BR** David R. Frazier Photolibrary, Inc./SPL; **p144BL** Pixtal Images/Photolibrary; **p144TR** photoL/Istockphoto; **p146L** Alain Juteau/Istockphoto; **p146R** Marshall Turner/Dreamstime; **p147** Rex Features; **p148** Robert Young/Istockphoto; **p149** Andrew Lambert Photography/SPL; **p150** Alistair Scott/Dreamstime; **p151TL** Rex Features; **p151TR** a4stockphotos/Fotolia; **p151BL** Clynt Garnham Medical/Alamy; **p151BR** Yasonya/Fotolia; **p152** Andrew Lambert Photography/SPL; **p153** Martyn F. Chillmaid/SPL; **p154TR** Aleksejs Pivnenko/Fotolia; **p154L** Melisback/Fotolia; **p154BR** UniqueLight/Shutterstock; **p161** Mark Kostich/Istockphoto; **p162** ©Diamond Light Source 2011 Ltd.; **p163T** Don Bayley/Istockphoto; **p163B** Mauro Fermariello/SPL; **p164L** Zephyr/SPL; **p164R** George Bernard/SPL; **p165B** SPL; **p165T** CNRI/SPL; **p166** Doncaster and Bassetlaw Hospitals/SPL; **p168** Gustoimages/SPL; **p169R** AJ Photo/Hop Americain/SPL; **p169L** Astier/SPL; **p170** Erich Schrempp/SPL; **p172** Jeffrey L. Rotman/Photolibrary; **p173** Phil Degginger/Alamy; **p174** Imagemore Co., Ltd./Alamy; **p176** Peter Burnett/Istockphoto; **p178** Suzanne Grala/SPL; **p179** Aaron Amat/Shutterstock; **p181** Diego Cervo/Shutterstock; **p182** Constant/Shutterstock; **p183** Mauro Fermariello/SPL; **p184** Jaume Gual/Photolibrary; **p185** Serg64/Shutterstock; **p186** Miroslav Georgijevic/Istockphoto; **p187** Giphotostock/SPL; **p189** Micro10x/Shutterstock ; **p190** Giphotostock/SPL; **p192R** Tek Image/SPL; **p192TR** Dr P. Marazzi/SPL; **p192BR** David M. Martin, Md/SPL; **p193L** Pascal Goetgheluck/SPL; **p193R** Geoff Tompkinson/SPL; **p199** Paulo Fridman/Corbis; **p200** Kristen Olenick/Photolibrary; **p201** Kkant1937/Istockphoto; **p202** Garret Bautista/Istockphoto; **p203BR** Aaron Haupt/SPL; **p203TR** Yuriy Brykaylo/Istockphoto; **p203L** Javier Larrea/Photolibrary; **p204** David H. Lewis/Istockphoto; **p205** Michael Maher/Istockphoto; **p206R** Pavel Losevsky/Istockphoto; **p206L** Esemelwe/Istockphoto; **p208R** Roman Milert/Fotolia; **p208L** Southern Illinois University/SPL; **p209L** Tetra Images/Corbis; **p209R** Ulisse/Dreamstime; **p210** Mustafa Deliormanli/Istockphoto; **p211L** NatUlrich/Shutterstock; **p211M** Paul Matthew Photography/Shutterstock; **p211R** Millbrook Proving Ground Ltd. and Wrightbus Ltd.; **p212R** AJ Photo/SPL; **p212L** Ron Niebrugge/Alamy; **p213** Brett Gonzales/Istockphoto; **p215R** Elena Elisseeva/Istockphoto; **p215L** Steve Nagy/Photolibrary; **p216** Inhaus Creative/Istockphoto; **p217B** Matt Jeacock/Istockphoto; **p217T** Spark62/Alamy; **p219** Lisa Denise Hillström/Istockphoto; **p220** David R. Frazier Photolibrary, Inc./Alamy; **p222** Zcw/Shutterstock; **p223** Andrew Lambert Photography/SPL; **p226** Jeronimo Create/Istockphoto; **p227** Vitaly Shabalyn/Istockphoto; **p228** Sheila Terry/SPL; **p229R** Mark Sykes Energy and Power/Alamy; **p229L** Edhar/Shutterstock; **p229LM** Mark Goble/Alamy; **p229RM** Judith Collins/Alamy; **p230T** Timur Arbaev/Istockphoto; **p230B** Parrus/Istockphoto; **p231** Paul Rapson/Alamy.

Cover image courtesy of GUSTO IMAGES/SCIENCE PHOTO LIBRARY.

Illustrations by Wearset Ltd, HL Studios, Peter Bull Art Studio, James Stayte, Trystan Mitchell.

OXFORD
UNIVERSITY PRESS

Great Clarendon Street, Oxford OX2 6DP

Oxford University Press is a department of the University of Oxford.
It furthers the University's objective of excellence in research,
scholarship, and education by publishing worldwide in

Oxford   New York

Auckland   Cape Town   Dar es Salaam   Hong Kong   Karachi
Kuala Lumpur   Madrid   Melbourne   Mexico City   Nairobi
New Delhi   Shanghai   Taipei   Toronto

With offices in
Argentina   Austria   Brazil   Chile   Czech Republic   France   Greece
Guatemala   Hungary   Italy   Japan   Poland   Portugal   Singapore
South Korea   Switzerland   Thailand   Turkey   Ukraine   Vietnam

Oxford is a registered trade mark of Oxford University Press
in the UK and in certain other countries

© Oxford University Press 2011

British Library Cataloguing in Publication Data

Data available

ISBN 978-0-19-913593-6

10 9 8 7 6 5 4 3 2

Printed in Great Britain by Bell and Bain, Glasgow

Paper used in the production of this book is a natural, recyclable product
made from wood grown in sustainable forests. The manufacturing process
conforms to the environmental regulations of the country of origin.